There Was Once a Slave

SHIRLEY GRAHAM

There Was
Once
a Slave . . .

The heroic story of
FREDERICK DOUGLASS

JULIAN MESSNER, Inc., NEW YORK

There Was Once a Slave, *The Heroic Story of Frederick Douglass* by Shirley Graham, received the sixty-five hundred dollar JULIAN MESSNER AWARD FOR THE BEST BOOK COMBATING INTOLERANCE IN AMERICA. The judges were: Carl Van Doren, Lewis Gannett, and Clifton Fadiman. Miss Graham's work was selected from over six hundred manuscripts submitted in the contest. The original award was augmented by a grant from the Lionel Judah Tachna Memorial Foundation, established by Max Tachna in memory of his son who lost his life in the Battle of the Coral Sea.

PUBLISHED BY JULIAN MESSNER, INC.
8 WEST 40TH STREET, NEW YORK 18

PRINTED IN THE UNITED STATES OF AMERICA
BY MONTAUK BOOK MANUFACTURING CO., INC.

To Peoples on the March

You cannot hem the hope of being free
With parallels of latitude, with mountain range or sea;
Put heavy padlocks on Truth's lips, be callous as you will,
From soul to soul, o'er all the world,
leaps the electric thrill.

—JAMES RUSSELL LOWELL

Contents

Prologue

I keep my eye on the bright north star and think of liberty.
—FROM AN OLD SLAVE SONG

THEY TOLD HIM that he was a slave, that he must bend his back, walk low, with eyes cast down, think not at all and sleep without a dream. But every beat of hoe against a twisted root, each narrow furrow reaching toward the hill, flight of a bird across the open field, creak of the ox-cart in the road—all spoke to him of freedom.

For Frederick Douglass had his eyes upon a star.

This dark American never knew the exact date of his birth. Some time in 1817 or 1818 or 1819 he was born in Talbot County on the Eastern Shore of the state of Maryland. Who were his people? "Genealogical trees," he wrote in his autobiography, "did not flourish among slaves. A person of some consequence in civilized society, sometimes designated as father, was literally unknown to slave law and to slave practices."

His first years were spent in a kind of breeding pen, where, with dogs and pigs and other young of the plantation, black children were raised for the fields and turpentine forests. The only bright memories of his childhood clung round his grandmother's log hut. He remembered touching his mother once. After he was four or five years old he never saw or heard of her again.

This is the story of how from out that breeding pen there came a Man. It begins in August of the year of our Lord, 1834. Andrew Jackson was in the White House. Horace Greeley was getting a newspaper going in New York. William Lloyd Garrison had been dragged through the streets of Boston, a rope around his neck. Slavery had just been abolished wherever the Union Jack flew. Daniel O'Connell was lifting his voice, calling the people of Ireland together. Goethe's song of the brotherhood of man was echoing in the hills. Tolstoy was six years old, and Abraham Lincoln was growing up in Illinois.

Part I

THE ROAD

The dirt receding before my prophetical screams
              —WALT WHITMAN

CHAPTER ONE

Frederick sets his feet upon the road

THE LONG DAY was ending. Now that the sun had dropped behind scrawny pine trees, little eddies of dust stirred along the road. A bit of air from the bay lifted the flaccid leaves and lightly rustled the dry twigs. A heap of rags and matted hair that had seemed part of the swampy underbrush stirred. A dark head lifted cautiously. It was bruised and cut, and the deep eyes were wide with terror. For a moment the figure was motionless—ears strained, aching muscles drawn together, ready to dive deeper into the scrub. Then the evening breeze touched the bloated face, tongue licked out over cracked, parched lips. As the head sagged forward, a single drop of blood fell heavily upon the dry pine needles.

Water! The wide nostrils distended gratefully, tasting the moisture in the air—cool like the damp bricks of the well. Cracked fingers twitched as if they wrapped themselves around a rusty cup—the rough red cup with its brimming goodness of cool water. It had stood right at the side of his grandmother's hut—the old well had—its skyward-pointing beam so aptly placed between the limbs of what had once been a tree, so nicely balanced that even a small boy could move it up and down with one hand and get a drink without calling for help. The bundle of rags in the bushes shivered violently. Benumbed limbs were coming alive. He must be quiet, lie still a little longer, breathe slowly.

But the stupor which had locked his senses during the heat of the August day was lifting. Pain which could not be borne made him writhe. He gritted his teeth. His head seemed to float somewhere in space, swelling and swelling. He pressed against the ground, crushing the pine needles against his lips. Faces and voices were blurred in his memory. Sun, hot sun on the road—bare feet stirring the dust. The road winding up the hill—dust in the road. He had watched his grandmother disappear in the dust of the road. His mother had gone too, waving goodbye. The road had swallowed them up. The shadows of the trees were blotting out the road. There were only trees here. He lay still.

Darkness falls swiftly in the pine woods. He raised himself once more and looked about. A squirrel scurried for cover. Then everything was still—no harsh voices, no curses, no baying of hounds. That meant they were not looking for him. With the dogs it would have been easy enough. Covey had not bothered to take time out from work. Covey knew he could not get away.

Masters who sent their slaves to this narrow neck of stubborn land between the bay and the river knew their property was safe. Edward Covey enjoyed the reputation of being a first-rate hand at breaking "bad niggers." Slaveholders in the vicinity called him in when they had trouble. Since Covey was a poor man his occupation was of immense advantage to him. It enabled him to get his farm worked with very little expense. Like some horse-breakers noted for their skill, who rode the best horses in the country without expense, Covey could have under him the most fiery bloods of the neighborhood. He guaranteed to return any slave to his master well broken.

Captain Auld had turned over to Covey this impudent young buck who had been sent down to the Eastern Shore from Baltimore. Among the items of his wife's property, Captain Auld had found this slave listed as "Frederick."

"Sly and dangerous!" The Captain's voice was hard. "Got to be broken now while he's young."

"Frederick!" Covey had mouthed the syllables distastefully, his small green eyes traveling over the stocky, well-formed limbs, broad shoulders and long brown arms. "Too much name—too much head!" The comment was a sort of low growl. But his tones were servile as he addressed the master.

"Know his kind well. Just leave him to me. I'll take it out of him."

Then Frederick had lifted his head. His broad, smooth face turned to his master. His eyes were eloquent. *Why?* But his lips did not move. Captain Auld spoke sternly.

"Watch yourself! Don't be bringing him back to me crippled. He'll fetch a fair price in a couple of years. Comes of good stock."

Thomas Auld (why "Captain" no one knew) had not been born a slaveholder. Slaves had come to him through marriage. The stench of the whole thing sickened him, but he despised himself for his weakness. He dreaded his wife's scorn. She had grown up on the Lloyd plantation where there were more slaves than anybody could count and there was always plenty of everything. Colonel Lloyd never had trouble with his slaves, she taunted her husband. Auld would tighten his colorless, thin lips. God knows he tried hard enough— starved himself to feed a parcel of no-good, lazy blacks. He thoroughly hated them all. This one now—this sleek young buck—he'd been ruined in the city by Hugh Auld. By his own brother and by that milk-faced wife of his. Teaching him to read! Ruining a good, strong field hand! Well, he'd try Covey. See what he could do.

"Take him along!"

That had been shortly after "the Christmas." It was now hot summer. For Frederick a long, long time had passed. He was indeed "broken."

A shuddering groan escaped the boy. Part of Covey's irritation could be understood. He *had* been clumsy and slow about the fields and barn. But he dared not ask questions, and since nobody took the trouble to tell him anything his furrows were shallow and crooked.

He failed at running the treadmill. He had never even seen horned cattle before. So it was not surprising that his worst experiences had been with them. The strong, vicious beasts dragged him about at will, and day after day Covey flogged him for allowing the oxen to get away. Flogging was Covey's one method of instruction.

At first Frederick tortured himself with questions. They knew he'd never learned field work. "Old Marse" had sent him to Baltimore when he was just a pickaninny to look after the favorite grandchild, rosy-cheeked Tommy. He remembered that exciting trip to Baltimore and the moment when Mrs. Auld had taken his hand and, leading him to her little son, had said, "Look, Tommy, here's your Freddy."

The little slave had shyly regarded his equally small master. The white child had smiled, and instantly two small boys became fast friends. Fred had gone everywhere with Tommy. No watchdog was ever more devoted.

"Freddy's with Tommy," the mother would say with assurance.

It was perfectly natural that when Tommy began to read he eagerly shared the new and fascinating game with his companion. The mother was amused at how quickly the black child caught on. She encouraged both children because she considered the exchange good for Tommy. But one day she boasted of Freddy's accomplishment to her husband. Mr. Auld was horrified.

"It's against the law," he stormed. "Learning will spoil the best nigger in the world. If he learns to read he'll never be any good as a slave. The first thing you know he'll be writing, and then look out. A writing nigger is dangerous!"

It was difficult for Mrs. Auld to see the curly-headed dark boy as a menace. His devotion to Tommy was complete. But she was an obedient wife. Furthermore she had heard dreadful stories of slaves who "went bad."

"Oh, well, no harm's done," she consoled herself. "Freddy's just a child; he'll soon forget all about this." And she took pains to see that no more books or papers fell into his hands.

But Freddy did not forget. The seed was planted. Now he wanted to know, and he developed a cunning far beyond his years. It was not too difficult to salvage school books as they were thrown away. He invented "games" for Tommy and his friends—games which involved reading and spelling. The white boys slipped chalk from their schoolrooms and drew letters and words on sidewalks and fences. By the time Tommy was twelve years old, Freddy could read anything that came his way. And Tommy had somehow guessed that it was best not to mention such things. Freddy really was a great help.

The time came when they were all learning speeches from *The Columbian Orator*. Freddy quite willingly held the book while they recited Sheridan's impressive lines on the subject of Catholic emancipation, Lord Chatham's speech on the American War, speeches by the great William Pitt and by Fox. Some things about those speeches troubled the boys—especially those on the American Revolution.

"Them folks—you mean they *fight* to be free?" Freddy asked.

The four boys were comfortably sprawled out on the cellar door, well out of earshot of grownups, but the question made them look over their shoulders in alarm.

"Hush your big mouth!"

"Slaves fight?" Freddy persisted.

"Wasn't no slaves!"

"Course not, them was Yankees!"

"I hate Yankees."

"Everybody hates Yankees!"

The crisis had passed. Freddy thoughtfully turned the page and they started on the next speech.

Then suddenly Tommy was growing up. It was decided to send him away to school. And so, after seven years, his dark caretaker, no longer a small, wide-eyed Pickaninny, was sent back to the Eastern Shore plantation.

"Old Marse" had died. In the division of property—live stock, farm implements and slaves—Frederick had fallen to Colonel Lloyd's ward, Lucille, who had married Captain Thomas Auld. So the half-grown boy went to a new master, whose place was near the oyster beds of St. Michaels. The inhabitants of that hamlet, lean and colorless as their mangy hounds, stared at him as he passed through. They stared at his coat and eyed the shoes on his feet—good shoes they were, with soles. They could not know that inside his bundle was an old copy of *The Columbian Orator*.

The book had brought him into Covey's hands. At the memory came a sudden stab of pain, blotting out everything in a wave of nausea. The trees assumed diabolical forms—hands stretching out to seize him. Words flaming in the shadows—leaping at him—burning him. What did he have to do with books? He was a slave—a *slave for life*.

His new master's shock and horror had been genuine. Nothing had prepared him for such a hideous disclosure. Fred, arriving at the plantation, had been quiet and obedient. Captain Auld appraised this piece of his wife's inheritance with satisfaction. The boy appeared to be strong and bright—a real value. But before he had a chance to show what he could do, "the Christmas" was upon them and all regular work on the plantation was suspended.

Throughout the South it was customary for everybody to knock off from work in the period between Christmas Day and New Year's. On the big plantations there were boxing, wrestling, foot-racing, a lot of dancing and drinking of whiskey. Masters considered it a good thing for the slaves to "let go" this one time of the year—an exhausting "safety valve." All kinds of wild carousing were condoned. Liquor was brought in by the barrel and freely distributed. Not to be drunk during the Christmas was disgraceful and was regarded by the masters with something like suspicion.

Captain Auld's place was too poor for much feasting; but complete license was given, and into half-starved bodies were poured jugs of rum and corn whiskey. Men and women careened around and sang hoarsely, couples rolled in the ditch, and little boys staggered as they danced, while the overseers shouted with laughter. Everybody had a "good time."

All this was new to the boy, Frederick. He had never witnessed such loose depravity. He was a stranger. Eagerly he inquired for those he had known as a child. No one could tell him anything. "Old Marse's" slaves had been divided, exchanged, sold; and a slave leaves no forwarding address. The youth had no feeling of kinship with the plantation folks. He missed Tommy and wondered how he was getting along without him. On the other hand, the field workers and oyster shuckers looked upon the newcomer as a "house nigger."

For a while he watched the dancing and "jubilee beating," tasted the burning liquid and then, as the afternon wore on, slipped away. The day was balmy, with no suggestion of winter as known in the north. Frederick had not expected this leisure. He had kept his book hidden, knowing such things were forbidden. Now, tucking it inside his shirt, he walked out across the freshly plowed fields.

So it happened that Captain Auld came upon him stretched out under a tree, his eyes fastened on the book which lay before him on the ground, his lips moving. The boy was so absorbed that he did not hear his name called. Only when the Captain's riding whip came down on his shoulders did he jump up. It was too late then.

And so they had called in Covey, the slave-breaker. All that was seven months ago.

The moon over Chesapeake Bay can be very lovely. This night it was full, and the pine trees pointing to a cloudless sky were bathed in silver. Far out on the water a boat moved with languid grace, her sails almost limp, sending a shimmering ripple to the sandy shore.

The dark form painfully crawling between the trees paused at the edge of the cove. The wide beach out there under the bright moonlight was fully exposed. Should he risk it?

"Water." It was a moan. Then he lifted his eyes and saw the ship sailing away on the water. *A free ship going out to sea. Oh, Jesus!*

He had heard no sound of footsteps, not the slightest breaking of a twig, but a low voice close beside him said,

"Rest easy, you! I get water."

The boy shrank back, staring. A thick tree trunk close by split in two, and a very black man bent over him.

"I Sandy," the deep voice went on. "Lay down now."

The chilled blood in Frederick's broken body began to race. Once more he lost consciousness. This time he did not fight against it. A friend was standing by.

The black man moved swiftly. Kneeling beside the still figure he slipped his hand inside the rags. His face, inscrutable polished ebony, did not change; but far down inside his eyes a dull light glowed as he tore away the filthy cloth, sticky and stiff with drying blood. Was he too late? Satisfied, he eased the twisted limbs on the pine needles and then hurried down to the river's edge where he filled the tin can that hung from a cord over his shoulders.

Frederick opened his eyes when the water touched his lips. He sighed while Sandy gently wiped the clotted blood from his face and touched the gaping wound in the thick, matted hair. His voice sounded strange to his own ears when he asked, "How come you know?"

"This day I work close by Mr. Kemp. Car'line come. Tell me."

At the name Frederick's bones seemed to melt and flow in tears. Something which neither curses, nor kicks, nor blows had touched gave way. Caroline—Covey's own slave woman, who bore upon her body the marks of his sadistic pleasure, who seldom raised her eyes and always spoke in whispers—Caroline had gone for help.

Sandy did nothing to stay the paroxysm of weeping. He knew it was good, that healing would come sooner. Sandy was very wise. Up and down the Eastern Shore it was whispered that Sandy was "voodoo," that he was versed in black magic. Sandy was a full-blooded African. He remembered coming across the "great waters." He remembered the darkness, the moans and the awful smells. But he had been fortunate. The chain which fastened his small ankle to the hold of the ship also held his giant mother, and she had talked to him. All through the darkness she had talked to him. The straight, long-limbed woman of the Wambugwe had been a prize catch. The Bantus of eastern Africa were hard to capture. They brought the highest prices in the markets. Sandy remembered the rage of the dealer when his mother was found dead. She had never set foot on this new land, but all during the long journey she had talked—and Sandy had not forgotten. He had not forgotten one word.

This mother's son now sat quietly by on his haunches, waiting. Long ago he had learned patience. The waters of great rivers move slowly, almost imperceptibly; big trees of the forest stand still, yet each year grow; seasons come in due time; nothing stays the same. Sandy knew.

After a long shuddering sigh Frederick lay silent. Then Sandy sprang up.

"We go by my woman's house. Come," he said.

Frederick made an effort to rise. Sandy lifted the boy in his strong arms and stood him on his feet. For a moment he leaned heavily; then, with Sandy supporting him, he was conscious of being half-dragged through the thicket. His body was empty of pain, of thought, of emotion. Otherwise he might have hesitated. He knew that Sandy was married to a free colored woman who lived in her own hut on the edge of the woods. In her case the penalty for sheltering or aiding a recalcitrant slave might be death. "Free niggers" had no property value at all. Further, they were a menace in any slaveholding community. Their lot was often far more precarious than that of plantation hands. Strangely enough, however, the slaves looked upon such rare and fortunate beings with almost awesome respect.

On the other side of the woods, where good land overlooked the bay, the woman, Noma, sat in the opening of her hut gazing at the fire. It was burning low. The pieces of coke, glowing red in the midst of charred wood, no longer turned the trees around the clearing to flickering shadows. On this warm evening the woman had built her fire outdoors and hung the iron pot over it. The savory odor coming from that pot hung in the air. It was good, for into it had gone choice morsels put by during the week of toil. Noma was part Indian. Here on the shore of the Chesapeake she lived much as her mother's people had lived for generations back. She made and sold nets for shad and herring, and she fished and hunted as well as any man. She was especially skilful at seine-hauling. Sandy had built the hut, but she planted and tended her garden. Six days and nights she lived here alone, but on the evening of the seventh day Sandy always came. Except in isolated communities and under particularly vicious conditions slaves did little work on Sunday. Sandy's master allowed him to spend that one day a week with his wife. She sat now, her hands folded, waiting for Sandy. He was later than usual, but he would come.

The fire was almost out when she heard him coming through the brush. This was so unusual that she started up in alarm. She did not cry out when he appeared, supporting a bruised and battered form. She acted instantly to get this helpless being out of sight. They carried the boy inside the hut and gently deposited him on the soft pile of reeds in the corner. No time was lost with questions.

Quickly she brought warm water and stripped off the filthy rags. She bathed his wounds and wrapped a smooth green leaf about his head. She poured oil on the back, which all along its broad flatness lay open and raw, an oozing mass. A rib in his side seemed to be broken. They bound his middle with strips which she tore from her skirts.

Then she brought a steaming bowl. Frederick had had nothing to eat all day. For the past six months his food had been "stock" and nothing more. Now he was certain that never had he tasted anything so good as this succulent mixture. Into the pot the woman had dropped bits of pork, crabs and oysters, a handful of crisp seaweed and, from her garden, okra and green peppers and soft, ripe tomatoes. In the hot ashes she had baked corn pone. Frederick ate greedily, smacking his lips. Sandy squatted beside him with his own bowl. A burning pine cone lighted them while they ate, and Sandy smiled at the woman.

But hardly had he finished his bowl when sleep weighted Frederick down. The soothing oil, the sense of security and now this good, hot food were too much for him. He fell asleep with the half-eaten pone in his hand.

Then the other two went outside. The woman poked the fire, adding a few sticks. Sandy lay down beside it. He told his wife how that afternoon he had spied Caroline hiding in the bushes near where he worked. She acted like a terrified animal, he explained, so he had gone to her. Bit by bit she told him how Covey had beaten Captain Auld's boy, striking his head and kicking him in the side, and left him in the yard. She had seen the boy crawl away into the woods. Surely this time he would die.

"I do not think he die now. Man die hard." Sandy thought a moment. "I help him."

"How?" Noma's question took in the encircling woods, the bay. How could this boy escape? Sandy shook his head.

"He no go now. This one time, he go back."

The woman waited.

"I hear 'bout this boy—how he read and write. He smart with white man's learning."

"Ah!" said the woman, beginning to understand.

"Tonight I give him the knowing of black men. I call out the strength in his bones—the bones his mother made for him."

Sandy lay silent looking up through the tall trees at the stars. He spoke softly.

"I see in him great strength. Now he must know—and each day he will add to it. When time ripe—he go. That time he not go alone." And the woman nodded her head.

It was not the dawn flooding the Bay with splendor which woke Frederick, though the sun did come up like a golden ball and the waters turned to iridescent glory. Nor was it the crying of crows high up in the pine trees, nor even the barking of a dog somewhere down on the beach. Rather was it a gradual awareness of flaming words. Had he found a book, a new book more wonderful even than his precious *Columbian Orator?* He didn't see the words; yet they seemed to be all around him—living things that carried him down wide rivers and over mountains and across spreading plains. Then it was people who were with him—black men, very tall and big and strong. They turned up rich earth as black as their broad backs; they hunted in forests; some of them were in cities, whole cities of black folks. For they were free: they went wherever they wished; they worked as they planned. They even flew like birds, high in the sky. He was up there with them, looking down on the earth which seemed so small. He stretched his wings. He was strong. He could fly. He could fly in a flock of people. Who were they? He listened closely. That's it: he was not reading, he was listening. Somebody was making a speech. But it wasn't a speech—not like any he had ever heard—not at all like the preacher in Baltimore.

Frederick opened his eyes. The dream persisted—a shaft of brightness surrounding a strange crouching figure swaying there beside him, the flowing sound of words. The light hurt his eyes, but now Frederick realized it was Sandy. He was sitting cross-legged on the floor, head erect, eyes two glowing balls of fire, making low musical sounds. If they were words, they conveyed no meaning to Frederick. Bright sunshine poured through an opening in the cabin where a door hung back. Outside a rooster crowed, and memory jerked Frederick to full consciousness. He raised his hand to his eyes. The flow of sound ceased abruptly, and while the boy stared a mask seemed to fall over the man's shining face, snuffing out the glow and setting the features in stone. For a moment the figure was rigid. Then Sandy was on his feet. He spoke tersely.

"Good. You wake. Time you go."

The words were hard and compelling, and Frederick sat up. His body felt light. His sense of well-being was very real, as real as the smell of pine which seemed to exude from every board of the bare cabin. He looked around. The woman was nowhere in sight, but his eyes fell on a pail of water near by; and then Sandy was back with food. The bowl was warm in his hands, and Sandy stood silent waiting for him to eat. Frederick drew a long breath.

He was remembering: black men, men like Sandy, going places! He must find out— He looked up at Sandy.

"When— When I sleep— You talking." Sandy remained silent. Frederick rubbed the back of his hand across his forehead. Suddenly he felt a little foolish. He'd had a silly dream. But— Something drove him to the question.

"You talk to me?"

"Yes." The simple statement made him frown.

"But, I do not understand. What you saying? I was asleep."

A flicker of expression crossed Sandy's face. When he spoke his voice was less guttural.

"Body sleep, the hurt body. It sleep and heal. But you," Sandy leaned over and with his long forefinger touched Frederick lightly on the chest, "you not sleep."

"But I— How could I—?" Before the steady gaze of those calm eyes Frederick's protest died. He did not understand, but he was remembering. After a moment he asked simply, "Where am I going?"

This was what it meant. Sandy had a plan for him to run away. Well, he would try it. He was not afraid. Freedom sang in his blood. And so Sandy's reply caught him like a blow.

"Back. Back to Covey's."

"No! No!"

All the horror of the past six months was in his cry; the bowl dropped to the floor; shivering, he covered his face.

The pressure of Sandy's hand upon his shoulder recalled him. The terror gradually receded and was replaced by something which seemed to surround and buoy him up. He could not have told why. He only knew he was not afraid. But he wanted to live. He must live. He looked up at Sandy.

"Covey will kill me—beat me to death." There was no terror in his voice now, merely an explanation. Sandy shook his head.

"No." He was picking up the thick bowl. It had not broken, but its contents had spilled over the scrubbed floor. Sandy scraped up the bits of food and refilled the bowl from an earthen crock on the hearth. Frederick sat watching him. Sandy observed how he made no move— just waited. And his heart was satisfied. *This boy will do,* he thought. *He has patience—patience and endurance. Strength will come.* Once more he handed the bowl to Frederick.

"Eat now, boy," he said.

And Frederick ate, emptying the bowl. The food was good and the water Sandy gave him from the pail was fresh and cool. Frederick wondered where the woman had gone. He wanted to thank her. He wanted to thank her before—he went back. He said, "I'm sorry I dropped the bowl."

Then Sandy reached inside the coarse shirt he was wearing and drew out a small pouch—something tied up in an old piece of cloth.

"Now, hear me well."

Frederick set the bowl down.

"No way you can go now. Wise man face what he must. Big tree bend in strong wind and not break. This time no good. Later day you go. You go far."

Frederick bowed his head. He believed Sandy's words, but at the thought of Covey's lash his flesh shivered in spite of the bright promise. Sandy extended the little bag.

"Covey beat you no more. Wear this close to body—all the time. No man ever beat you."

Frederick's heart sank. He made no move to take the bag. His voice faltered.

"But—but Sandy, that's—that's voodoo. I don't believe in charms. I'm—I'm a Christian."

Sandy was very still. He gazed hard into the boy's gaunt face below the bloodstained bandage wrapped about his head; he saw the shadow in the wide, clear eyes; he thought of the lacerated back and broken rib, and his own eyes grew very warm. He spoke softly.

"You be very young."

He untied the little bag and carefully shook out its contents into the palm of his hand—dust, fine as powder, a bit of shriveled herb and several smooth, round pebbles. Then he held out the upturned hand to Frederick.

"Look now!" he said. "Soil of Africa—come cross the sea close by my mother's breast."

Holding his breath Frederick bent his head. It was as if a great hand lay upon his heart.

"And here"—Sandy's long fingers touched the withered fragment—"seaweed, flowered on great waters, waters of far-off lands,
waters of many lands."

Holding Frederick's wrist, Sandy carefully emptied the bits upon
the boy's palm, then gently closed his fingers.

"A thousand years of dust in one hand! Dust of men long gone,
men who lived so you live. Your dust."

He handed Frederick the little bag. And Frederick took it reverently. With the utmost care, lest one grain of dust be lost, he emptied
his palm into it. Then, drawing the cord tight, he placed the pouch
inside his rags, fastening the cord securely. He stood up, and his
head was clear. Again the black man thought, *He'll do!*

The boy stood speechless. There were things he wanted to say,
things he wanted to promise. This day, this spot, this one bright
morning was important. This man had saved his life, and suddenly
he knew that his life was important. He laid his hand on the black
man's arm.

"I won't be forgettin'," he said.

They walked together out into the morning and stood a moment
on the knoll, looking down at the bay. Then Frederick turned his
back and walked toward the trees. At the edge of the woods he
stopped and waved his hand, then disappeared in the hidden lane.

CHAPTER TWO

The road winds about Chesapeake Bay

THE ROOF of the colorless house needed mending. Its sagging made the attic ceiling slope at a crazy angle. Rainy weather—it always started in the middle of the night—it leaked, and Amelia had to pull her bed out onto the middle of the floor. The bed was a narrow iron affair, not too heavy to move. Amelia never complained. She was grateful for the roof her sister's husband had put over her head.

Edward Covey was considered a hard man. Amelia's neighbors could barely hide their pity when she announced that she was going to live with her sister.

"You mean the one who married Ed Covey?"

Then they sort of coughed and wished they hadn't asked the question. After all, where else could Tom Kemp's poor widow go? Lem Drake chewed a long time without a word after his wife told him the news. Then he spat.

" 'Melia never did no harm to nobody," he said.

"Old devil!"

Lem knew his wife was referring to Edward Covey. Otherwise he would have reproved her. Wasn't fitting talk for a woman.

So Amelia Kemp came down to the Bay to live in Edward Covey's house. Amelia was still bewildered. At thirty, she felt her life was over. Seemed like she hadn't ought to take Tom's death so hard. She'd known her husband was going to die: everybody else did. But Tom had kept on pecking at his land up there on the side of the hill. His pa had died, his ma had died, his brother had died. Now he was dead—all of them—pecking at the land.

Edward Covey was different. He was "getting ahead." Her sister

Lucy had stressed that difference from the moment of her arrival. Unnecessarily, Amelia was sure; because in spite of her heavy heart she had been properly impressed. What almost shook the widow out of her lethargy was her sister Lucy. She wouldn't have known her at all. True, they had not seen each other for years, and they were both older. Amelia knew that hill women were apt to be pretty faded by the time they were thirty-four. But Lucy, living in the low country, looked like an old hag. Amelia was shocked at her own thoughts.

"Mr. Covey's a God-fearing man."

These were almost her sister's first words, and Amelia had stared at her rather stupidly. All of her thoughts kept running back to Tom, it seemed. Amelia was sure her sister hadn't meant to imply that Tom hadn't been a "God-fearing" man. Though, as a matter of fact, she was a little vague in her own mind. She'd never heard Tom *say* anything about fearing God. He'd never been very free with talk about God.

That was before she met Mr. Covey. She had come up on the boat to St. Michaels where, on the dock, one of Edward Covey's "people" was waiting for her. This in itself was an event. There weren't any slaves in her county, and she felt pretty elegant being driven along the road with an obsequious black man holding the reins. After a time they had turned off the highway onto a sandy lane which carried them between fields jutting out into the bay. She could see the place from some distance, and in the dusk the sprawling building with barn and outhouses loomed like a great plantation manor. This impression hardly survived the first dusk, but Covey's passion to "get ahead" was plain to see.

Very soon Amelia Kemp was glad that she had been given a bed in the attic. The first few evenings, climbing up the narrow ladder from the lower floor, she had wondered about several rooms opening out on the second floor. They seemed to be empty. Soon she blessed her good fortune, and it wasn't long before she became convinced the idea had been her sister's—not Covey's.

Only when she lowered the attic trap door could she rid herself of him. Then she couldn't see the cruel, green eyes; she didn't feel him creeping up behind her or hear his voice. It was his voice particularly that she wanted to shut out, his voice coming out of the corner of his mouth, his voice that so perfectly matched the short, hairy hands. At the thought of the terrible things she had seen him do with those hands her flesh chilled.

Lucy had married Covey down in town where she had gone to work. He had not come to her home to meet her folks. So Amelia didn't know about the "slave-breaking." When she saw the slaves about, she assumed that her brother-in-law was more prosperous than she had imagined; and that first evening she could not understand why her sister was so worn.

Her education began the first morning, when they called her before dawn. She was used to getting up early, only she'd thought folks with slaves to do their work could lie abed till after sun-up. Though she dressed hastily and hurried downstairs, it was quite evident she was keeping them waiting in the big room. The stench of unwashed bodies stopped her in the doorway.

Her first impression was one of horror. Covey seated at the table, a huge book spread open in front of him, thrust his round head in her direction and glared wolfishly. The oil lamp's glare threw him into sharp relief. The light touched Lucy's white face and the figure of another man, larger than Covey, who gave her a flat, malignant stare. But behind them the room was filled with shadows frozen into queer and grotesque shapes.

"You're late, Sister Amelia." Her brother-in-law's tone was benign. "This household starts the day with worship—all our big family."

He waved his arm, taking in all the room. A ripple of movement undulated the darkness, quivered, and then was gone.

"I'm so sorry," Amelia managed to murmur as she groped her way to a chair. Gasps came from behind her. She dared not turn around, and sat biting her lips. Covey seemed to hear nothing. He was peering at the book, his short, stubby finger tracing each word as he began to read slowly and painfully:

"O give thanks unto the Lord, for he is good; for his mercy endureth for ever.
Let the redeemed of the Lord say so, whom he hath redeemed from the hand of the enemy;
And gathered them out of the lands, from the east, and from the west, from the north, and from the south.
They wandered in the wilderness in a solitary way; they found no city to dwell in.
Hungry and thirsty, their soul fainted in them.
Then they cried unto the Lord in their trouble and he delivered them out of their distresses.

And he led them forth by the right way, that they might
   go to a city of habitation."

"Praise the Lord!" added Covey and closed the Bible with a heavy
thump. "Now then, Fred, lead us in song."

Amelia heard the choked gasp behind her. She could feel the
struggle that cut off the panting breath. Waiting was unbearable.

"You, Fred!" The command jerked a cry from the shadows. A
memory flashed across Amelia's mind. *Sid Green lashing his half-
crazed horse, which had fallen in the ditch—Tom grabbing the whip
and knocking Sid down.*

Then a strained voice began to quiver. It missed several beats
at first but gathered strength until Amelia knew it was a boy behind
her, singing. In a moment, from Covey's twisted mouth there came
uneven, off-key notes, then Lucy's reed-like treble sounded. From the
shadows the music picked up, strange and wild and haunting. At
first Amelia thought this was an unfamiliar chant, then she recognized the rolling words:

      "O for a thousand tongues to sing
       My great Redeem's praise,
       The glories of my God and King,
       The triumphs of his grace."

When the music died away Covey fell on his knees, his face lifted
beside the oil lamp. His words poured forth with a passion and fervor
which pounded like hammers in the stifling gloom. He groveled in
shameless nakedness, turning all the hideousness of his fear upon
their bowed heads. Then he rose, face shining and picking up a
heavy, many-pronged cowhide from the corner, drove the shuffling
figures out into the gray morning. Amelia remembered the cold:
she had shivered in the hallway.

The only slave left to help her sister was a slow, silent creature
who now moved toward the kitchen.

"We've et. The—the—" Lucy was speaking with a hesitation
which Amelia recalled later. "The—woman will show you. Then you
can help me with the renderin'."

It was warm in the big kitchen. A smoking lamp hanging from
the ceiling swayed fretfully as the door closed and Lucy threw a
piece of wood on the fire. Remains of a hasty meal were scattered
upon the table.

"Clean up this mess and give Miss Amelia some breakfast."

Amelia saw her sister shove the woman forward as she spoke. The tight hardness in her voice fell strangely upon Amelia's ears. Without another word Lucy disappeared into the pantry.

Amelia was afraid. She suddenly realized that it had been fear that had first stopped her on the threshold, and nothing had taken place to dissipate that fear—not the scripture reading, not the singing, not the prayer. She was afraid now of this silent, dark woman, whose face remained averted, whose step was noiseless. Surely some ominous threat lay behind the color of such—such creatures. Irrelevantly she remembered Tom's black horse—the one on which he had come courting. Amelia made a peremptory gesture.

"I'll eat here!" Fear hardened her voice. She would eat like a grand lady being served by a nigger.

And then the woman turned and looked at her. She was not old. Her brown skin was firm and smooth, her quivering mouth was young, and her large eyes, set far apart, were liquid shadows.

A man could drown himself in those shadows. The thought was involuntary, unwilled, horrible—and instantly checked—but it added to her fear.

She picked up bits of information throughout the long morning, while Lucy stirred grease sizzling in deep vats, dipped tallow candles and sewed strips of stiff, coarse cloth. The work about the house seemed endless, and Lucy drove herself from one task to another. Amelia wondered why she didn't leave more for the slave woman. Finally she asked. The vehement passion in Lucy's voice struck sharply.

"The lazy cow!" Then, after a pause she added, "She's a breeder." Her lips snapped shut.

"A breeder? What's that? Does she have some special work?"

Lucy laughed shortly.

"Ain't they no niggers up home yet?" she asked.

Amelia shook her head.

Lucy sighed. It was a sound of utter weariness.

"Mr. Covey says you can't git ahead without niggers. You jus' can't."

"But you said—" began Amelia.

"Mr. Covey bought her," Lucy explained with a sort of dogged grimness, "for—for more—stock. Mr. Covey's plannin' on buyin' all this land. Niggers come high. You wouldn's believe what Mr. Covey paid for that there Caroline." Pride puckered her lips like green persimmon.

Amelia swallowed. Her mouth felt very dry. She cleared her throat.

"Well, he's makin' a good start."

"Oh, them!" Lucy bit her thread. "They ain't all hissen. He takes slaves over from the plantations hereabouts to—train."

"Then he—"

A cry of stark terror coming from the yard brought Amelia up in alarm. Lucy calmly listened a moment.

"Sounds like Mr. Covey's having to whop that Fred again," she said. "He's a bad one!"

What Amelia was hearing now bleached her face. Lucy's composed indifference rebuked her. She tried to control the trembling of her lips.

"You mean—the boy—who sang this morning?"

"That's him—stubborn as a mule. Reckon that singin' will be a mite weaker tomorrow."

And Mrs. Covey giggled.

The day unwound like a scroll. By mid-afternoon fatigue settled all along Amelia's limbs. Outside the sun shone brightly—perfect February weather for early plowing. The kitchen door stood open to the sunshine, and Amelia paused a moment looking out toward the bay.

A small child two or three years old crawled out from under a bush and started trotting across the littered back yard. Amelia stood watching her. Beneath the tangled mass of brown curls the little face was streaked with dirt. It was still too cool for this tot to run about barefoot, Amelia thought, looking around for the mother. She held out her hand and the child stopped, staring at her with wide eyes.

"Well, little one, where do you come from?" There was no answering smile on the child's face. In that moment Amelia heard a swift step behind her.

"Don't touch that nigger!" Lucy's voice cracked like a whip. Her face was distorted with fury. Amelia saw the dark woman, bending over a tub in the corner, lift her head. Lucy leaped at her and struck her full in the face.

"Get that brat out of here," she screamed. "Get her back where she belongs. Get her out!"

With one movement the woman was across the floor and outside the door. She swept up the child in her arm and, holding her close, ran behind the barn.

"How dare she! How dare she!"

Lucy was shaking as with an ague—she seemed about to fall. Still Amelia did not understand.

"But, Lucy—what are you saying? That child's white."

"Shut up, you fool!" Her sister turned on her. "You fool! It's her's. It's her's, I tell you. And what is she? She's a nigger—a filthy, stinking nigger!"

She began to cry, and Amelia held her close, remembering the large green eyes, set in the little girl's pinched face.

Nothing much was happening in Maryland that spring of 1834. In Virginia they hanged Nat Turner. John Brown, on a wave of prosperity, was making money in his Ohio tannery. William Lloyd Garrison was publishing the *Liberator* in Boston, and a man named Lovejoy was trying to start an Abolitionist paper out West, trying both Kansas and Ohio. But Maryland had everything under control.

The Coveys had no neighbors. The farm, surrounded on three sides with water, lay beyond a wide tract of straggling pine trees. The trees on Covey's land had been cut down, and the unpainted buildings were shaken and stained by heavy northwest winds. From her attic window Amelia could see Poplar Island, covered with a thick black forest, and Keat Point, stretching its sandy, desert-like shores out into the foam-crested bay. It was a desolate scene.

The rains were heavy that spring, and Covey stayed in the fields until long after dark, urging the slaves on with words or blows. He left nothing to Hughes, his cousin and overseer.

"Niggers drop off to sleep minute you turn your back," he groaned. "Have to keep right behind 'em."

Amelia battled with mud tracked from one end of the house to the other.

Then came summer with its oppressive heat and flashing thunder storms that whipped the waters to roaring fury.

"Family" prayers were dispensed with only on Sunday mornings. Regardless of the weather, Mr. Covey and his wife went to church. It was regrettable that the slaves had no regular services. Big plantations could always boast of at least one slave preacher. Mr. Covey hadn't reached that status yet. He was on his way. He observed the

Sabbath as a day of rest. Nobody had to go to the fields, and nothing much had to be done—except the cooking, of course.

So Amelia could lie in bed this Sunday morning in August. All night the attic had been like a bake-oven. Just before dawn it had cooled a little, and Amelia lay limp. By raising herself on her elbow she could see through a slit in the sloping roof. White sails skimmed across the shining surface of the bay. Amelia sighed. This morning the white ships depressed her. They were going somewhere.

The heat, she thought, closing her eyes, had made things worse than usual. Mr. Covey would certainly kill that Fred—that is, if he wasn't already dead. Well, why didn't he do his work? She had thought at first the boy had intelligence, but here of late he'd lost every spark of sense—just slunk around, looking glum and mean, not paying any attention to what was told him. Then yesterday—pretending to be sick!

"Reckon I 'bout broke every bone in his body," Mr. Covey had grunted with satisfaction.

"Captain Auld won't like it," Lucy warned.

That made Mr. Covey mad as hops. Lucy kept out of his way the rest of the evening. Amelia saw him twist Caroline's arm till she bent double. That wench! *She* wasn't so perk these days either—sort of dragged one leg behind her.

Well, Amelia thought, swinging her own bony shanks over the side of the bed, *I'm glad they didn't send the hounds after him.* He was sulking somewhere in the woods. But Mr. Covey said the dogs would tear him to pieces. *A bad way to die—even for a nigger.*

"He'll come back," Covey had barked. "A nigger always comes crawlin' back to his eatin' trough."

Amelia left the cotton dress open at the neck. Maybe it wouldn't be so hot today. Lucy was already down, her eyes red in a drawn face. Her sister guessed that she had spent a sleepless night, tossing in the big bed, alone. Caroline was nowhere in sight.

When he appeared, dressed in his Sunday best, Mr. Covey was smiling genially. This one day he could play his favorite rôle—master of a rolling plantation, leisurely, gracious, served by devoted blacks. He enjoyed Sunday.

"Not going to church, Amelia?" he asked pleasantly as he rose from the table.

Amelia was apologetic. "No, Mr. Covey, I— I don't feel up to it this mornin'. Got a mite of headache."

"Now that's too bad, Sister. It's this awful heat. Better lie down a while." He turned to his wife. "Come, my dear, we don't want to be late. You dress and I'll see if Bill has hitched up." Picking his teeth, he strolled out to the yard.

Amelia started scraping up the dishes.

"Leave 'em be." Lucy spoke crossly. "Reckon Caroline can do something."

So Amelia was out front and saw Fred marching up the road! Funny, but that's exactly the way it seemed. He wasn't just walking. She was digging around her dahlias, hoping against hope they would show a little life. She had brought the bulbs from home and set them out in front of the house. Of course they weren't growing, but Amelia kept at them. Sometimes dahlias surprised you.

She straightened up and stared. It was Fred, all right, raising a dust out there in the road.

Mr. and Mrs. Covey were coming down the porch steps just as Fred swung in the gate. He kept right on coming. Poor Lucy's mouth sagged open, but Mr. Covey smiled like a saint.

"Well, now, you're back, and no worse for wear." He paused, taking in the discolored bandage and the spattered tatters. He spoke impatiently. "Get yourself cleaned up. This is Sunday." The boy stepped aside. Mr. Covey and his wife moved toward their buggy. As Fred turned to go around back, Mr. Covey called to him. "Oh, yes, round up those pigs that got into the lower lot last night. That's a good boy."

Then the master leaned over, waved his hand at Amelia and drove away, sitting beside his good wife. It made a pretty picture! Amelia could see Fred, standing at the side of the house, facing the road. There was a funny look on his face.

Amelia's thoughts kept going back to the way he'd come marching up the road. Her mind kept weaving all sorts of queer fancies. Did slaves really think like people? Covey had beaten him half to death. How could he walk so? Just showed what a thick skin they had. And that great head of his! She hadn't noticed how big it was till this morning.

Covey's manner didn't fool her a mite. He never flogged slaves on Sunday, but he'd sure take it out of that boy in the morning.

She woke up Monday morning thinking about the look on Fred's face and hurried downstairs. Seemed like Mr. Covey cut the prayers short. Maybe he had something on his mind, too. As they started out,

Amelia heard him tell Fred to clean out the barn. That meant he wouldn't be going to the fields with the others. Covey lingered a few minutes in the house, tightening the handle on his lash.

Amelia had always tried to get away from the awful floggings. Lucy said she was chicken-hearted. But this morning she was filled with an odd excitement. She wanted to see. She decided against going out in the yard. With a quick look at Lucy's bent back, she slipped out of the kitchen and almost ran up the stairs. Her attic window overlooked the yard.

It was fully light now. Covey and the overseer were standing a few feet from the back door. Hughes held a looped cord in his hand and was showing something to Covey, who listened closely. Amelia could see them plain enough, but they were talking too low for her to hear. Then Fred swung the barn doors back and fastened them. Both men turned and watched him. He certainly was going about his job with a will. He wasn't wasting any time standing around. Evidently he was getting ready to lead out the oxen.

She saw Hughes start away, stop and say something. Then she heard Covey's, "Go ahead. I'll manage."

Her attention was attracted by the way Fred was handling the oxen. They were ornery beasts, but he didn't seem afraid of them at all. Covey too was watching. Amelia couldn't see what he had done with his lash. He held in his hand the cord Hughes had handed him. Fred seemed to be having some trouble with one of the oxen. He couldn't fasten something. He backed away, turned and in a moment started climbing up the ladder to the hayloft.

The moment the boy's back was turned, Covey streaked across the yard. The movement was so unexpected and so stealthy that Amelia cried out under her breath. She saw what he was going to do even before he grabbed Fred by the leg and brought him down upon the hard ground with a terrible jar. He was pulling the loop over the boy's legs when, with a sudden spring, the lithe body had leaped at the man, a hand at his throat! Amelia gripped the ledge with her hands and leaned out. They were both on the ground now, the dark figure on top. The boy loosened his fingers. Amelia could see Covey's upturned face. He was puffing, but it was bewilderment, not pain, that made his face so white and queer. The boy sprang up and stood on his guard while Covey scrambled to his feet.

"You ain't resistin', you scoundrel?" Covey shouted in a hoarse voice.

And Frederick—body crouched, fist raised—said politely, "Yessir." He was breathing hard.

Covey made a move to grab him, and Fred sidestepped. Covey let out a bellow that brought Lucy running to the door.

"Hughes! Help! Hughes!"

Amelia saw Hughes, halfway across the field, start running back. Meanwhile the boy held his ground, not striking out but ready to defend himself against anything Covey could do.

The slave boy has gone mad! She'd heard of slaves "going bad." She ought to go down and help. They'd all be murdered in their beds. But she couldn't leave her window. She couldn't take her eyes off the amazing sight—a dumb slave standing firmly on his feet, his head up. Standing so, he was almost as tall as Covey.

Now Hughes came bolting into the yard and rushed Fred. He met a kick in the stomach that sent him staggering away in pain. Covey stared after his overseer stupidly. The nigger had kicked a white man! Covey dodged back—needlessly, for Fred had not moved toward him. He stood quietly waiting, ready to ward off any attack. Covey eyed him.

"You goin' to keep on resistin'?"

There was something plaintive about Covey's question. Amelia had a crazy impulse to laugh. She leaned far out the window. She must hear. The boy's voice reached her quite distinctly—firm, positive tones.

"Yessir. You can't beat me no mo'—never no mo'."

Now Covey was frightened. He looked around: his cowhide—a club—anything. Hughes, at one side, straightened up.

"I'll get the gun," he snarled.

Covey gave a start, but he spoke out of the corner of his mouth. "It's in the front hall."

Amelia saw Hughes coming toward the house; his face was livid. Then she heard Lucy's shrill voice and Hughes's curses. She guessed what Lucy was saying—that they dare not kill Captain Auld's slave.

The boy had not moved. He was watching Covey, whose eyes had fallen on a knotty piece of wood lying just outside the stable door. He began easing his way toward it. Amelia's breath was coming in panting gulps. Her knees were shaking.

Her fingers felt numb on the splintery wood of the ladder. She nearly slipped. Her legs almost doubled up under her when she leaned over the banister, peering down into the hall below. She couldn't see the gun, but she could still hear Hughes's angry voice out back.

Shadows seemed to clutch at her skirts, the stairs cracked and creaked as she crept down, while the thick, heavy smell that lurked in the hall nearly sickened her. Her cold, shaking fingers clutched the barrel of the gun standing upright in the corner, and she somehow managed to get up the stairs before the door at the back of the hall opened. She crouched against the wall, listening, not daring now to climb her ladder. She heard Hughes clumping about below, his heavy boots kicking objects aside. She heard him curse, at first softly, then with a roar. A few feet away a door stood partly open. Holding the gun close, she tiptoed along the wall and into one of the rooms.

Meanwhile, Frederick knew that Hughes had gone for a gun, but that was not as important as Covey's cautious approach to the thick, knotty stick of wood.

He'll knock me down with it, Frederick thought. He breathed evenly, knowing exactly what he was going to do. The moment Covey leaned over to grab the stick, the boy leaped forward, seized his shirt collar with both hands and brought the man down, stretched out full length in the cow dung. Covey grabbed the boy's arms and yelled lustily.

Feet, suddenly no longer tired, were hastening toward the back yard. The news was spreading.

Bill, another of Covey's "trainees," came around the house. He stared—open-mouthed.

"Grab him! Bill! Grab him!" Covey shouted.

Bill's feet were rooted to the ground, his face a dumb mask.

"Whatchu say, Massa Covey, whatchu say?"

"Get hold of him! Grab him!"

Bill's eyes were round. He swallowed, licking out his tongue.

"I gotta get back to mah plowin', Massa. Look! Hit's sun-up." With a limp hand he indicated the sun shooting its beams over the eastern woods and turned vaguely away.

"Come back here, you fool! He's killing me!"

A flash of interest flickered across the broad, flat face. Bill took several steps forward. Frederick fixed him with a baleful gaze and spoke through clenched teeth.

"Don't you put your hands on me!"

Bill sagged. "My God, ye crazy coon, I ain't a-gonna tech ye!" And he shuffled around the barn.

Covey cursed. He could not free himself. The boy was like a slippery octopus, imprisoning him with his arms and legs.

Frederick was panting now. His heart sank when he saw Caroline.

She must have been milking in the shed, for she carried a brimming pail. Covey could make her help him. She really was a powerful woman, and Frederick knew she could master him easily now, exhausted as he was.

Covey, too, saw her and called out confidently. Caroline stopped. She set down the pail of milk. Covey relaxed, an evil grin on his face.

And then—Caroline laughed! It wasn't loud or long; but Covey sucked in his breath at the sound.

"Caroline! Hold him!" The iron in his voice was leaking out.

Caroline's words were low in her throat—rusty because so seldom used. Two words came.

"Who? Me?"

She picked up the pail of milk and walked toward the house, dragging her leg a little.

Frederick felt Covey go limp. And in that moment he sprang up, himself grabbed the knotty chunk of wood and backed away. Covey rolled over on to his side. He was not hurt, but he was dazed. When he did get to his feet, swaying a bit, the yard seemed crowded with dark, silent forms. Actually only four or five slaves, hearing the outcries, had come running and now showed the whites of their eyes from a safe distance. But Covey's world was tottering. He must do something.

The boy stood there, holding the stick. Now Covey went toward him. Frederick saw the defeat on his face, and he made no move to strike him. So Covey was able to take him by the shoulders and shake him mightily.

"Now then, you wretch," he said in a loud voice, "get on with your work! I wouldn't 'a' whipped you half so hard if you hadn't resisted. That'll teach you!"

When he dropped his hands and turned around, the dark figures had slipped away. He stood a moment blinking up at the sun. It was going to be another hot day. He wiped his sleeve across his sweating face, leaving a smear of barnyard filth on his cheek. The kitchen door was closed. *Just like that skunk, Hughes, to go off and leave me!* He'd send him packing off the place before night. But he didn't want to go into the house now. He was tired. Covey walked over to the well and stood looking out toward the bay.

Frederick once more started up the ladder. He would get some sweet, fresh hay for the oxen. Then he could lead them out.

CHAPTER THREE

An old man drives his mule

WHEN COVEY CAME down sick right after Hughes was fired, his wife was certain things would go to rack and ruin. Strangely enough, they did not. The stock got fed; the men left for the fields every morning; wood was cut and piled, and the never-ending job of picking cotton went on.

Amelia thought she'd never seen anything prettier. Cotton didn't grow up in the hills, and now the great green stalks with their bulbs of silver fascinated her. With no more floggings going on out back, she began to notice things. She found herself watching the rhythm of a slave's movements at work, a black arm plunged into the gleaming mass. She even caught the remnants of a song floating back to her. There was peace in the air. And the boy Fred went scampering about like a colt.

Inside the house, Covey groaned and cursed. After a time he sat silent, huddled in a chair, staring at the wall.

He'd sent Hughes packing, all right. But there had been hell to pay first. Hughes had been all set to go in town and bring out the authorities. The nigger had struck him, he blubbered, and should get the death penalty for it. The young mule certainly had given his dear cousin an awful wallop. Had Covey let himself go, he would have grinned. But, after all, it was unthinkable for a black to strike a white man. *The bastard!* But had it got about that he, Covey, couldn't handle a loony stripling—not a day over sixteen—he would be ruined. Nobody would ever give him another slave to break. So Hughes's mouth had to be shut. He was willing to go, but he had forced a full month's salary out of Covey. The worst thing was Hughes's taking the gun along in the bargain!

Hughes swore he couldn't find the gun. But Covey knew he had cleaned that gun just the day before and stood it right behind the hall door. That's where he always kept it, and he knew it was there. No use telling him one of the boys took it. A black won't touch a gun with a ten-foot pole. No, it had gone off with Hughes, and he'd just have to get himself another one next time he went to Baltimore.

By now Covey had convinced himself that most of his troubles stemmed from Hughes. Take the matter of Captain Auld's boy. After Hughes left, he'd handled him without a mite of trouble.

Frederick for his part had tasted freedom—and it was good. "When a slave cannot be flogged," he wrote many years later, "he is more than half free."

So it was as a free man that he reasoned with himself. He would prove to Covey—and through him to Captain Auld—that he could do whatever job they assigned. When he did not understand, he asked questions. Frederick was not afraid. He was not afraid of anything. Furthermore, his fellow-workers looked up to him with something like awe. Until now he had been just another link in the shackles that bound them to the mountain of despair. Their hearts had been squeezed of pity, as their bodies had been squeezed of blood and their minds of hope. But they had survived to witness a miracle! They told it over and over, while they bent their backs and swung their arms. They whispered it at night. Old men chewed their toothless gums over it, and babies sucked it in with their mothers' milk.

The word was passed along, under cover, secret, unsuspected, until all up and down the Eastern Shore, in field and kitchen, they knew what had happened in "ole man Covey's back yard on 'at mawnin'!" And memories buried beneath avalanches of wretchedness began to stir.

Something heard somewhere, someone who "got through!" A trail—footprints headed "no'th"—toward a star! And as they talked, eyes that had glazed over with dullness cleared, shoulders straightened beneath the load, and weary, aching limbs no longer dragged.

It was a good fall. Even Covey, forcing himself through the days, had to admit that. Crops had done well, and the land he had put in cotton promised much. Undoubtedly cotton was the thing. Next year he would buy a gin and raise nothing else. But now it was a big job to weigh, bale, and haul his cotton into town.

Covey's strength came back slowly. He had Tom Slater in to help him for a spell, but Tom wasn't much good at figuring; and figuring was necessary, if he didn't want those town slickers to cheat him out of every cent.

One Sunday evening he was sitting out front, waiting for it to get dark so he could go to bed. Around the house came Amelia, trowel in hand. Covey didn't mind Amelia's flowers. That little patch of purple was right nice. But Amelia had hardly knelt down when from out back came the boy Fred. He stopped at a respectful distance and bowed.

"You sent for me, Miss Amelia?"

Covey sucked his tongue with approval. They had said this nigger was house-broke. He sure had the manners. Amelia had jumped up and was talking brightly.

"Yes, Fred. I wonder if you can't fix that old gate. Even with our netting this yard has no protection as long as the gate's no good."

She indicated the worm-eaten boards sagging between two rotten posts. Fred turned and studied them a moment before replying.

"Miss Amelia," he said slowly, "I better make you a new gate."

Damn! thought Covey.

"Can you do that?" Amelia was delighted.

"Yes, ma'm. I'll measure it right now."

Covey watched him hurry across the yard, draw a piece of string from somewhere about him, and with clear-cut, precise movements measure the height and width between the two posts.

"I'll have to allow for straightenin' these posts and the swing in and out, but I'm sure I can find the right sort of pieces in the barn," he explained. "If it's all right with Mr. Covey."

"Oh, I'm sure he won't mind."

The next thing, Amelia was coming toward him. His wife's sister certainly wasn't as droopy as she used to be. Didn't seem to be moping around any more.

"Mr. Covey, don't you think it would be very nice if Fred makes us a new gate? He says he can. It'll help the appearance of the whole yard."

Yes, she sure had perked up.

"Go ahead," he grunted.

Fred made one last calculation with his string. "I'll go see about the wood right away," he said, and turned to leave.

"Wait till tomorrow," Covey barked. "It's still the Sabbath."

"Yes, sir," said Fred and disappeared around the house. Amelia bent over her flowers.

A thought was breaking through the thick layers of Covey's brain. Damned if that fresh nigger didn't sound just like one of those city slickers! The way he had measured that opening! *I'll bet he can figure!*

It was a staggering thought and struck him unprepared. Full on like that, it was monstrous. But when the first shock had passed— when the ripples sort of spread out—he calmed down and began to cogitate.

He went back over what Captain Auld had said—how the buck had been ruined by the Captain's city kin, coddled and taught to read until he was too smart for his own or anybody else's good.

"Take it out of him!" Captain Auld had stormed. "Break him!" And he had promised he would. *Well!*

Covey was so still that Lucy, coming to the door and peeping out, thought he was dozing. She went away shaking her head. *Poor Mr. Covey! He's not himself these days.*

He was turning it over in his mind, weighing it. Really big plantations all had some smart niggers on them, niggers who could work with tools, niggers who could measure and figure, even buy and sell. Naturally he hated such niggers when he came across them in town, often as not riding sleek, black horses. But having one on your own plantation was different. Like having a darky preacher around, like being a Colonel in a great white plantation house with a rolling green and big trees.

The last faint streaks of color faded from the sky. For a little while the tall pines in the distance loomed black against soft gray. Then they faded, and overhead the stars came out.

Covey rose, yawned and stretched himself. Tomorrow he would talk to Fred about that figuring. It was still the Sabbath.

There was nothing subtle about Covey the next day. He was clumsy, disagreeable and domineering. Frederick suspected that he was being tricked. But there was no turning back. He said, "Yes, sir, I can chalk up the bales."

So he marked and counted each load of cotton, noted the weighing of the wheat and oats, set down many figures. And Covey took his "chalk man" to town with him. It got about among the white folks that the "Auld boy" could read and write. The white masters heard other whisperings too—vague, amusing "nigger talk." But it was disturbing. Couldn't be too careful these days. There had been that Nat Turner! And a cold breath lifted the hair on the backs of their necks.

Frederick's term of service with Edward Covey expired on Christmas day, 1834. The slave-breaker took him back to Captain Auld. The boy was in good shape, but Captain Auld regarded both of them sourly. The talk had reached his ears, and he had been warned that he had better get rid of this slave. "One bad sheep will spoil a whole flock," they said. Captain Auld dared not ignore the advice of his powerful neighbors. His slave holdings were small compared to theirs. Yet he did not want to sell a buck not yet grown to his full value. Therefore he arranged to hire the boy out to easy-going Mr. William Freeland, who lived on a fine old farm about four miles from St. Michaels.

Covey covered the dirt road back to his place at a savage pace. He was in a mean mood. That night he flogged a half-wit slave until the black fainted. Then he stomped into the house and, fully dressed, flung himself across the bed. Lucy didn't dare touch him and Caroline wouldn't.

Frederick's return to the Auld plantation was an event among the slaves. Little boys regarded him with round eyes; the old folks talked of his grandmother. There were those who claimed to have known his mother; others now recalled that they had fed from the same trough, under the watchful eye of "Aunt Katy." He had returned during "the Christmas" so they could wine and dine him. He saw the looks on their faces, felt the warm glow. For the first time he saw a girl smiling at him. Life was good.

Early on the morning of January 1 he set out from St. Michaels for the Freeland plantation. He had been given a fresh allotment of clothes—a pair of trousers, a thin coarse jacket, and even a pair of heavy shoes. Captain Auld did not intend his slave to show up before "quality" in a state which would reflect shame on his owner. Though not rich, the Freelands were one of the first families of Maryland.

Life would be easier for him now, Frederick knew. But, as he walked along the road that morning, he was not hastening toward the greener grass and spreading shade trees on Mr. Freeland's place. He was whistling, but not because he would sleep on a cot instead of on the floor, nor because his food would be better and ampler. He might even wear a shirt. But that wasn't it. Two strong, brown legs were carrying his body to the Freeland plantation, but Frederick was speeding far ahead.

He carried his shoes in his hand. Might need those good, strong shoes! They'd take him over sharp rocks and stubby, thorn-covered fields and through swamplands. *Rub them with pepper and they leave no scent!* He kicked the sand up with his bare feet. It felt good. He stamped down hard, leaving his footprints in the damp earth.

He met an old man driving a mule.

"Whar yo' goin', boy?" the old man asked.

"I'm on my way!" It was a song.

The old man peered at him closely. He was nearly blind and knew his time was almost over. But he wanted to see the face of this young one who spoke so.

"Whatchu say, boy?" He spoke sharply.

"My master's sending me over to Mr. Freeland's place," Frederick explained.

"Oh!" the old man said, and waited.

Frederick lowered his voice, though there was no one else in sight.

"It is close by the bay."

The old man's breath made a whistling sound as it escaped from the dried reeds of his throat.

"God bless yo', boy!" Then he passed on by, driving his mule.

Several hours later Amelia passed the same old man. She had offered to drive into town and pick up some things for the house. When Covey had snarled that all the boys were busy, she said cheerfully she could drive herself.

"I did all of Tom's buying," she reminded him. Covey frowned. He didn't like opinionated women.

Amelia urged Lucy to go along; the drive would do her good. But poor Lucy only shrank further into herself and shook her head.

The fact was that Amelia was expecting some mail at the post office. Also, she wanted to mail a letter. She was writing again to Tom's cousin who lived in Washington.

Tom had missed Jack terribly when he went away. They had shot squirrels and rabbits together, but Jack never took to plowing. He was kind of wild. Jack had urged Tom to give up, to leave the hills. Tom had hung on—and now he was dead. They had told Amelia she must be resigned, that it was "God's will."

When Amelia began to wonder, she wrote Jack. *Why did Tom die?* she asked him. From there she had gone on to other questions, many questions. Words had sprawled over the thin sheets. She had never written such a long letter.

Jack had replied immediately. But that letter had been only the first. He had sent her newspapers and books. As she read them her astonishment increased. She read them over and over again.

Now she was thinking about going down to Washington. She was thinking about it. She hardly saw the old man, driving his mule.

The old man did not peer closely at her. His mule turned aside politely.

CHAPTER FOUR

Frederick comes to a dead end

Wᴵᴸᴸᴵᴬᴹ Fʀᴇᴇʟᴀɴᴅ, master of Freelands, gave his rein the slightest tug as he rode between the huge stone columns. It was good to be alone and let all memory of the Tilghmans drain from his mind, including Delia's girlish laughter. He was glad the Christmas was over. Now he could have peace.

Just inside the wrought-iron gates, where the graveled drive was guarded by a stately sycamore, the big mare came to a quivering pause. She knew this was where her master wished to stop. From this spot the old dwelling far up the drive, with tulip poplars huddled around it, was imposing.

It was a good house, built in the good old days when Maryland boasted noble blood. Beside the winding staircase of the wide hall hung a painting of Eleanor, daughter of Benedict Calvert, sixth Lord Baltimore. William Freeland was not a Calvert; but the families had been close friends, and the lovely Eleanor had danced in those halls. That was before Maryland had broken her ties with England. For a long time there were those who regretted the day Maryland signed the Articles of Confederation; but when ambitious neighbors crowded their boundaries, loyal Marylanders rallied round; and in 1785 William Freeland's father, Clive Freeland, had gone to Mount Vernon to contest Virginia's claim to the Potomac. He had spoken eloquently, and Alexander Hamilton had accompanied the young man home. There Hamilton had been received by Clive's charming bride, had rested and relaxed and, under the spell of Freelands, had talked of his own coral-strewn, sun-drenched home in the Caribbeans.

In those days the manor house sat in the midst of a gently rolling green. Spreading trees towered above precise box borders; turfed walkways, bordered with beds of delicate tea-roses, crossed each other at right angles; Cherokee rose-vines climbed the garden walls; and wistaria, tumbling over the veranda, showed bright against the white-washed bricks, joined with pink crêpe myrtle by the door and flowed out toward the white-blossomed magnolias in the yard. The elegant, swarthy Hamilton lingered, putting off his return to New York as long as he could. He told them how he hated that city's crooked, dirty streets and shrill-voiced shopkeepers.

All this was fifty years ago. The great estate had been sold off in small lots. On the small plantation that was left, the outhouses were tumbling down, moss hung too low on the trees, the hedges needed trimming and bare places showed in the lawn. Everything needed a coat of paint. Slowly but surely the place was consuming itself, as each year bugs ate into the tobacco crop.

"It will last out our time." More than that consideration did not concern the present master of Freelands.

There was a faint wild fragrance of sweet shrub in the air—the smell of spring. It was the first day of January, but he knew that plowing must be got under way. Spring would be early. He sighed. Undoubtedly, things would have been very different had his elder brother lived. For Clive, Jr., had had will and energy. He would have seen to it that the slaves did their work. He would have made the crops pay. Clive had been a fighter. In fact, Clive had been killed in a drunken brawl. The whole thing had been hushed up, and young William sent off to Europe. For several years they spoke of him as "studying abroad." Actually, William did learn a great deal. He met lots of people who became less queer as the days and months passed. He ran into Byron in Italy.

A cable from his mother had brought him hurrying back home. His father was dead when he arrived.

Everything seemed to have shrunk. For a little while he was appalled by what he saw and heard. Then gradually the world outside fell away. His half-hearted attempts to change things seemed silly. He had forgotten how easy life could be in Maryland.

Now he looked at the substantial old house. Someone was opening the second-floor shutters. That meant his mother was getting up. He smiled, thinking how like the house she was—untouched, unmarred, unshaken by the passing years. At seventy she was magnificent—the real master of Freelands. He bowed to her every wish, except one. Here he shook his head and laughed softly. At forty, he remained unmarried.

His mother could not understand that the choice young bits of femininity which she paraded before him amused, but did not intrigue, him. So carefully guarding their pale skin against the sun, so daintily lifting billowing flowered skirts, so demure, waiting behind their veils in their rose gardens. He knew too well the temper and petty shrewishness that lurked behind their soft curls. In some cases there would be brains, too, but brains lying dormant. None of them could hold a candle to his mother! He would tell her so, stooping to kiss her ear.

The mare pawed restlessly. Someone was whistling just outside the gate. Freeland drew up closer to the low wall. It was a black who had sat down on the stump beside the road. He was pulling on a shoe. The other shoe lay on the ground beside him. Apparently he had been walking along the sandy road in his bare feet. Freeland chuckled. Just like a nigger! Give them a good pair of shoes, and the minute your back's turned they take them off. Don't give them shoes, and they say they can't work. This fellow was undoubtedly turning in at Freelands and didn't want to appear barefoot.

He was standing up now, brushing himself off carefully. A likely looking youngster, well built. Freeland wondered where he belonged. He wasn't black, rather that warm rich brown that indicated mixed blood.

"Bad blood," his mother always called it. And she would have rapped her son smartly with her cane had he questioned the verdict. Why should he? It would seem that the Atlantic Ocean produced some queer alchemical changes in bloods. In Europe "mixed blood" was, well, just mixed blood. Everybody knew that swarthy complexions in the south of France, in Spain, in Italy, indicated mixed blood. Over here things were different. Certainly there was nothing about slavery to improve stock. He had seen enough to know that.

He suspected that his mother had doubts and suspicions which she did not voice. Her feverish anxiety to get him safely married didn't fool him. He shrugged his shoulders. She need not worry. He knew men who blandly sold off their own flesh and blood. He rubbed elbows with them at the tobacco market, but he never invited them to his table.

In the road Frederick stood looking at the gates a moment. They were swung back, so he had no hesitancy about entering; but he had never seen such large gates before. He touched the iron trimmings. Close by a horse neighed. Frederick turned and knew it must be the master sitting there so easily on the big red mare. He jerked off his hat and bowed.

"Well, boy, what do you want?" The voice was pleasant.

"I'm Captain Auld's boy, sir. He sent me to work."

Freeland studied the brown face. This young darky was unusual; such speech was seldom heard on the Eastern Shore. He asked another question.

"Where are you from, boy?"

Frederick hesitated. It was hardly likely that his master had told his prospective employer about the year at Covey's. Had he heard from some other source? That would be a bad start. He temporized.

"I walked over from St. Michaels just now, sir."

"Must have got an early start. We haven't had breakfast here yet."

The master slid easily to the ground, tossing the reins in the boy's direction. "Come along!"

He had not the faintest idea what this was all about. But things had a way of clearing up in time. He started walking up the driveway toward the house. Frederick followed with the horse.

"Did you bring a note?" Freeland asked the question over his shoulder.

"No, sir. Captain Auld just told me to get along."

Who the devil is Captain Auld? Oh, he remembered, *St. Michaels —yes*. Had said he could send him some help this spring, a good strong hand. Now what would poor trash like Auld be doing with a slave like this? He spoke his thoughts aloud, impatiently.

"You're not a field hand! What do you know about tobacco?"

Frederick's heart missed a beat. He didn't want him; didn't like his looks! He saw the big gates of Freelands—this lovely place— swinging shut behind him. He swallowed.

"I—I can do a good day's work. I mighty strong."

Freeland flipped a leaf from a bush with his riding crop before he spoke.

"You weren't raised up at St. Michaels, and you're no field hand. Don't lie to me, boy!" He turned and looked Frederick full in the face. The boy stopped but did not flinch. Nor did he drop his eyes in confusion. After all, the explanation was simple.

"When I was little, Old Marse sent me to Baltimore to look after his grandson, Tommy. I was raised up there."

"I see. Who's your folks?"

The answer came promptly. "Colonel Lloyd's my folks, sir."

"Oh!"

So that was it! Colonel Edward Lloyd—one of the really great places in Talbot County—secluded, far from all thoroughfares of travel and commerce, sufficient unto itself. Colonel Lloyd had transported his products to Baltimore in his own vessels. Every man and boy on board, except the captain, had been owned by him as his property. The plantation had its own blacksmiths, wheelwrights, shoemakers, weavers and coopers—all slaves—all "Colonel Lloyd's folks." Freeland's mother had known dashing Sally Lloyd, the Colonel's eldest daughter. They had sailed together in the sloop called the *Sally Lloyd*. Yes, the old master was dead now. Naturally many of the slaves had been sold. He was in luck.

They had reached the house. Freeland mounted the veranda steps. He did not look around. His words were almost gruff.

"Go on round back. Sandy'll take care of you."

He disappeared, leaving Frederick's "Yessir" hanging in the air.

Frederick patted the mare's neck and whispered in her ear, "It's all right, old girl. Let's go find Sandy!"

From the road the big house and its tangled yard made a charming picture of sleepy tranquility. But "round back" all was bustling activity. "The Christmas" was over. Aunt Lou had emphasized the fact in no uncertain terms.

"Yo black scamps clean up all dis hyear trash!"

Rakes, brooms, mops and wheelbarrows were whisking. There were sleepy groans and smart cuffs. Already one round bottom had been spanked. Everybody knew New Year's was a day to start things *right*. Aunt Lou's standards and authority were unquestioned. Mis' Betsy would be coming along soon. And Lawd help if everything wasn't spick and span by then! 'Course Master William was already up and out on that mare of hissen. But nobody minded Master William too much. Though he could lay it on if he got mad! Most of the time he didn't pay no 'tention to nothin'—not a thing.

Then came a strange nigger leading Master William's horse. *Well!* The young ones stopped and stared, finger in mouth. Susan, shaking a rug out of an upstairs window, nearly pitched down into the yard. John and Handy regarded the intruder with eager interest. Sandy turned and just looked at him.

Frederick's pulse raced, but he made no sign of recognition either. Then "voodoo" Sandy smiled, and everybody relaxed. *So!*

In the high wainscoted dining room young Henry was serving breakfast. Old Caleb always served dinner—and even breakfast when there were guests—but Henry was in training under the eye of his mistress. Polished silver, gleaming white linen and sparkling glasses —all the accoutrements of fine living were there. A slight woman in a soft black silk dress with an ivory-colored collar, sat across from Master William. Her hair was white, but her blue-veined hands had not been worn by the years and her eyes remained bright and critical. The mistress of Freelands had not aged; she had withered.

"Henry!" She rapped the table with her spoon. "Be careful there! How many times have I told you not to use those cups for breakfast?"

"Please, Mis' Betsy." Henry's tone was plaintive. " 'Tain't none of mah fault. Caleb set 'em out, ma'm. They was sittin' right hyear on tha sideboard."

"Stop whining, Henry!" Her son seldom spoke with such impatience. Mrs. Freeland glanced at him sharply.

"Yessah, Massa William, but—" began Henry.

"He's quite right, Mother," Freeland interrupted. "Caleb served coffee to the Tilghmans before they left. I had a cup myself."

"I'm glad of that." The cups were forgotten. "I had no idea they were leaving so early. I should have been up to see my guests off."

"No need at all, Mother. I accompanied the carriage a good piece down the road. They'll make it back to Richmond in no time."

"It was nice having them for the holidays." She tasted her coffee critically.

Mornings were pleasant in this room. The canary, hanging beside the window, caught the gleam of sunshine on its cage and burst into song. Some place out back a child laughed. The mistress suppressed a sigh. It would be a black child. Her son lounged so easily in his chair. She bit her lips.

"I never thought Delia Tilghman would grow up to be such a charming young lady." She spoke casually. "She's really lovely."

"She is, indeed, Mother," her son assented; but at his smile she looked away.

"I reckon Caleb better wash these cups himself." Her eyes grew indulgent as they rested on Henry. He shuffled his feet as she added, "Henry here was probably out skylarking all night."

"Yes, *ma'm*." Henry gave a wide grin before vanishing kitchen-ward.

His master's snort was emphatic. "Henry probably slept twelve hours last night. The silly ass!"

"Really, William, I do not understand your attitude toward our own people. Henry was born right here at Freelands."

He laughed and took another hot biscuit.

"Which undoubtedly should make him less an ass. But does it?" At his mother's stricken look he was contrite. "Forgive me, Mother, but I've just found much better material for you to work on, worthy of your efforts."

"What are you talking about?"

Henry had returned with golden-brown baked apples, swimming in thick syrup.

"Henry," Freeland said, "step out back and fetch in that new boy." Henry's eyes widened, but he did not move. "Run along! You'll see him."

Henry disappeared, moving faster than was his wont. Freeland smiled at his mother.

"I took on a new boy this morning. You'll like him."

Mrs. Freeland was incredulous. "You bought a boy this morning?"

"I'm hiring this fellow from a peckawood over at St. Michaels." His mother's sniff was audible. "But he's really one of Colonel Lloyd's people."

"Oh! That's different. Should be good stock."

"Unquestionably. I'd like to buy him."

The old lady's eyes had grown reminiscent. She shook her head.

"I wonder if that fine old place is going to pieces. How sad that the Colonel died without a son."

The door behind her was shoved open noisily, admitting Henry who breathed as if he had been running.

"Hyear he is!" he blurted out.

Frederick stopped on the threshold. The room made him hold his breath—sunlight reflected on rich colors and pouring through the singing of a little bird. He wanted to stoop down to see if his shoes carried any tiny speck of sand or dust. He must step softly on the beautiful floor.

"Come in, boy!"

The man's voice was kind. Mrs. Freeland turned with a jerk and stared keenly at the new acquisition. She noted at once his color, or lack of color. That meant—the thought was rigorously checked. Who was this boy her son had picked up in St. Michaels? Why this sudden interest in buying the half-grown buck? She spoke brusquely.

"Come here!"

He drew near, walking quietly but firmly, and bowed. Under her merciless scrutiny he neither shuffled his feet nor lowered his eyes. It was the master who broke the silence.

"Well, Mother—"

She waved him to silence with a peremptory gesture.

"Do you have a name?" she questioned.

"My name is Frederick, ma'm." His words were respectfully low and distinct.

The man nodded his head in approval. His mother did not move for a moment. When she spoke there was a harsh grating in her voice.

"Who gave you such a name?"

Frederick was conscious of something tightening inside of him. His name always surprised people. He had come to wish that he did know how he got it. From his grandmother? His mother? His father? In Baltimore he and Tommy had talked about it. Then the young master had said to his little slave, "Aw, fiddlesticks! What difference does it make? That's your name, ain't it? Just tell 'em!"

"Answer me, boy!" this frightening old lady was saying.

His back stiffened and he said in the same respectful tone, "Frederick is my name, ma'm."

She struck him, hard, with her cane. The master pushed back his chair and half rose.

"Mother!"

"Impudence!" Her eyes blazed. "Get out of my sight!"

Frederick backed away. He dare not run, he dare not answer. He would not cower. He had no need of asking how he had offended her. He had the fierce satisfaction of knowing. "Impudence" could be committed by a slave in a hundred different ways—a look, a word, a gesture. It was an unpardonable crime. He knew he was guilty. Henry had backed to the wall, eyes popping, mouth open.

Now William Freeland was on his feet. He spoke to Henry rather than to Frederick, and his voice was hard.

"Take him out back. I'll come along in a moment."

Frederick had a crazy impulse to laugh at Henry's face as he came toward him. The lumbering dark fellow was heavier, perhaps a year or two older, but in a fair fight Frederick knew he could outmarch him. There was no question of resistance in his mind now, however. The timid way Henry took his arm was silly.

The moment the door had closed behind them, Henry's entire demeanor changed.

"Look-a-hyear, boy," he whispered, dropping Frederick's arm, "ain't you dat crazy nigger what whopped a white man?"

Frederick shrugged his shoulders. His tiny spurt of exaltation had passed. He felt sick.

"I *am* crazy." His words were a groan.

"I knowed it!" exulted Henry. "I knowed it! Come on out to tha barn. I gotta tell tha others." There was no suggestion of whine in his voice, nor was his head cocked to one side.

At Henry's silent arm-wavings they gathered round—the numerous yard boys and men working in the stables and barns. Frederick dropped on an empty box, but Henry delivered a dramatic account of what had just occurred. They kept their voices low, and when Handy slapped his knee and laughed out loud, John whirled on him.

"Shut yo' big mouth! Wanta bring tha house down on us?"

"Standin' up to Ole Missus!"

"Lawd! Lawd! She'll skin you!"

They looked at him admiringly. Only Sandy shook his head. "Not good!" was his only comment.

And Frederick, sitting there on the empty box, agreed with Sandy.

Mrs. Freeland's cane slipped to the floor as the door closed behind the two slaves. Her hand was shaking. Her son was puzzled as he bent to pick up the cane.

"Mother, you have upset yourself. I'm so sorry. But I declare I don't see why."

The small white head jerked up.

"You don't! So this is your idea of better material. That— That mongrel!" Her words were vehement.

"Oh, Mother! For heaven's sake!" The scene he had witnessed suddenly took on meaning. Was "bad blood" getting to be an obsession with her?

"Strutting in here with his airs and impudence!"

"I'll confess he is a little cocky." Then he sought to mollify her. "He's probably been spoilt. I told you he was from Colonel Lloyd's place. He's not just a common hand."

She managed to control the trembling of her lips. *I must not fight with William.* She pressed back her tears and got to her feet.

"Keep him, if you like. He looks strong. Only I will not have him in the house."

She started across the floor, her cane muffled by the rug. In the hallway she turned.

"I don't like him. A nigger who looks you straight in the eye is dangerous. Send Tessie to me!" The keys hanging at her side rattled.

She ascended the stairs, the cane taps growing fainter.

"I'll be damned!" He spoke the words under his breath, looking after her. Then, returning to the room, he reached for his pipe. Standing there, he crushed the bits of dried tobacco leaf into its bowl. "Wonder if the old girl's right."

He sat a while smoking before he went out back. He forgot about Tessie.

The folks in the yard were surprised when Frederick was sent to the fields. Obviously he had been considered for houseboy. Then, after he offended Old Missus, they thought he would go scuttling. But, after a time, Master William came stomping into the yard. He wore his high boots and he carried his riding crop. In a loud voice he asked where that boy was hiding. One little pickaninny began to whimper. Everybody thought that boy was going to get it. But he came right on out of the barn. The master just stood there, waiting, drawing the whip through his hands. He didn't say anything until the boy was quite close. Then he spoke so low they couldn't hear.

"Do you want to work on my place?"

Frederick was so surprised by the question that he barely managed to gasp, "Oh, yes, sir! I do, sir!"

The master's next words were louder.

"Then get down to the bottom tract." He pointed with his whip. "And hurry!" he almost shouted.

Without another word the boy streaked off across the field. Master William yelled for his horse and went riding lickety-split after him. The yard folks stared: *Well!*

Some of the boys tried to console Frederick that evening. They considered field work low drudgery and held themselves aloof from the "fiel' han's." But Frederick considered himself fortunate. He liked Mr. Freeland, liked the way he had told an older worker to show him, liked the way he had gone off, leaving them together.

He found he was to bunk over the stable with Sandy and John. John was Henry's brother, but Henry slept in the house where he could answer a summons. Handy occupied a cabin with his mother and sister. Before Frederick went to sleep that first night he knew all there was to know about these four, who were to be his closest friends. Sandy, though still owned by Mr. Grooms, had been hired out for the season as usual to Mr. Freeland. He told Frederick that his wife Noma was well. He spent every Sunday with her as always. Some Sunday, he promised, he would take Frederick to see her. The mother of John and Handy had died while they were quite young. They had never been away from Freelands, and were curious about what went on "outside."

Never had Frederick enjoyed such congenial companionship. The slaves at Freelands had all they wanted to eat; they were not driven with a lash; they had time to do many things for themselves. Aunt Lou was an exacting overseer, but Aunt Lou could be outwitted. After his grueling labor at Covey's, Frederick's duties seemed very light indeed. He was still a field hand, but he preferred work in the open to any service which would bring him under the eyes of the Old Missus. Since he had no business in the house or out front, he could stay out of her sight. Once in a while he would look up to find Master William watching him at work, but he seldom said anything.

Frederick was growing large and strong and began to take pride in the fact that he could do as much hard work as the older men. The workers competed frequently among themselves, measuring each other's strength. But slaves were too wise to keep it up long enough to produce an extraordinary day's work. They reasoned that if a large quantity of work were done in one day and it became known to the master, he might ask the same amount every day. Even at Freelands this thought was enough to bring them to a dead halt in the middle of a close race.

The evenings grew longer and more pleasant, and Frederick's dreams for the future might have faded. But now he found himself talking more and more earnestly to his friends. Henry and John were remarkably bright and intelligent, when they wished to be. Neither could read.

"If I only had my *Columbian Orator!*"

He told them how he lost his precious book and how he had learned to read it. Perhaps such a book could be found.

"What's in a book?" they asked.

Frederick told them everything he knew—about stories he and Tommy had read together, spelling books, newspapers he had filched in Baltimore, how men wrote down their deeds and thoughts, about things happening in other places, how once white men fought a war,

and a speech one of the boys had learned from the *Columbian Orator*
—a speech that said "Give me liberty or give me death!"

"All dat in a book?" But then they noticed Master William sitting
with a book. Evening were long now and warmer. The master rode
only in the mornings. They saw him on the veranda, for hours at a
time, sitting with a book. One day Henry made up his mind.

"I'll git me a book!"

It was easy. Just walk into the room which was usually empty and
take a book! It was his job to dust them, anyhow, so no one noticed.
Henry could hardly wait for evening when Frederick would come in
from the fields. Henry and John and Handy—waiting with a book.
They were excited.

Frederick's heart leaped too when he saw the book. He took it
eagerly and opened to the title page. He frowned. The words were
very long and hard-looking. Pictures would have made it easier, but
no matter. He turned to the first page. They held their breath. Frederick was going to read.

But Frederick did not read. Letters were on the page in front of
him, but something terrible had happened to them. He strained his
eyes searching—searching for one single word he recognized. Had
he forgotten everything? That could not be. With his mind's eye he
could see pages and words very clearly. But none of the words he
remembered were here. What kind of book was this? Slowly he spelt
out the title, vainly endeavoring to put the letters together into something that would make sense.

"G–a–r–g–a–n–t–u–a–e–t–p–a–n–t–a–g–r–u–e–l." And underneath
all that were the letters "R–a–b–e–l–a–i–s."

He shook his head. Many years later, in Paris, Frederick Douglass
read portions of Rabelais' *Gargantua et Pantagruel*. And he vividly recalled the awful sense of dismay which swept over him the first time
he held a copy of this masterpiece of French literature in his hands.

They were waiting. He swallowed painfully.

"G'wan, big boy! Read!" Handy was impatient.

"I— I—" Frederick began again. "This— This book— It's not—
the one I meant. I can't make— This book—" He stopped. John
drew nearer.

"Hit's a book, ain't it?" He was ready to defend his brother.

"Yes, but—"

"Then read hit!"

Frederick turned several pages. It was no use. He wished the ground would open and swallow him up. He forced his lips to say the words.

"I—can't!"

They stared at him, not believing what they heard. Then they looked at each other and away quickly. They'd been taken in. He had been lying all the time.

Handy spat on the ground, disgusted.

But Henry was puzzled. Frederick looked as if he were going to be sick. He hadn't looked like that when the old lady struck him, or when Master William came out after him with his whip. Henry shifted his weight.

"Looky, Fred! What all's wrong wid dat book?"

Gratitude, like a cool breeze, steadied Frederick. He wet his lips.

"I don't know, Hen. It's all different. These funny words— Everything's mixed up."

"Lemme see!" Henry took the book and turned several pages. He liked the feel of the smooth paper.

"Humph!" Handy spit again.

"Huccome they's mixed?" John's suspicions sounded in his voice. The recklessness of desperation goaded Frederick.

"Henry, could you get another book? I— I never said I could read *all* the books. Could you try another one? Could you, Henry?"

Henry sighed. He tucked the rejected book under his arm.

"Reckon."

His brief reply brought Hand's withering scorn.

"Yo' gonna lose yo' hide! Hyear me!" With this warning Handy walked away. His disappointment was bitter.

The next day stretched out unbearably. Frederick forced himself through the motions of his work while his mind went round and round in agonizing circles. Then suddenly it was time to stop, time for the evening meal, time to return to the yard. He knew Henry would be waiting with another book. His moist hands clung to his hoe, his feet seemed rooted in the cool, upturned earth. Then his legs were carrying him back.

He saw them standing behind the barn—John and Henry and, slightly removed, leaning against a tree, Handy. He went on whittling when Frederick came up. Handy's demeanor was that of a wholly disinterested bystander. But Henry said, "I got hit—anodder one." His tone was cautious.

Frederick took the book with hands that trembled. Handy's knife paused. Then Frederick gave a whoop, and Handy, dropping his stick, came running.

"The Last of the Mo–hi–cans!" read Frederick triumphantly. He didn't know what "Mohicans" meant, but what was one small word? He turned the pages and shouted for joy. Words, words, words— beautiful, familiar faces smiled up at him! He hugged the book. He danced a jig, and they joined him, making such a disturbance that Sandy came out of the barn to see what was going on.

Sandy was their friend, so they told him—all talking together. They hid the book and went to eat, swallowing their food in great gulps. Afterward they went down to the creek, and Frederick read to them until darkness blotted out the magic of the pages. They talked, then, turning over the words, examining them.

This was the beginning. As summer came on and the long evenings stretched themselves over hours of leisure, the good news got around; and additional trusted neophytes were permitted to join them at the creek. Learning to read was now the objective. More books disappeared from the house. After Frederick slipped up in the attic and found several old school books, real progress began. Then trouble arose.

Seemed like everybody wanted to learn "tha readin'." That, argued the select few, would not do. This certainly was not a matter for "fiel' han's." Field hands, however, were stubborn in their persistence. The fact that the teacher was a field hand seemed to have erased their accustomed servility. One of them even brought in Mr. Hall's Jake, an uncouth fellow from the neighboring plantation. They vouched for Jake's trustworthiness, and he proved an apt pupil. Then Jake brought a friend!

Sandy counseled caution. Frederick, happy in what he was doing, was hardly aware of the mutterings. So they wrestled with their first problem in democracy.

Then, one Sunday afternoon, they were nearly caught.

It was a scorcher, late in July. The noon meal was over, and they were sitting in the shade of a big oak tree at the edge of the south meadow, ten or twelve of them under the big tree. Jake appeared, coming over the ridge that marked the boundary of Freelands. He saw them and waved, then started walking down.

"Glad I ain't walkin' in no hot sun." John had just learned a new word, and he felt good. Suddenly Jake was seen to straighten up, wave both arms frantically and start running in the opposite direction.

Books were whisked out of sight, papers disappeared as if by magic. When Master William and his guest came trotting around the clump of trees, all they saw was a bunch of lazy niggers stretched out in the shade.

"Watch out, there!" Freeland's mare shied away. With a sleepy grunt, Henry rolled over.

The guest was from Baltimore. He had been speaking vehemently for such a hot day.

"Look at that!" he burst out. "Show me a bunch of sleek, fat niggers sleeping through the day in Boston."

The master of Freelands laughed indulgently. His guest continued.

"Those damned Abolitionists ought to come down here. Freein' niggers! The thieving fools!" He jerked his horse's head savagely.

William Freeland spoke in his usual, pleasant, unheated voice.

"I'd kill the first Abolitionist who set foot on my land, same as I would a mad dog."

They rode on out of hearing.

No one moved for a long minute. Then Henry sat up abruptly.

"Where is mah book?" He jerked it from under the belly of a sweating stable boy.

Black Crunch, long, lean and hard like a hound, moved more slowly. He was thinking.

"Fred," he asked, leaning forward, "does yo' know whar is dat dar Boston place?"

After this, the "Sunday School" grew in numbers. There was no more talk of restricting "members." The name was Frederick's idea, and everybody followed the lead with complete understanding. It was well known that masters seldom raised any objection to slaves leaving the plantation for Sunday services, even when they went some distance away. So now it was possible to talk freely about the Sunday School over on Mr. Freeland's place!

Somebody hailed William Freeland one day as he rode along.

"Hear your niggers are holding some kind of a revival, old man," he called. "Got a good preacher?"

"I wouldn't know." Freeland laughed back, waving his whip. Next morning, however, he spoke to Henry.

"Oh, Henry, what's this I hear about a revival going on?"

"Whatchu sayin', Massa William?" Henry's lips hung flabby. Not a trace of intelligence lighted his face.

"A revival! You know what a revival is." Freeland tried to curb his impatience.

"Oh, yessuh!" Henry showed his teeth in a wide grin. "Yessuh, Ah knows a revival. Yes, *suh!*"

"Well, is there a revival going on around here?"

"Revival? Roun' hyear?" The whites of Henry's eyes resembled marbles.

Freeland kicked back his chair. What the hell difference did it make?

At the end of the year William Freeland rode over to St. Michaels and renewed his contract with Captain Auld for his boy's services. He reported that the slave had worked well; he had no complaints to make. Captain Auld's eyes glittered when he took the money. Evidently that buck was turning out all right. Another year and he'd bring a good price in the market.

The master was really touched by Frederick's gratitude when told that he was to remain on. As a matter of fact, Frederick had been deeply worried. As the year had drawn to a close he felt he had wasted valuable time. There was much to do—plans to make and lines to be carefully laid—before he made his break for freedom.

Another Christmas and a new year. And New Year's Day was a time to start things right. Everybody knew that!

They heard it first in the yard, of course. Black Crunch had run away! When the the horsemen came galloping up the drive not a pickaninny was in sight. Old Caleb opened the front door and bowed with his beautiful deference. But they shoved him out of the way unceremoniously, calling for the master. Old Missus sniffed the air disdainfully, standing very straight, but Master William rode off with them.

The next night all along the Eastern Shore slaves huddled, shivering in dark corners. The baying of the hounds kept some white folks awake, too. They didn't find Black Crunch. They never found Black Crunch.

There was a hazy tension in the air. The five friends bound themselves together with a solemn oath of secrecy—Frederick, Handy, Henry, John, and Sandy. They were going together—all five. John pleaded for his sweetheart, little Susan, to be taken along; and Sandy knew the danger that threatened his wife if he left her. Though a free woman herself, she could be snatched back into bondage if he ran away. Noma knew this also. Yet the woman said simply, "Go!"

The Eastern Shore of Maryland lay very close to the free state of Pennsylvania. Escape might not appear too formidable an undertaking. Distance, however, was not the chief trouble. The nearer the lines of a slave state were to the borders of a free state, the more vigilant were the slavers. At every ferry was a guard, on every bridge sentinels, in every wood patrols and slave-hunters. Hired kidnapers also infested the borders.

Nor did reaching a free state mean freedom for the slave. Wherever caught they could be returned to slavery. And their second lot would be far worse than the first! Slaveholders constantly impressed upon their slaves the boundlessness of slave territory and their own limitless power.

Frederick and his companions had only the vaguest idea of the geography of the country. "Up North" was their objective. They had heard of Canada, they had heard of New York, they had heard of Boston. Of what lay in between they had no thoughts at all.

After many long discussions they worked out their plan for escape. On the Saturday night before the Easter holidays they would take a large canoe owned by a Mr. Hamilton, launch out into Chesapeake Bay and paddle with all their might for its head, a distance of about seventy miles. On reaching this point they would turn the canoe adrift and bend their steps toward the north star until they reached a free state.

This plan had several excellent points. On the water they had a chance of being thought fishermen, in the service of a master; hounds could not track them; and over Easter their absence might not be noted. On the other hand, in bad weather the waters of the Chesapeake are rough, and there would be danger, in a canoe, of being swamped by the waves. Furthermore, the canoe would soon be missed; and, if absent slaves were suspected of having taken it, they would be pursued by some fast-sailing craft out of St. Michaels.

They prepared for one quite possible emergency. Any white man, if he pleased, was authorized to stop a Negro on any road and examine and arrest him. Many a freeman, being called upon by a pack of ruffians to show his free papers, presented them, only to have the hoodlums tear them up, seize the victim and sell him to a life of endless bondage.

The week before their intended start, Frederick wrote a pass for

each of the party, giving him permission to visit Baltimore during
the Easter holidays. He signed them with the initials of William
Hamilton, tobacco planter whose place edged on the bay and whose
canoe they had planned to take. The pass ran after this manner:

> This is to certify that I, the undersigned, have given the
> bearer, my servant John, full liberty to go to Baltimore to
> spend the Easter holidays.
> Near St. Michaels, Talbot Co., Md.   W. H.

Although they were not going to Baltimore and intended to land
east of North Point, in the direction they had seen the Philadelphia
steamers go, these passes might be useful in the lower part of the
bay, while steering toward Baltimore. These were not, however, to
be shown until all other answers had failed to satisfy the inquirer.
The conspirators were fully alive to the importance of being calm
and self-possessed when accosted, if accosted they should be; and they
more than once rehearsed to each other how they would behave under
fire.

With everything figured out, the days and nights of waiting were
long and tedious. Every move, every word, every look had to be carefully guarded. Uneasiness was in the air. Slaveholders were constantly
looking out for the first signs of rebellion against the injustice and
wrong which they were perpetrating every hour of the day. And their
eyes were skilled and practiced. In many cases they were able to read,
with great accuracy, the state of mind and heart of the slave through
his sable face. Any mood out of the common way gave grounds for
suspicion and questioning.

Yet, with the plowing over, with spring in the air and an Easter
holiday drawing near, what more natural than that the slaves should
sing down in their quarters—after the day's work was over?

> "Oh Canaan, sweet Canaan,
> Ah'm boun' fo' the lan' o' Canaan."

They sang, and their voices were sweet. William Freeland, sitting on
the veranda, took his pipe from between his teeth and smiled at his
mother.

"I always say there's nothing like darkies singing—nothing. Some
of our folks have really beautiful voices. Listen to that!" The master
of Freelands spoke with real pride.

Inside the house old Caleb fussed with the curtains. He felt a trembling inside of him. That clear, young voice out there in the dusk:

> "Ah thought Ah heared them say
> There was lions in the way
> I don' expect to stay
> Much longah here."

The buoyant refrain—all the voices singing triumphantly:

> "Oh Canaan, sweet Canaan,
> Not much longah here!"

"Crazy fools!" whispered Caleb. "Singin' lak dat!"

Singing for all the world to know! He wanted to warn them. He shook his head. Caleb had been young once, too. And he had dreamed of freedom. He was old now. He would die a slave. He shuffled back to the pantry. Shut in there he could no longer hear the singing.

Two days before the appointed time Sandy withdrew. He could not go off and leave his wife. They pleaded with him.

"You young ones go! You make good life. I stay now!"

John was the most visibly shaken. John whose little Susan had wept several times of late because of his moody silences and bad temper. After saying that nothing could change his mind or intention he walked away stiffly.

Then Sandy confessed that he had had a dream, a bad dream.

"About us?" Frederick asked the question, his heart heavy. This was bad, coming from Sandy. And Sandy spoke, his voice low and troubled.

"I dream I roused from sleep by strange noises, noises of a swarm of angry birds that passed—a roar like a coming gale over the tops of the trees. I look up. I see you, Frederick, in the claws of a great bird. And there was lots of birds, all colors and all sizes. They pecked at you. Passing over me, the birds flew southwest. I watched until they was clean out of sight." He was silent.

Frederick drew a long breath.

"And they took me with them?"

"Yes."

Frederick did not meet his eyes. He stiffened his back.

"It was just a dream, Sandy. Look, we're worried and jumpy. That's all. Hen, that's right—don't you think? What's a little dream?"

Henry spoke with unaccustomed firmness.

"Ain't no little ole dream gonna stop *me*!"

Frederick gripped his arm, thankful for Henry's strength and determination. He keenly felt the responsibility of the undertaking. If they failed it would be his fault. He wished Sandy had not told him the dream.

The day dawned. Frederick went out to the field earlier than usual. He had to be busy. At breakfast Henry broke one of the precious cups. He was roundly berated by Old Missus. Her son said nothing. Henry had been more clumsy than usual lately.

The morning dragged. Frederick had been spreading manure for what seemed to him an eternity when—for no apparent reason at all —he experienced a sudden blinding presentiment.

"We've failed!"

It was as if a hundred eyes were watching him—as if all his intentions were plainly written in the sky. A few minutes after this, the long, low, distant notes of the horn summoned the workers from the field to the noon-day meal. Frederick wanted nothing to eat. He looked around probing the landscape for some reason for the awful certainty in his mind. He shook himself. He pressed the back of his hand hard against his mouth.

As he crossed the field he saw William Freeland come out of the house and go toward the barn. He came nearer, and the long graveled driveway was in full view. And so he saw the four men on horseback turn into the drive and approach the house. Then he saw two blacks whom he could not identify walking behind. One of them seemed to be tied!

Something has happened! We've been betrayed!

No need to run now. He came on, cutting across the front yard; he climbed over the low hedge and was stooping to pass under the rotting rose trellis as one horseman, far in the lead and riding very rapidly, reached the house. It was the tobacco planter, Mr. William Hamilton. The horseman pulled his horse to an abrupt stop and hailed Frederick.

"Hey, boy! Where's your master?"

Even in this bitter moment of defeat some perverse imp inside Frederick forced him to reply, speaking very politely, "Mr. Freeland, sir, just went to the barn."

Hamilton's whip jerked in his hand, but he did not bring it down on Frederick. He wheeled about in a flurry of gravel and rode off toward the stables. By this time the other three had come up, and Frederick saw that they were constables.

He burst into the kitchen, heedless of Aunt Lou's wrath. But the kitchen was quiet with an ominous stillness. Only John was there, his back to the room, looking out the window. He turned quickly, and Frederick saw his quivering face. They grasped each other by the hand and stood together, waiting.

The outside door opened a second time, admitting Master Freeland. His eyes were glinting steel in a grim face. His voice was harsh.

"So, here you are!" He was looking at Frederick. "Go outside! These men want to question you."

"He ain't done nothin', Massa William." There was panic in John's appeal.

"Shut up!" Freeland shoved Frederick toward the door.

As he stepped outside, two constables seized him.

"What do you want? Why do you take me?"

A blow in the mouth cut his lip. They twisted his arm, throwing him to the ground.

Hamilton, standing beside his horse, pointed to John, who had followed Frederick to the door.

"That one, too. Take him!" He held a rifle in his hand.

John cried out when they seized him.

All this was taking place just outside the kitchen door, some distance from the barns and outhouses. Motionless black figures could be seen. Now a kind of hushed wail was heard.

Henry, running with Sandy behind him, was coming from the barn. A constable met him, a heavy gun at his side. He carried a rope. Hamilton had pointed to Henry, nodding his head.

"Tie him!"

"Cross your hands!" ordered the constable. Henry was panting. He did not speak at once. In that moment he had seen everything. Then, looking straight at the man in front of him, he said, "I won't!"

They were all taken by surprise. The master of Freelands stared at a Henry he had never seen before. The constable sputtered.

"Why you black ——! You won't cross your hands!" He reached for his revolver.

"Henry!" His master's voice cracked.

And Henry looked at him and said, with added emphasis, "No! I won't!"

The three constables now cocked their revolvers, surrounded him. Mr. Hamilton was agitated. He also drew his rifle.

"By God, Freeland, he's dangerous!"

William Freeland could say nothing. Iron bands seemed to be choking him. *Henry!* That clumsy, silly slave had grown a foot.

"Shoot me! Shoot me and be damned! I won't be tied!"

And at the moment of saying it, with the guns at his breast, Henry quickly raised his arms and dashed the weapons from their hands, sending them flying in all directions.

In the confusion which followed Frederick managed to get near John.

"The pass?" he asked. "Do you have the pass?"

"It's burned. I put it in the stove."

"Good!" This much evidence was gone, anyway.

Henry fought like a tiger. Inside the house, Old Missus heard the uproar and came out back.

"Henry! Henry! They're killing Henry!" she shrieked. Her son rushed to her, trying to explain. She pushed him away. "Stop them! Stop those ruffians!"

Finally they had Henry overpowered. As he lay on the ground trussed and bleeding, Frederick and John, helpless though they were, stood accused in their own eyes because they too had not resisted. John cried bitterly, in futile rage. Frederick stood rigid, every breath a separate stab of pain. Mrs. Freeland, her own eyes wet, tried to comfort John.

"Don't, Johnny. I know it's all a mistake. We'll fix it. We'll get you and Henry out of it!"

They took Sandy, whose black face remained unfathomable. Then the tobacco planter spoke.

"Perhaps now we'd better make a search for those passes we understand Captain Auld's boy has written for them."

Freeland was almost vehement, insisting that they be taken immediately to the jail and there carefully examined. To himself he said that his mother's outburst had unnerved him. He wanted to get the whole business over and done with—get it out of his sight.

As they stood, securely bound, ready to start toward St. Michaels, the mistress came out with her hands full of biscuits which she divided between John and Henry, ignoring both Sandy and Frederick. And as they started around the house she pointed her bony finger at Frederick.

"It's you! You yellow devil!" she called out after him. "You put it in their heads to run away! John and Henry are good boys. You did it! You long-legged, yellow devil!"

At the look which Frederick turned on her, she screamed in mingled wrath and fright and went in, slamming the door.

The constables fastened them with long ropes to the horses. Now Frederick recognized the two dark forms he had seen from a distance as Handy and a boy owned by Mr. Hamilton. Handy had slipped off that morning to hide their supplies near the canoe. This boy had somehow become involved. Maybe Handy had solicited his aid—maybe that was what happened. Frederick turned the possibility over inside his aching head. The boy had been beaten. His shirt hung in stained tatters. Under the watchful eyes they gave no sign of knowing each other. They waited while the horses pawed restlessly, kicking up sharp bits of gravel into their faces.

As Freeland mounted his big mare, the tobacco planter pointed at Sandy.

"Is that one of your own niggers?"

"No," the master of Freelands shook his head. "I hire him from a man named Groomes, over in Easton." His lips twisted into a wry smile. "I hate to lose the best carpenter we've had in a long time."

"I've seen him somewhere before." Hamilton looked thoughtful. "Believe he's the one they call a voodoo." Freeland shrugged his shoulders, settling himself firmly in the saddle. Hamilton continued, his voice grim. "Best keep an eye on him."

"Don't tell me you take stock in nigger black magic!" Freeland mocked him.

It was Hamilton's turn to shrug his shoulders, as his ungracious host headed the procession down the drive and out into the highway.

Inside the house old Caleb straightened the worn, brocaded curtains, his stiff fingers shaking. He felt old and useless. Upstairs Susan sought to muffle her sobs in Old Missus' feather bolster, heedless of the fact that she was staining the fine linen slip. The children down in the slave quarters were very still, hardly breathing.

Easter was in the air. The sun shone bright and warm. Folks were thinking about the holiday, and overseers were relaxed. In the fields, slaves leaned on their hoes and watched them go by—five white men, their hats pulled low, their shirts open at the neck, riding on horses; and behind them, jerking, grotesque figures, pulled by the horses, dust blinding and choking them, their bare feet stumbling over rocks and raising a cloud of dust, their bare heads covered with sweat and grime.

Frederick, fastened with Henry to the same horse, pulled hard on the rope, endeavoring to slacken the pace. He knew what torture Henry was enduring. The constable, noticing this tugging, lashed out once with his whip. Then he chose to ignore the matter. It was a long, hot drive to the Easton jail, and the constable was in no particular hurry.

Henry managed to get his breath. The mistress had made them loose one of his hands. In this free hand he still clinched his biscuits. Now, looking gratefully at Frederick, he gasped, "The pass! What shall I do with my pass?"

Frederick answered immediately. "Eat it with your biscuit!"

A moment later Henry had managed to slip the piece of paper into his mouth. He chewed well on the biscuit and swallowed with a gulp. Then he grinned, a trickle of blood starting from his cut lip.

The word went round from one bound figure to another, "Swallow your pass! Own nothing! Know nothing."

Though their plans had leaked out—somehow, some way—their confidence in each other was unshaken. Somebody had made a mistake, but they were resolved to succeed or fail together.

By the time they reached the outskirts of St. Michaels it was clear that the news had gone on ahead.

A bunch of runaway niggers! Fair sport on a Saturday afternoon. The "insurrection"—the word stumbled off their tongues—had been started by that "Auld boy," the "smart nigger."

"A bad un!"

"Ought to be hanged!" They laughed and ordered another drink of burning whiskey. *Wish something would happen in this Godforsaken hole!*

The procession stopped first at Captain Auld's. The Captain was loud in his cries of denunciation.

"Done everything for this boy, everything! I promise you he'll be punished—I'll take all the hide off him! I'll break every bone in his body!"

He was reminded that Frederick and the others were already in the hands of the law. Beyond a shadow of doubt they would be punished. At this the Captain calmed down. Here was a horse of another color. Frederick was *his* property. His slow mind began to revolve. He dared not offend either Mr. Freeland or Mr. Hamilton. He had no stomach for losing a valuable piece of property to anything as vague and unrewarding as "the law." He fixed a stern eye on Frederick—noting the thick broad shoulders and long legs.

"What have you done, you ungrateful rascal?"

"Nothin', Massa, nothin', nothin', nothin'! The whistle blowed, I come in to eat—an' they took me! They took me!"

Frederick's mind also had been working. He was resolved to throw the burden of proof upon his accusers. He could see that the passion of his outcry now had its effect. The Captain grunted with satisfaction. He asked the gentlemen for more details. Just exactly what *had* the boy done?

Of course, no single pass was found on them. All six of the accused said the same thing—they had been going about their work as usual. They had not the slightest idea why they had been arrested. Handy explained in great detail how he had been sent over to Mr. Hamilton's place by Aunt Lou. He was returning from that errand. The Hamilton boy had been down on the beach mending a net. Their protestations of innocence were loud and voluble. Too voluble, each master thought to himself. But he did not put his thoughts into words. It would never do to admit that they were being outwitted by a bunch of sniveling darkies.

They were taken to the county jail and locked up. It was a ramshackle, old affair. A good wind coming in from the bay could have knocked it over, and a very small fire would have wiped it out in short order. But it was prison enough for the six. Henry, John, and Frederick were placed in one cell and Sandy, the Hamilton boy, and Handy in another. They had plenty of space, since the cells really were rooms of the building. They were fed immediately and were left completely alone throughout the night. They were thankful for this respite.

Early Easter morning they were at them—a swarm of slave-traders and agents of slave-traders who, hearing of the "catch" in the county jail at Easton, hurried over to ascertain if the masters wanted to rid themselves of dangerous "troublemakers." Good bargains could often be picked up under such circumstances. Rebellious slaves were usually strong and vigorous. Properly manacled, they were rendered helpless. And there was a demand for them on the great plantations where they were beginning to grow enormous crops of cotton. Word had gone out that these captured slaves were young and in unusually good condition.

The sheriff willingly obliged the traders. So they fell upon the prisoners like a bunch of vultures, feeling their arms and legs, shaking them by the shoulders to see if they were sound and healthy, making them jump up and down on one foot, examining their teeth, examining their testicles.

"This one, now,"—the trader was "going over" Frederick—"he'd go fine with a piece I picked up last week. She's swellin' with heat. They'd make a litter!"

The two men laughed.

"How'd you like to go with me, buck boy?" He kicked him lightly. Frederick, his rage choking him, did not answer.

"Um—no tongue," the second trader grunted.

"Look at his eyes!" the first man said. "If I had 'im, I'd cut the devil out of him pretty quick!"

This went on for several days, with no further questions nor any beatings. The suspense was terrible. The dream of freedom faded.

Then one afternoon the master of Freelands appeared with Mr. Hamilton and took away all the prisoners except Frederick. They were going back with no further punishment. Old Missus had persuaded her son that this was the just and correct course.

"Nobody's to blame but that hired boy! Bring our folks home!"

He talked it over with Hamilton. For want of an alternative, he assented.

Freeland could not have explained to himself why he allowed them to tell Frederick goodbye. All that his mother had said about him had been proven true. He *was* dangerous. He was certain that this boy, standing there so quietly, had planned an escape for his slaves. How many were involved and where were they going? Why should they wish to leave Freelands? They had far less to worry them than the master had—a shelter over their heads, clothing, food. His mother nursed them when they were sick. Their work was not heavy. He would have liked to ask this boy some questions.

It was evident that the others did not want to go. Henry clung to Frederick's arm, his big, ugly face working. He heard Sandy, who seldom spoke, say, "Big tree bow in the wind. Big tree stand!"

"I will not be forgettin'!" Frederick answered.

They went away then and climbed into the waiting wagon. They were going back in state—riding with one of Mr. Hamilton's men driving the mules. The masters were on horseback. Frederick, standing beside the barred window, saw them wave as the wagon turned into the road.

Alone in the prison Frederick gave way to complete misery. He felt certain now that he was doomed to the ever-dreaded Georgia, Louisiana, or Alabama. They would be coming for him now, to take him "down the river." Even in his despair he was glad that the others were not going with him. At least they were no worse off than before their heads had been filled with dreams of freedom. And now they could read. Eventually they would get away. But he was too young to derive much comfort from this thought—too young and too much alive.

A long week passed, and then to Frederick's joyful relief Captain Auld came for his boy. In a loud voice he told the sheriff that he was sending him off to Alabama to a friend of his.

The sheriff looked at Frederick. Pity a clean-looking hand like that couldn't behave himself! He spat out a fresh cud of tobacco. It had lost its taste.

Frederick's heart fell, but obediently he went with his master. The next several days went by in comparative idleness on the Auld place just outside St. Michaels. Frederick's stature with the other slaves had grown. By them he was treated as an honored guest, and in this he found some comfort. But the Alabama friend did not put in an appearance, and finally Captain Auld announced that he had decided to send him back to Baltimore again, to live with his brother Hugh. He told Frederick that he wanted him to learn a trade, and that if he behaved himself properly he might emancipate him in time.

Frederick could hardly believe his ears. The morning came when they went into St. Michaels, and there he was placed in the custody of the captain of a small clipper. They set sail over the waters of the Chesapeake Bay toward Baltimore.

CHAPTER FIVE

One more river to cross

ON ITS WAY to the sea, the Patapsco River cuts through the old city of Baltimore. Here the fall line—the point where the harder rocks of the Piedmont meet the softer rocks of the coastal plain—moves close to the coast, and the deep estuary affords a large sheltered harbor. Baltimore was a divided city: by temperament, dreamily looking toward the South; but, during business hours at least, briskly turning her face to the North. The old English families seemed to be dwindling, and the "upstarts" wanted business.

Early in the nineteenth century, Baltimore became second only to New York as port of entry for immigrants from Europe—Irish, Italians, Greeks, Poles, Scandinavians. They spread out from Baltimore all over Maryland. The increase of population in Baltimore, especially foreign or non-British population, made the counties afraid. When the Federalists were overthrown in 1819 the issue of apportioning of delegates by population came up in the Assembly. It was defeated because the counties refused to place the great agricultural state of Maryland "at the feet of the merchants, the bank speculators, lottery office keepers, the foreigners and the mob of Baltimore."

For many years this attitude helped to retard enfranchisement of Jews. Not until 1826 were Jews allowed to vote. This was just two years after thin, stoop-shouldered Benjamin Lundy came walking down out of the backwoods of Tennessee, a printing press on his back, and began turning out the *Genius of Universal Emancipation*, first antislavery journal to appear in the whole country.

After the "Jew Bill" got by, Baltimoreans paid more attention to Lundy's journal. There was talk of "outside influence"; and one day Austin Woolfolk, a notoriously mean slave-trader, beat up the editor on the street and nearly killed him.

The city's business was expanding. Shipbuilding had started in the Colonial days. With the new roads bringing in products from the west, merchants were soon making shipments in their own vessels and the town's prominence as a seaport was assured. By 1810 the city had become the third largest in America. The population had quadrupled since the Declaration of Independence, mainly because of the maritime business. Baltimore clippers brought coffee from South America, tea and opium from China, and slaves from Africa.

It was well known that smuggling sprang up, after the importation of African slaves was made a felony. By 1826 the interstate traffic was enormous. Boatloads of slaves, manacled together, were conveyed in sailing vessels along the Atlantic and Gulf coasts to New Orleans, great slave mart of the South. These cargoes of living freight were listed openly in the papers with the regular shipping news. Law or no law, the great city of Baltimore had little patience with "loose talk" about so lucrative a market. A meddling outsider, William Lloyd Garrison, was thrown in jail. Publication of the *Genius* ceased, and all copies of the incendiary journal were destroyed. At least that's what the merchants thought. But old marked sheets had a way of turning up in the queerest places!

Even as a child—a slave child, following his young master from place to place—Frederick had not been wholly unaware of the swelling, pushing traffic of the growing city. As he sat on the school steps waiting for Tommy to come out, he watched heavy carts go by on their way to the wharf. Sometimes one would get stuck in the mud; and then, while the mule pulled and backed, the "furriners" yelled funny-sounding words. A stalk of sugar cane dropped from the load made a good find. If it was not too large, Frederick would hide it until night. Then he and Tommy would munch the sweet fiber, the little master in his bed, the slave stretched out on the floor. The day came when the growing boys slipped off to the wharves where vessels from the West Indies discharged their freight of molasses, to gorge themselves on the stolen sweet, extracted on a smooth stick inserted through a bunghole.

Frederick had seen coffles of slaves trudge through Baltimore streets—men and women and sometimes little children chained together. The boys always stopped playing and stared after them.

The year 1836 had been a good year for the South. Cotton was rolling up into a gleaming ball—an avalanche which would one day bring ruin; but now prices were soaring. On the June evening when

Frederick sailed into Baltimore's harbor, tall masts of square-rigged vessels bowed and dipped. They spoke to him of places in the far corners of the world; they beckoned to him. He nodded, his heart leaping.

He had left Baltimore a child; he returned a man. He looked around now, thinking, evaluating, remembering places he must go, people he must look up.

But first, there was Mr. Hugh Auld waiting for him on wharf. Tommy was nowhere in sight. Then he remembered. Tommy also was a man—a free, white man. A little stab of pain shot through Frederick.

Hugh Auld and his brother Thomas had come South to seek their fortunes. Raised in Vermont, they had found the lush softness of Maryland very pleasant. Employed by Colonel Lloyd on his rolling tidewater acres, Hugh had in due time married the Colonel's youngest daughter and set up business in Baltimore. Hugh Auld had prospered. He was now part owner of a shipyard. Soon it would be Auld & Son.

"Good evening, Captain. I see you've got my boy."

Mr. Auld greeted the captain though Frederick had hurried forward, his face alight.

"Yes, sir; shipshape, sir. And not a mite of trouble." Nantucket Bay was more familiar to the captain than Chesapeake, but he liked the southern waters and he found Baltimore people friendly. They stood chatting a while and Frederick waited.

"Well, I thank you." Mr. Auld was adjusting his panama hat. "Now I'll be taking him off your hands."

"Go along, boy!" the Captain said.

Mr. Auld stepped to the waiting rig, motioning Frederick to climb up beside the driver, and they were off toward Lower Broadway. They wound their way between warehouses, great piles of cotton bales and tobacco, pyramided kegs of rum and stinking fish markets; and finally Mr. Auld spoke.

"So, Fred, we're going to make a caulker out of you!"

"Yes, sir." Frederick turned his head.

"Well, you're big and strong. Ought to make a good worker. Watch yourself!"

After that they drove in silence, the driver casting sidelong glances at Frederick, neither slave saying anything. Their time to talk would come later. The rig bumped over the cobblestones on Thames Street with its shops and saloons, and came out into a pleasant residential section of shuttered windows, dormered roofs and paneled doors.

Here the June evening was lovely. They passed a fine old house beside which a spreading magnolia tree, all in bloom, spilt its fragrance out into the street. In gardens behind wrought-iron handrails children were quietly playing. Young dandies passed along the sidewalks, parading before demure young misses. On white stoop or behind green lattice, the young ladies barely raised their eyes from their needlework. Negro servants moved to and fro, wearing bright red bandanas and carrying market baskets tilted easily on their heads. They passed a gray cathedral and came to a small brick house with white marble steps and white-arched vestibule.

Frederick's heart turned over. The house had been freshly painted, the yard trimmed and cut. The place with its lace curtains had an air of affluence which Frederick did not recall; but this had been the nearest thing to a home that he had ever known, and he felt affection for it. Was Tommy at home? After the master had descended, they drove around back. There was the cellar door down which he and Tommy had slid; the gnarled tree was gone. He wondered what Tommy had done with the notebooks they had hid inside the trunk—those notebooks in which Frederick had so painfully traced his young master's letters. As they climbed down from the rig Frederick, trying to keep the urgency from his voice, turned to the boy.

"Is Master—Master Tommy at home?"

The black boy stared at him a moment without answering. Then he asked, "Young Massa?" And at Frederick's nod, "Yes—Massa Thomas, he hyear."

So it was "Master Thomas" now. Frederick checked his sigh as he smiled at this boy of his own color.

"My name's Fred. What's yours?" he said cordially.

"I Jeb." The boy answered immediately, but there was a puzzled look on his face. They were unhitching the horse now. He cleared his throat and burst out, "Say, yo'— Yo' talks lak white folks. Huccome?"

Frederick hesitated. Should he tell him about the notebooks and reading lessons—that he and the Young Master had learned together? He decided not. So he only laughed and said, "Fiddlesticks!"

Jeb studied the newcomer covertly as they went inside. He liked this Fred—liked the way he looked at you—liked the way he walked; but Jeb recognized that here was something to think about.

The ugly, gaunt woman at the stove turned when they entered

the kitchen. She did not smile, and Frederick felt her dark eyes, set deep in bony sockets, take him in from head to foot. Then she motioned them to places at the scrubbed pine board. They sat down on stools.

"Hit's Nada." Jeb leaned forward and whispered. "She free! She free 'oman!"

Now it was Frederick's turn to stare at the big woman. She moved slowly, clumsily, as if the springs of her body were giving way. The deep ridges of her face were pitted with smallpox, the scars extending from her eyes to the wide sad space of her mouth. But she was free, and Frederick looked at her with envy.

There were several hundred "free people of color" in Baltimore at this time. Their lot was one of inconceivable hardship. Yet no slave having purchased or having been granted his freedom ever voluntarily went back into slavery. Under the laws of the state, he had no rights as a citizen. At times he was restrained from working at certain occupations, from selling tobacco and other commodities without a certificate from the justice of peace. He couldn't keep a dog, carry firearms, belong to a secret order, or sell spirituous liquors. The mere word of a white man could convict the Negro of any offense. And punishment was swift and severe.

These people did what work they could for the smallest possible wages—as caulkers in the shipyards, hod carriers, dock workers. A few were good bricklayers and carpenters. No matter what their work, they had to take what they were given. Therefore, they were despised and hated by white workers who were often ousted by this cheaper labor. The rising merchant and business class of the city found it cheaper to employ such help for a few cents a week than to buy slaves to work in their homes. A master had some responsibility for his slave's upkeep. He had none for his "paid servants." So, Nada worked for Mrs. Hugh Auld from six o'clock in the morning until eight or nine at night. Then she disappeared down the alley—no one ever bothered to find out where.

After supper Mrs. Auld came back to speak to Frederick. She was a Lloyd and remembered Frederick's grandmother. Now she asked after her foster sister, Captain Auld's wife, whom she had not seen for many years. She had a moment of nostalgia for those girlhood days on the plantation, and patted his arm.

"You've grown to be a fine, upstanding boy," she said. "We're proud of you!"

Master Thomas did not come.

It was not until the next afternoon when he had been set to work in the shipyard that he heard a pleasant voice at his elbow.

"Hello, Fred! They tell me you're going to build ships."

He looked up at the tall, clean young man in his tailored suit. He tried to smile.

"Yes, Massa Thomas," he said, but his voice was gruff.

Something like a veil slipped over the white man's face. They stood there a moment facing each other. And the cloud, which in their boyhood had been no larger than a man's hand, now enveloped them. Frederick hardly heard his words as he turned away.

"Well— Good luck! So long!"

Frederick never saw him again. A few days afterward Thomas Auld sailed on one of his father's ships. A year later he was drowned in a gale off the coast of Calcutta.

William Gardiner, big shipbuilder on Fells Point, was having trouble. Some time before he had put down demands for higher wages in his yard by peremptorily hiring a number of colored mechanics and carpenters.

"And damned good mechanics!" he had pointedly informed his foreman. "Now you can tell those blasted micks, kikes and dagos they can leave any time they don't like what we're paying."

Labor organizations were getting troublesome in Baltimore, but so far he had been fairly lucky in getting around them. He shuddered, however, looking into the bleak future. He'd better save all the money he could now by hiring more cheap niggers.

The white workers had swallowed their disappointment. Some of the more skilled did leave, swearing vengeance, but most of them hung on to their jobs.

"If we could only kill off these niggers!"

They did what they could, seriously injuring several, and bided their time.

Their chance came when Gardiner ambitiously contracted to build two large man-of-war vessels, professedly for the Mexican government. It was a rush job. The vessels were to be launched in August. Failure to do so would cause the shipbuilder to forfeit a very considerable sum of money. Work was speeded up. Some of the blacks were given jobs requiring the highest skill.

Then, all at once, the white carpenters swore they would no longer work beside the freedmen.

William Gardiner saw his money sinking to the bottom of Chesapeake Bay. Frantic, he appealed to his friend and associate, Hugh
Auld. The small shipbuilder was flattered. Gardiner was a powerful
man. Mr. Auld took the matter under consideration and came up
with a solution.

"Let some of the niggers go," he said. "Then take over a lot of
apprentices—whites and blacks. Work them at top speed under good
supervision. You'll pull through."

The older man frowned, pulling at his stubby mustache.

"Oh, come now." Mr. Auld clapped his friend on the back. "I've
got several good boys I can let you have."

Frederick was one of the apprentices sent to the Fells Point shipyard. He had worked hard and under very good instruction. But when
he arrived at Gardiner's yard he found himself in a very different
situation.

Here everything was hurry and drive. His section had about a
hundred men; of these, seventy or eighty were regular carpenters—
privileged men. There was no time for a raw hand to learn anything.
Ferderick was directed to do whatever the carpenters told him. This
placed him at the beck and call of about seventy-five men. He was to
regard all of them as his masters. He was called a dozen ways in the
space of a single minute. He needed a dozen pairs of hands.

"Boy, come help me cant this here timber."

"Boy, bring that roller here!"

"Hold on the end of this fall."

"Hullo, nigger! Come turn this grindstone."

"Run bring me a cold chisel!"

"I say, darky, blast your eyes! Why don't you heat up some pitch?"

It went on hour after hour. "Halloo! Halloo! Halloo!"—"Come
here—go there—hold on where you are." "Damn you, if you move
I'll knock your brains out!"

Although Frederick was only an apprentice, he was one of the
hated threats to their security. They had no mercy on him. The white
apprentices felt it degrading to work with him. Encouraged by the
workmen, they began talking contemptuously about "the niggers,"
saying they wanted to "take over the country" and that they ought to
be "killed off."

One day the powder keg exploded.

It was a hot afternoon. Frederick had just lowered a heavy timber
into place. Someone called him. He stepped back quickly, jostling
against Edward North, meanest bully of them all. North struck him

viciously. Whereupon, with one sweep, Frederick picked up the white fellow and threw him down hard upon the deck.

They set on him in a pack. One came in front, armed with a brick, one at each side, and one behind. They closed in, and Frederick, knowing he was fighting now for his life, struck out on all sides at once. A heavy blow with a handspike brought him down among the timbers. They rushed him then and began to pound him with their fists. He lay for a moment gathering strength, then rose suddenly to his knees, throwing them off. Just as he did this one of their number planted a blow with his boot in Frederick's left eye. When they saw his face covered with blood there was a pause.

Meanwhile scores of men looked on at this battle of four against one.

"Kill him!" they shouted. "Kill the nigger. He hit a white boy!"

Frederick was staggering, but he grabbed up a handspike and charged. This time they were taken by surprise. But then several of the carpenters grabbed Frederick and held him powerless. He was sobbing with rage. What could he do against fifty men—laughing, jeering, cursing him? At that moment the division superintendent was seen coming to investigate the uproar. They thinned out. Taking advantage of the lull, Frederick dropped over the side of the hull and escaped from the yard. He knew he would find no justice at the hands of the authorities there.

Bleeding and battered, he made his way home, nearly frightening the wits out of Jeb. At Nada's call, Mrs. Auld came running to the kitchen. She had them carry him to his attic room, and herself saw that his wounds were bathed. She bound up his battered eye with a piece of fresh beef.

"The brutes! The beastly brutes!" she kept saying while she rubbed his head with ointment.

There was no question about Mr. Auld's reaction when he reached home that evening. He was furious. It never entered his head that his friend, William Gardiner, was in any way to blame. He heaped curses on the shipyard ruffians; it might well be some "Irish plot," and he was going to see that the scoundrels were punished.

Just as soon as Frederick was somewhat recovered from his bruises, Mr. Auld took him to Esquire Watson's office on Bond Street, with a view to procuring the arrest of the four workers. The Master gave the magistrate an account of the outrage. Mr. Watson, sitting quietly with folded hands, heard him through.

"And who saw this assault of which you speak, Mr. Auld?" he coolly inquired.

"It was done, sir, in the presence of a shipyard full of hands." The magistrate shrugged his shoulders.

"I'm sorry, sir, but I cannot move in this matter, except upon the oath of white witnesses."

"But here's my boy. Look at his head and face!" Mr. Auld was losing his temper.

"I am not authorized to do anything unless white witnesses come forward and testify on oath as to what took place."

For one flashing moment the veil was torn from Hugh Auld's eyes. His blood froze with horror. It would have been the same had the boy been killed! He took Frederick by the arm and spoke roughly.

"Let's get out of here!"

For several days Hugh Auld fussed and fumed. He went to call on Mr. Gardiner. The big shipbuilder received the younger man coolly.

"You're loosing your head, Auld," he observed shrewdly, "and you're following a line that may cause you to lose your shirt. Do you think I'm going to upset my shipyard because one fresh nigger got his head cracked? I've got contracts to fill."

"But—" Mr. Auld's confidence was oozing out.

"Of course," continued Mr. Gardiner, still cold, "I'll compensate you for any expense you've had. Did you have to get a doctor to patch him up?" He reached for his wallet.

Outside, with the August sun blistering the boardwalks, Hugh Auld shivered.

Before the year had passed it was decided that Frederick would be more valuable to his master as a journeyman caulker than working in his small shipyard. He was therefore allowed to seek paying employment. He was in the enviable position of being able to pick his job and demand wages. He was known as "Hugh Auld's boy" and was reputed remarkably bright and dependable. He made his own contracts and collected his earnings, bringing in six and seven dollars a week during the busy season. At the end of some weeks he turned over nine dollars to his master.

Frederick congratulated himself. His lot was improving. Now he could increase his little stock of education. On the Eastern Shore he had been the teacher. As soon as he had got work in Baltimore, he began looking up colored people who could teach him. So it happened that he heard about the East Baltimore Mental Improvement Society and met a free colored girl named Anna Murray.

The Oblate Sisters of Providence had been attracted by dark-eyed, slender Anna Murray. Madame Montell herself had brought the girl to the side door of St. Mary's Seminary. She told the sisters she was of free parentage and employed in her household. Madame wished the girl carefully instructed.

Then Madame Montell died. And the weeping girl was told that she had been provided with a dowry—a great feather bed, eider-down pillows, some real silver and linen, dishes. Her heart was filled with gratitude. Madame's relatives did not deprive the faithful girl of her wealth. They had packed a trunk for her and seen her safely installed with the nice Wells family on South Carolina Street. All this before they returned to their beloved France, where Madame had once planned to take Anna.

The Wellses were not French, but they were gentle people and Anna was not unhappy with them.

Anna was a great favorite among the free Negroes of Baltimore. She had had access to Madame's books, and anything she said was likely to start an inspiring line of thought. The Negroes from Haiti were drawn to her. She understood their French, though she herself seldom tried to speak it.

In spite of the staggering obstacles, groups of free Negroes did manage to sustain themselves even within the boundaries of slave states. They ran small businesses, owned property, were trusted in good jobs. In the 1790's statesmen from Washington and merchants from Richmond and Atlanta came to Baltimore to buy the clocks of Benjamin Banneker, Negro clockmaker.

Any meeting of Negroes was safest in a church. The whites readily encouraged religious fervor among the "childlike" blacks. "Slaves, obey your masters" was a Biblical text constantly upon the lips of the devout. Over all blacks the ease and glories of heaven were sprayed like ether to deaden present pain. It was especially good for free Negroes to have lots of religion.

The East Baltimore Mental Improvement Society usually met in the African Methodist Episcopal Church on Sharp Street. Having carefully established their purpose by lusty singing and a long, rolling prayer, watchers were set and copies of the *Freedom's Journal*, published in New York, or a newer paper called the *Liberator*, were brought out.

One evening a group of shipyard workers from Fells Point had something to say. They wanted to present a new name for membership.

"He is a young man of character," their spokesman said.

"A good caulker, steady and industrious," added his companion.

"He writes and ciphers well," put in another.

"Invite this newcomer, by all means." The chairman spoke cordially. "What is his name?"

There was a moment of embarrassment among the Fells Point workers.

"He is— He is still a—slave."

A horribly scarred old man with only one leg spat contemptuously. He had been one of the followers of Gabriel in the Virginian insurrection. He had seen the twenty-four-year-old giant die without a word. He himself had been one of the four slaves condemned to die, who had escaped. Now, he had little patience with "strong young men" who were content to remain slaves.

"Let 'im be!" He rumbled deep in his throat.

One of the caulkers turned to him. He spoke with deference, but with conviction.

"Daddy Ben, I have seen him fight. He is a man!"

"His name?" asked the chairman.

"He is known as Frederick."

So Frederick was admitted to membership. At his first meeting he sat silent, listening. He felt very humble when these men and women rose to their feet and read or spoke. His head whirled. It seemed that he could not bear any more when a young woman, whom he had noticed sitting very quietly in a corner, rose. She held a paper in her hand, and when she spoke her voice was low and musical. At first he heard only that music. He shook himself and tried to attend to what she was saying.

"This third edition of the *Appeal* has been wholly reset and contains many corrections and important additions. David Walker is dead, but let us remember that his words are addressed to us, to every one of us. Remember the preamble to his four articles, his own words 'To the Colored Citizens of the World, but in particular, and very expressly, to those of the United States of America.' The hour is too late for you to hear the entire text of his final message. But in this time of great stress and discouragement I should like to call your attention to this one paragraph."

And then, standing close to the smoking oil lamp, she read from the paper in her hand:

"For although the destruction of the oppressors God may not effect by the oppressed, yet the Lord our God will bring other destruction upon them, for not infrequently will He cause them to rise up one against the other, to be split, divided, and to oppress each other. And sometimes to open hostilities with sword in hand."

She sat down then amid complete and thoughtful silence. The meeting broke up. They dispersed quickly, not loitering on the street, not walking together. But first Frederick buttonholed his friend from Fells Point.

"What's her name?" he whispered. His friend knew whom he meant.

"Anna Murray."

The bonds of slavery bit deeper than before. The calm, sweet face of Anna Murray shimmered in his dreams. He had to be free!

He was living and working among free men, in all respects equal to them in performance. Why then should he be a slave? He was earning a dollar and a half a day. He contracted for it, worked for it, collected it. It was paid to him. Turning this money over to Mr. Auld each Saturday became increasingly painful. He could see no reason why, at the end of each week, he should pour the rewards of his toil into the purse of a master.

It is quite possible that Mr. Auld sensed some of this rebellion, though not its intensity. Each time he carefully counted the money and each time he looked searchingly at the young man and asked, "Is that all?"

It would not do to let the boy consider himself too profitable. On the other hand, when the sum was extra large he usually gave him back a sixpence or shilling along with a kindly pat.

This dole did not have the intended effect. The slave took it as an admission of his right to the whole sum. In giving him a few cents the master was easing his conscience.

Frederick could not think what to do. At this rate he could not even *buy* his freedom. To escape he needed money. His free friends offered a suggestion: that he solicit the privilege of buying his time.

It was not uncommon in the large cities. A slave who was considered trustworthy could, by paying his master a definite sum at the end of each week, dispose of his time as he liked.

Frederick decided to wait until his actual master, Captain Auld, came up to Baltimore to make his spring purchases. Master Hugh was only acting as the Captain's agent, but Frederick was confident that the report concerning him given to the Captain would be a good one.

In this he was not disappointed. Captain Auld was told that his slave had learned well, had worked diligently. But when Frederick presented his request, the Captain's face turned red.

"No!" he shouted. "And none of your monkey business!"

He studied the slave's gloomy face. His own eyes narrowed.

"Get this through your black skull. You can't run away! There's no place you can go that I won't find you and drag you back." His voice was grim. "Next time I won't be so easy. It'll be the river!"

He meant he'd "sell him down the river." Frederick turned away.

"Give 'em an inch and they want an ell," grumbled the Captain to his brother.

Hugh Auld shook his head sympathetically. He was having his own troubles. Along with a lot of other speculators he was beginning to doubt the wisdom of his "sure" investments. He had taken out stock in both the Baltimore and Ohio Railroad and the Chesapeake and Ohio Canal. Now there were dire whispers of an impending crash. The Bank of Maryland had closed—temporarily, of course— but the weeks were passing and business was falling off.

Therefore, when, a month later, Frederick came to him with the same proposition, he said he would think about it. Jobs for journeymen caulkers were going to be fewer, wages were coming down. He had this big hulk of a fellow on his hands. No telling what would happen within the next months. Let him try himself. He told Frederick he could have all his time on the following terms: he would be required to pay his master three dollars at the end of each week, board and clothe himself and buy his own caulking tools. Failure in any of these particulars would put an end to the privilege.

His words staggered Frederick. The week just ended had not been good. He had worked only four and a half days. That meant there would be no sixpence for him tonight. They were standing in the kitchen. Frederick had been eating when the master came in.

"Well? Speak up?"

Frederick watched his week's earning go into the small black pouch. A slight movement from Nada at the stove caused him to look at her. She was forming the word "Yes" with her lips, nodding her head vigorously at him. Mr. Auld spoke complacently.

"You see, being your own boss means more than just keeping your money. Do you want your time or don't you?"

Frederick's face did not change expression, but he squared his shoulders.

"Yes, sir," he said to Mr. Auld. "I'll take my time."

"Very well. You can start Monday." The master joined his wife in the living room. She did not like what he told her.

"You shouldn't let him," she frowned over her mending. "They can't look out after themselves. It's wicked!"

"He'll be back." Mr. Auld settled himself comfortably in his favorite chair. "The young buck's restless. This will be a good lesson to him."

Back in the kitchen Frederick turned worried eyes on Nada. She gave him one of her rare smiles.

"No worry!" she said. "Yo' come live by me."

Jeb was appalled. Frederick had taught him to read, and he regarded the young man with something akin to adoration. That night in their attic room they talked.

"Yo' gonna run away! Yo' gonna run away!" All the terrors of pursuing hounds, starvation and dragging chains choked the boy's voice.

"Hush!" Frederick gripped his shoulder. Then he whispered fiercely, "Do you want to be a slave all your life?"

"No! Oh, Jesus! No!" He began to sob.

"Then keep still—and let me go!"

The boy gulped piteously. He put his mouth close to Frederick's ear.

"Take me wid yo', Fred, take me wid yo'! I not feared." But Frederick pushed him away gently.

"Don't talk. Wait!"

"Yo' not forget me?"

And Frederick promised. "I will not forget."

The following evening when Nada disappeared down the alley, Frederick was with her.

Events now moved rapidly. The entire membership of the East Baltimore Mental Improvement Society was concerned with Frederick.

They all knew what he was trying to do. The caulkers were on the alert for any extra jobs, older men advised, and Anna Murray's eyes began to glow softly. Sometimes Frederick entered into the discussions at the meeting now, but usually he sat silent, listening. Afterward he walked home with Anna, avoiding the lighted streets. And he poured into her willing ear his whole mad scheme. The stringent cordon thrown around Baltimore to prevent slaves from escaping demanded a bold plan. Frederick knew that he had to get well away or he would surely be captured, and he knew that a second failure would be fatal.

The railroad from Baltimore to Philadelphia was under such rigid regulations that even free colored travelers were practically excluded. They had to carry free papers on their persons—papers describing the name, age, color, height and form of the traveler, especially any scars or other marks he had. Negroes were measured and carefully examined before they could enter the cars, and they could only go in the daytime. The steamboats had similar rules. British seamen of color were forbidden to land at Southern ports. An American seaman of African descent was required to have always on him a "sailor's protection," describing the bearer and certifying to the fact that he was a free American sailor.

One night Frederick was introduced to a sailor who appeared to be well known to the group. The older ones, standing round, studied the two young men talking together. Then Daddy Ben said briefly, "It will do!"

After that Frederick spent every moment away from his work in the sailor's company. They leaned over bars in crowded saloons off Lower Broadway and swapped talk with old salts who had not yet recovered their land legs. They swore at the fresh young landlubber, but his friend, laughing heartily, warded off their blows.

On the last Sunday in August, as was his custom, Frederick reported with his three dollars.

"I'm taking Mrs. Auld to the country over next Sunday," Mr. Auld said. "This awful heat is bad for her. Come in next Monday."

Frederick knew the time had come. He reported at each place punctually that week. He took every extra job he could find. Sunday evening he slipped into the little garden behind the house on South Carolina Street. Anna was waiting.

"Take care! Oh, take care!" she whispered.

"You'll be getting a letter from up North—soon!" he boasted.

The next morning the Philadelphia train was puffing into the Baltimore and Ohio station when a swaggering young sailor strode across the platform. Several Negro passengers stood in a huddled group to one side. All had passed their examinations. The impatient young sailor did not join them. His bell-bottom trousers flopped about his legs, the black cravat fastened loosely about his neck was awry, and he pushed his tarpaulin hat back on his head, as he peered anxiously up the street. The conductor had yelled "All aboard!" when a ramshackle old hack drew up. The sailor ran to it, flung open the door before the stupid old hackman could move, and grabbed a big, battered bag, plastered with many labels and tied with strong hemp.

"Damn you!" cursed the sailor, "yo' makin' me miss ma ship!"

He sprinted for the last car of the train, leaving the blinking old hackman unpaid. The conductor laughed.

The train was well on the way to Havre de Grace before the conductor reached the last car to collect tickets and look over the colored folks' papers. This was rather perfunctory, since he knew they had all been examined at the station. He chuckled as he spied the sailor slumped in a back seat, already fast asleep. Bet he'd made a night of it—several nights, no doubt! Probably overstayed his time and knew the brig irons were waiting for him. *Oh, well, niggers don't care.* So long as they had their whiskey and women! He shook the sailor playfully. Frederick stared up at him, blinking.

"All right, sailor boy, your ticket!"

"Yes, *suh*." Frederick fumbled in his blouse, producing a not too clean bit of cardboard. He appeared to be groggy.

"I reckon you got your free papers?"

The fellow showed the whites of his eyes. He shook his head.

"No, suh. Ah nevah carries mah papahs to sea wid me."

"But you do have something to show you're a free man, haven't you?"

The sailor's face beamed.

"Yes, *suh*. Ah got a papah right hyear wid da 'Merican eagle right on hit. Dat little ole bird carries me round da world!"

From somewhere about himself he drew out a paper and unfolded it carefully. The conductor immediately recognized it as a sailor's protection. He looked at the spread American eagle at its head, nodded and went on down the aisle.

Frederick's hand was trembling as he folded the paper. It called for a man much darker than himself. Close examination would have brought about not only his arrest, but the arrest and severe punishment of the sailor who had lent it to him.

The danger was not over. After Maryland they passed through Delaware, another slave state, where slave-catchers would be awaiting their prey. It was at the borders that they were most vigilant.

They reached Havre de Grace, where the Susquehanna River had to be crossed by ferry. Frederick was making his way to the rail so that he could stand with his back to the other passengers, when he literally bumped into Henry!

Henry saw him first. In a second the big fellow pushed him violently to one side; and so Mr. William Freeland did not catch a glimpse of the young sailor. A sailor who no longer swaggered but whose legs hardly managed to bear him up as he clung to the rail. On shore Henry, watching the ferry pull away from the dock, was also trembling.

"What's the matter with you, Henry?" asked Mr. Freeland. The fellow looked as if he was going to be sick.

"Nothin', suh! Nothin' at all!" Henry answered quickly.

On the other side of the river Frederick ran into a new danger. A German blacksmith for whom he had worked only a few days before looked him full in the face. Two trains had stopped on tracks next to each other—one going south, the other going north. The blacksmith was returning to Baltimore. The windows were open and Frederick, sitting close to his window, was bareheaded. The German opened his mouth. Then his face froze like Frederick's. He flicked ashes from his big cigar and turned away from the window.

Frederick sank back into his seat, closed his eyes and pulled his hat over his face as if he were asleep.

The last danger-point, and the one he dreaded most, was Wilmington. Here he had to leave the train and take the steamboat for Philadelphia. It was an hour of torture, but no one stopped him; and finally he was out on the broad and beautiful Delaware on his way to the Quaker City.

He had eaten nothing and his head felt very light as he stood on the deck. He knew that never would he see anything so beautiful as that river. Yet he dared not relax one moment of watchfulness.

They reached Philadelphia late in the afternoon. The sky was a crimson glow as he stepped first upon free soil. He wanted to shout and sing, but he had been warned not to pause until he reached New York—there only might he savor the taste of freedom. He asked the first colored man he saw in Philadelphia how he could get to New York. The man directed him to the Willow Street depot. He went there at once, and had no trouble buying a ticket. During the several hours' wait for his train, he did not leave the station. It seemed as if the train would never come, but at last he was safely aboard.

He thought something was wrong. It was still dark, but all the passengers were getting off. He was afraid to ask questions.

"Come on, sailor!" the conductor said. And when he looked up stupidly, the conductor added, "It's the ferry. You have to take the ferry over to Manhattan."

He watched the skyline of New York come up out of the dawn. The hoarse whistles along the waterfront made a song; the ships' bells rang out freedom. He walked across the gangplank, set his battered bag down on the wharf and looked back. The busy river was like a crowded thoroughfare. A barefoot Negro had leaned against a pile, watching him.

"What river is this, boy?" Frederick asked. The boy stared.

"That's tha Hudson River. Where you come from, sailor?"

The fugitive from slavery's Eastern Shore smiled.

"A long way, boy. I've crossed a heap of rivers!"

Then, early in the morning of September 4, 1838, he walked up into New York City. He was free!

Part II

THE LIGHTNING

And what man moves but on the crest of history!
The spark flashes from each to each.
The incandescence fuses—
Blooms out of the ghetto pit—
Roars to the sky—
Fans into a fiery liberty tree
Showering its seed to the last beaches of the em-
  battled earth!

—HARRY GRANICK

CHAPTER SIX

Is this a thing, or can it be a man?

F REEDOM IS A HARD-BOUGHT thing! Frederick expected to remain in New York. He was free, he had money in his pocket, he would find work. He had no plans beyond reaching this big city, where there were Abolitionists who printed papers calling for the freeing of the slaves, and many free Negroes. Here he could work in safety.

"*Voila!*" murmured a little French seamstress, peeping through the slits of her blinds as the jaunty figure came in view. She had seen such stepping before, such lifting of the head, such a singing with the shoulders. She remembered free men marching into the Place de la Concorde. She smiled and hummed a few bars of the "*Marseillaise.*" "*Allons, enfants. . . . Marchons. . . .*" She threw the shutters open. What a beautiful morning!

But Frederick didn't find work that first day. By nightfall he was feeling uneasy. Job-hunting had brought him up against an unexpected wall. The colored people he saw seemed to be avoiding him. He walked straight up to the next Negro he saw and spoke to him. From his bespattered appearance, and his pail and brush, Frederick judged the man to be a house painter.

"Good evening, mister! Could you tell me where I might find a place to stay? I just got here and—"

The man's eyes in his sunken, dark face were rolling in every direction at once.

"Lemme be. I donno nothin'." He was moving on, but Frederick blocked his path.

"Look, mister, I only want—"

The man's tones were belligerent, though his voice was low.

83

"Donno nothin' 'bout you, sailor. An' I ain't tellin' you nothin'!"

Frederick watched him disappear around a corner. As night came on he followed a couple of sailors into a smoke-filled eating place. There he ate well, served by a swarthy, good-natured fellow, whose father that day had picked olives on a hillside overlooking Rome. Garlic, coarse laughter, warmth and the tangy smell of seamen mingled in the dimly lighted room. Some of the men lifted their foamy mugs in greeting as Frederick sank into a corner. He waved back. But he hurried through his meal, not daring to linger long for fear of betraying himself.

He walked aimlessly in the gathering gloom. He thought a lamplighter, lifting his wick to the corner lamp, eyed him suspiciously. Frederick turned down a dimmer thoroughfare. He was tired. The suitcase was heavy.

Across the street a bearded seaman took his stubby pipe from between his teeth and looked after the solitary figure. *Young sailors do not carry heavy suitcases, bumping against their legs!* The man grunted, crossed the street and came up behind the young man. He spoke softly.

"Hi, sailor!"

With a start Frederick turned. Now it was his turn to hesitate. In the fading light he could not distinguish whether the face behind the thick beard was white or colored. So he only answered, "Hi, yo'self!"

The stranger fell in beside him. "When'd you get in?"

"Yesterday. Up from the West Indies." The answer came easily. *But*, the seaman thought to himself, *it's the wrong answer*. Out of the corner of his eye he studied the young man and threw out another question.

"What's your ship?"

Frederick was well prepared for this question.

"The *Falcon*."

They walked along in silence, the bearded seaman puffing his pipe. Frederick waited.

"Might you be headin' toward the—north star?"

Frederick's heart leaped. The words could have only one meaning. Yet was this man friend or foe? Dared he trust him?

"I hear tell the north star leads us straight," he said.

The stranger took Frederick's arm.

"It has led you well. Come!"

In the little house on Centre Street, Frederick met Tom Stuart's mother, a bright-eyed little woman who greeted him warmly. But hardly could he blurt out an outline of his story before he had fallen asleep—for the first time in nearly forty-eight hours.

Then Tom Stuart went quickly to the corner of Lispenard and Church Streets and knocked on the door of David Ruggles, secretary of the New York Vigilance Committee.

"You are right," said the secretary, when he heard what the seaman had to say. "He is not safe here."

"New York's full of Southerners. They're beginning to come back from the watering-places now," Stuart added.

"Looking for work down on the waterfront, he'll be caught."

The scar on Ruggles' black face twisted into a smile.

"God's providence protected him today. Now we must do our part and get him away." He covered his sightless eyes with his hand and sat thinking.

David Ruggles had been born free. He was schooled, alert, and he had courage. But once he had dared too much for his own good. In Ohio an irate slave-chaser's whip had cut across his face. Its thongs had torn at his eyes, and he would never see again. But the slave whom he was helping to escape had got away. And David Ruggles had said, "My eyes for a man's life? We were the winners!"

The seaman cleared his throat.

"There is a girl—a freewoman. She is to meet him here."

The secretary frowned.

"Good heavens! Haven't we enough to do without managing love trysts?"

Tom Stuart grinned in the darkness as he walked home. He knew the heart of this black man. He would show no sign of annoyance the next morning when he welcomed the young fugitive.

As for Frederick, he wanted to kiss the hands of this blind man when they clasped his own so firmly. *An agent of the Underground Railroad! Underground Railroad!*—a whisper up and down the Eastern Shore. Now Frederick was to hear them spoken aloud.

The increasing numbers of slaves who were escaping, in spite of the rigid cordons thrown round the slave states and the terrifying penalties for failure in the attempt, gave rise to wild rumors. The bayous of Louisiana, the backlands of Alabama and Mississippi, the swamps of Florida and the mountains of the Atlantic states, seemed to suck them in like a man-eating plant. People said there was a colony of blacks deep in the Florida scrub, where they lived a life of ease far inside the bayous that no white man could penetrate. Another group, so they said, raised crops on the broad flat plains that ran toward the border of Georgia; and two thousand more hid inside the dismal swamps of Virginia, coming out to trade with Negroes and whites.

There was no denying the fact that Negroes showed up across the border of Canada with surprising regularity—slaves from the rice fields of Georgia and South Carolina, the tobacco lands of Virginia and Maryland, and the cotton fields of Alabama.

"One thousand slaves a year disappear!" John Calhoun thundered in Congress. "They go as if swallowed up by an underground passage."

The idea caught on. Young America expanding—passages opening to new territory. To a people still using the stagecoach, trains symbolized daring and adventure. An underground railway to freedom! Men cocked their hats rakishly, cut off their mustaches and tightened the holsters at their belts; small shopkeepers put heavy padlocks on their doors and slipped out to meetings; tall, lean men wearing linen and nankeen pantaloons—sons of planters among them—emptied their mint juleps and climbed into the saddle; the devout Quaker put a marker in his Bible and dug a new deep cellar underneath his house, partitioned off rooms with false walls and laid in fresh supplies of thick wide cloaks and long black veils.

What more natural than that slaves down in their quarters sang, *Dat train comin', hit's comin' round da bend!* and *Git on board, lil' chillun, git on board!*

The "train" might be a skiff, securely fastened under overhanging reeds. Or it might be a peddler's cart, an open wagon filled with hay, or the family carryall, driven by a quiet man in a wide-brimmed Quaker hat, who spoke softly to the ladies sitting beside him, neatly dressed in gray, with Quaker bonnets on their heads and veils over their faces. The "train" might simply be a covered-up path through the woods. But the slave voices rose, exulting:

> "Da train am rollin'
> Da train am rollin' by—
> Hallelujah!"

"Conductors" planned the connections. And David Ruggles in the house on Church Street routed the train in and out of New York City.

He collected and paid out money, received reports and checked routes. David Ruggles was a busy man.

He heard Frederick through quietly. Frederick was worried. If he could not stay in New York, where would he go?

"It's a big country," Mr. Ruggles assured the young man. "A workman is worthy of his hire. We shall look about." Then he asked abruptly, "Have you written the young lady?"

Frederick felt his face burn. Being among people with whom he could share his precious secret was a new experience.

"Y-es, sir," he stammered. "I—I posted a letter this morning— On my way here."

He looked toward Tom Stuart, whose eyes were laughing at him. The seaman put in a word.

"Got up and wrote the letter before dawn!"

"Since she is a freewoman," Mr. Ruggles smiled, "she can no doubt join you immediately."

"Yes— Yes, sir."

"Very well. Then you must remain under cover until she comes."

"He's safe at my house," Tom Stuart said quickly, and the secretary nodded.

"That is good," he said. "And now for the record."

At this word a slender boy of nine or ten years, who had been sitting quietly at the table, opened a large ledger and picked up a quill pen. He said nothing but turned his intelligent, bright eyes toward Frederick. Mr. Ruggles laid his hand on the boy's arm.

"My son here is my eyes," he said.

Frederick regarded the little fellow with amazement. He was going to write with that pen!

"You are called Frederick?" the father asked.

Frederick gave a start. "I have sometimes heard of another name —Bailey," he said. "I—I really don't know. They call me Frederick."

"For the present, we shan't worry about the surname. It is safer now to lose whatever identity you might have. Write Frederick Johnson, son!" The boy wrote easily. "There are so many Johnsons. But now that you are a free man, you must have a name—a family name.

"Oh, yes, sir!"

The days passed swiftly. Anna arrived—warmly welcomed by Tom Stuart's mother and whisked quickly out of sight until the moment when she stood beside him. Anna, her eyes pools of happiness, wearing a lovely plum-colored silk dress! They were married by the Reverend J. W. C. Pennington, whose father, after having been freed by George Washington, had served him faithfully at Valley Forge. He refused the fee offered by the eager young bridegroom.

"It is my wedding gift to you, young man. God speed you!"

They were put aboard the steamer *John W. Richmond*, belonging to the line running between New York and Newport, Rhode Island.

"New Bedford is your place," David Ruggles had said. "There are many Friends in New Bedford, and the shipyards are constantly fitting out ships for long whaling voyages. A good caulker will find work. Good luck, my boy!"

Since colored passengers were not allowed in the cabins, the bride and groom had to pass their first night on the deck. But what mattered whether they were cold or hot, wet or dry; whether they stood leaning over the rail, jammed against sticky kegs, or sat on the hard boards? They were free—they were young—they were on their way, to make a home, to build a life *together*.

Oh, how bright the stars shone that night! Anna saw Frederick's lips move as he gazed at them. She leaned closer and he tightened his arm about her. "I must not forget!" he murmured.

The nights on the open deck—they had two of them—enfolded them and shut out all the world. The ache of all their lonely years dissolved before the new happiness in their hearts. Then, out of the gray mist and the darker shadows, emerged the gaunt shores of their new world. Anna gripped her husband's arm and trembled. But he lifted her face to his and kissed her.

As the boat approached New Bedford, the crowded harbor, with its stained, weather-beaten ships and dirty warehouses, was a golden gate—let down from the clouds just for them. Frederick wanted to shout.

"Look! Look!" He was pointing at an imposing house that stood on a hill behind the town. "That's the kind of house we'll have. A fine, big house! I'll make it with my own hands. I'm free, Anna, I'm free to build a house like that!"

Her eyes laughed with him.

So it was that they landed on the rocky shores of New England, where free men had set their feet before them. Leif, son of Eric the Red, touched this coast with his Norsemen. In 1497 and '98 John Cabot, Venetian navigator, explored here and gave England her claim to the region. Cabot under the British flag, Verrazzano under the *fleur de lis*, and Gomez under the flag of Spain, all of them had come even before the Pilgrim Fathers.

It was from Rhode Island—from Roger Williams and Anne Hutchinson, all part of the rising winds of rebellion—that New Bedford got its start. Time and again this salty breeze had blown through the Massachusetts commonwealth. It rose and blew steadily during most of the eighteenth century, bringing gains in political freedom and education and religious tolerance. Impoverished farmers had followed Daniel Shays; and an early governor, James Sullivan, had been stirred to say, "Where the mass of people are ignorant, poor and miserable, there is no public opinion excepting what is the offspring of fear." The winds had died down during the rise of Federalism, but now once more a little breeze fanned the cheeks of the mill girls in Lowell and the mechanics in Boston. It rustled the dead, dry leaves piled high in Cambridge and Concord. It was scattering the seeds of Abolitionism.

Boston had William Lloyd Garrison, whom neither jails, fires, threats, nor the elegant rhetoric of William Ellery Channing could stifle. He waved his paper, the *Liberator*, high in the air, whipping the breeze higher. He stood his ground and loosed a blast destined to shake the rafters of the nation.

"Urge me not to use moderation in a cause like the present. I am in earnest. I will not equivocate. I will not excuse. I will not retreat a single inch—and I will be heard!"

Certain slave states had set a price on William Lloyd Garrison's head. But in February, 1837, the Massachusetts Anti-Slavery Society had convened in the hall of the House of Representatives in Boston, and after every space was filled nearly five thousand people were turned away. Nathan Johnson had been one of the delegates from New Bedford.

Nathan Johnson was proud of the commonwealth of Massachusetts. His people had lived in the midst of a group of Dutch dairy farmers comfortably spread out over the meadowlands near Sheffield. They had owned a tiny piece of land. Nathan had gone to school, learned a trade and, like many another Massachusetts farm boy, made a trip to sea. For a time he had lingered in Scotland where a Negro was a curiosity. There was something about the hills and valleys with their jutting rocks that drew him. Then he realized he was homesick. He returned to Massachusetts, married and plied his trade—he was a carpenter—near the sight and sound and smell of the sea. He had seen the face of slavery, but he believed the State of Massachusetts would educate the nation away from such evil practices.

David Ruggles had written Nathan Johnson about Frederick. The answer had come back: "Send him along!" And Johnson had hurried to the dock to meet the "poor critters."

But the young man who stepped from the boat and took his hand with such a firm grip did not call forth pity. To the Yankee he had the look neither of a fugitive nor a slave.

Ma Johnson blocked all questions while she bustled about setting a good, hot meal before the newcomers.

"Dead beat, I know," was her comment. "Now you just wash up and make yourselves right at home." She poured water and handed them thick white towels, while little Lethia and Jane stared with wide eyes.

Everything floated in a dreamy mist. This house, this abundant table, this room were unbelievable. Frederick's fingers itched to take down the books from their shelves, to pick up papers lying about. With an effort he brought his eyes back to the animated face of his host.

"There ain't a thing in the laws or constitution of Massachusetts to stop a colored man being governor of the state, if the folks sees fit to elect him!" Lethia nodded her small head gravely and smiled at Frederick.

Ma Johnson sighed gently. Nathan was off on his favorite topic—Massachusetts! But that was safe talk for these two nice young people. They could just eat in peace. She set a plate of savory clam chowder in front of Anna.

"No slaveholder'd dare try takin' a slave out of New Bedford!" The glasses quivered as Johnson thumped the table. Frederick smiled.

"I'm glad to hear that—after what they told me about New York."

"Humph!" The Yankee snorted. "New York ain't in Massachusetts, young man. All sorts of people there. Can't count on 'em!" Ma Johnson gently intervened.

"Reckon we have some troublemakers, too, even in New Bedford."

"Ay, and I reckon we know how to take care of 'em!"

It was Indian summer in New England. The evenings were still long, with no suggestion of frost in the air. After supper they sat in the yard, and between long puffs on his pipe the host talked and gradually drew out the young man. Came the moment when he took his pipe from his mouth and sat forward on his chair, lips pressed together in a grim line.

"I cannot understand how such things be!" he said, shaking his head.

The women had gone inside. Lights shone in the cottage across the way, and on the other side of the white picket fence a girl laughed. Frederick stood up. Even in the dusk, Johnson was conscious of the broad shoulders and the long, lithe limbs. He was looking up at the trees.

"Almost— Almost I am afraid," Frederick said.

"Afraid? Now? Your time to be afraid is gone. Now you are safe!"

"That's it! *I* am safe. I'm afraid of so much happiness."

"A mite o' happiness won't spoil you, my boy. There's strength in you. And now I reckon your wife is waiting." Nathan Johnson stood up.

Inside the house Frederick turned and clasped the hand of his host.

"How can I thank you?" he asked.

The older man smiled. "Fine words ain't needed, son. The two of you are good for Ma and me. Now go 'long with you!"

And he sent him to Anna.

They were awakened by church bells. Then they heard the children getting off to church. Anna started up guiltily. Perhaps they were delaying Mrs. Johnson.

But over the house lay a sweet Sabbath calm; it ran all up and down the street—and over all New Bedford. The day passed in unhurried discussion of jobs and plans for the young folks. Now indeed Frederick must have a name.

"Some take the name of their old master."

"I won't." Frederick spoke emphatically.

"Ay," agreed Nathan. "No sense in tying a stone round your children's necks. Give 'em a good name." He grinned at Frederick and Anna. "When I look at you I think of somebody I read about— fellow by the name of Douglass."

"You want to name him from a book, Pa?" His wife laughed.

"Why not? He's already got a heap out of books. And this Scotchman, Douglass, was a fine man. The book says he had a 'stalwart hand'."

Then Nathan launched into a vivid description of Scotland as he had seen it. He came back to the name.

"Ay, Douglass is a bonny name."

Anna spoke softly. "Frederick Douglass— It has a good, strong sound."

"You like it, Anna?" Frederick's eyes drew her to him.

And Anna smiled, nodding her head. So Douglass was the name he passed on to their children.

The next day he went down to the wharves and caught his first view of New England shipping.

"The sight of the broad brim and the plain, Quaker dress," he recalled later, "which met me at every turn, greatly increased my sense of freedom and security. *I am among the Quakers*, thought I, *and am safe*. Lying at the wharves and riding in the stream, were full-rigged ships of finest model, ready to start on whaling voyages. Upon the right and the left, I was walled in by large granite-fronted warehouses, crowded with the good things of this world. On the wharves, I saw industry without bustle, labor without noise, and heavy toil without the whip. There was no loud singing, as in Southern ports where ships are loading or unloading—no loud cursing or swearing—but everything went on as smoothly as the works of a well-adjusted machine. How different was all this from the noisily fierce and clumsily absurd manner of labor-life in Baltimore and St. Michaels! One of the first incidents which illustrated the superior mental character of Northern labor over that of the South, was the manner of unloading a ship's cargo of oil. In a Southern port, twenty or thirty hands would have been employed to do what five or six did here, with the aid of a single ox hitched to the end of a fall. Main strength, unassisted by skill, is slavery's method of labor. An old ox worth eighty dollars was doing in New Bedford what would have required fifteen thousand dollars' worth of human bone and muscle to have performed in a Southern port. . . . The maid servant, instead of spending at least a tenth part of her time in bringing and carrying water, as in Baltimore, had the pump at her elbow. Wood-houses, indoor pumps, sinks, drains, self-shutting gates, washing machines, pounding barrels, were all new things, and told me that I was among a thoughtful and sensible people. The carpenters struck where they aimed, and the caulkers wasted no blows in idle flourishes of the mallet." *

* Douglass, *My Bondage and My Freedom*, chap. xxii, pp. 345–46.

He remembered little about the hardships of that first winter in the North, and only mentioned in passing that he was not permitted to use his skill as a caulker. Even here white labor shut the black worker out. The difference between the wage of a caulker and that of a common day-laborer was 50 per cent. But Frederick would not be stopped. He was free. So he sawed wood, dug cellars, shoveled coal, rolled oil casks on the wharves, loaded and unloaded vessels. It was the cold that he remembered.

Nothing had prepared them for the cold—the silent, thick, gray cold that shut down like a vise over the land. The tiny house on a back street, which had seemed the fulfillment of their dreams, now was a porous shed. It had none of the Northern conveniences, and each trip through the snowdrifts to the distant well with its frozen buckets was a breath-taking effort.

Each morning Anna got her husband's breakfast by candlelight, and Frederick set out for work. Odd jobs were not as easy to find nor as steady as he would have liked. Many cotton mills in New England were still that winter, and many ships lay idle all along Cape Cod. Down in Washington a new President was proving himself weak and ineffectual. Banks were tottering and business houses were going down in ruins. This was the year Susan B. Anthony's father lost his factory, his store, his home; and the eighteen-year-old Quaker girl, with Berkshire hills mirrored in her eyes, went out to teach school.

During the hardest part of the winter, Frederick's wages were less than ten dollars for the month. He and Anna were pinched for food. But they were never discouraged: they were living in a new world. When he could, Frederick attended the meetings of colored people of New Bedford. These meetings went far beyond the gatherings of the East Baltimore Mental Improvement Society, and once more Frederick sat silent, listening and learning. He was constantly amazed at the resolutions presented and discussions which followed. All the speakers seemed to him possessed of marvelously superior talents.

Two events during his first months in New Bedford had a decisive effect upon his life.

"Among my first concerns on reaching New Bedford," he said years later, "was to become united with the church, for I had never given up, in reality, my religious faith. I had become lukewarm and in a backslidden state, but I was still convinced that it was my duty to join the church . . . I therefore resolved to join the Methodist church in New Bedford and to enjoy the spiritual advantage of public worship. The minister of the Elm Street Methodist Church was the Reverend Mr. Bonney; and although I was not allowed a seat in the body of the house, and was proscribed on account of my color, regarding this proscription simply as an accommodation of the unconverted congregation who had not yet been won to Christ and his brotherhood, I was willing thus to be proscribed, lest sinners should be driven away from the saving power of the Gospel. Once converted, I thought they would be sure to treat me as a man and a brother. *Surely*, thought I, *these Christian people have none of this feeling against color. . . .*

"An opportunity was soon afforded me for ascertaining the exact position of Elm Street Church on the subject. . . . The occasion . . . was the sacrament of the Lord's Supper. . . . At the close of his (Mr. Bonney's) discourse, the congregation was dismissed and the church members remained to partake of the sacrament. I remained to see, as I thought, this holy sacrament celebrated in the spirit of its great Founder.

"There were only about a half dozen colored members attached to the Elm Street Church, at this time. . . . These descended from the gallery and took a seat against the wall most distant from the altar. Brother Bonney was very animated, and sung very sweetly, 'Salvation, 'tis a joyful sound,' and soon began to administer the sacrament. I was anxious to observe the bearing of the colored members, and the result was most humiliating. During the whole ceremony, they looked like sheep without a shepherd. The white members went forward to the altar by the bench full; and when it was evident that all the whites had been served with the bread and wine, Brother Bonney—pious Brother Bonney—after a long pause, as if inquiring whether all the white members had been served, and fully assuring himself on that important point, then raised his voice to an unnatural pitch, and looking to the corner where his black sheep seemed penned, beckoned with his hand, exclaiming, 'Come forward, colored friends!—come forward! You, too, have an interest in the blood of Christ. God is no respecter of persons. Come forward, and take this holy sacrament to your comfort.' The colored members—poor, slavish souls—went forward, as invited. I went *out,* and have never been in that church since, although I honestly went there with the view of joining that body." *

The second event was happier. Not long after they moved into the

* Douglass, *My Bondage and My Freedom,* chap. xxii, pp. 351–53.

little house a young man knocked on their door. Frederick had just come in from a particularly hard and unproductive day. Anna, turning from the stove where she was about to serve the evening meal, listened attentively. She wanted to say something. Then she heard Frederick's tired voice, "Subscribe? the *Liberator?*"

"Yes," the young man spoke briskly, "You know, William Lloyd Garrison's Abolitionist paper. Surely *we* ought to support him!"

Anna moved to the doorway, but Frederick was shaking his head.

"I wish I could, but— We— I can't—now."

Anna slipped her hand in his. It was warm and a little moist. The young man understood. He cleared his throat.

"You'd *like* to read it?" he asked.

"Oh, yes!" It was Anna who breathed the answer.

"Then—you can pay me later!"

"Oh, Freddie, that's wonderful!" Anna said, but her eyes were beaming at the young man, who grinned and disappeared around the corner.

"*She's* got brains!" he thought, with thorough appreciation.

Back at the stove, Anna was fairly singing.

"We hardly dared get the *Liberator* through the mail in Baltimore. Now to think we can sit in our own yard and read it!"

Every week Anna watched eagerly for the paper. When it came she waved the sheet triumphantly over her head as she walked back from the mailbox. Garrison was a hero. The authorities had run the New Englander out of Baltimore. But it had been from the sparks he drew that the East Baltimore Improvement Society had come into being. Anna sent their copies to Baltimore after they had finished with them.

"E–man–ci–pa–tion," Frederick stumbled over the long word. "What does it mean, Anna?"

"Freedom, Frederick—or rather *setting* the people free. Listen to this!" The two dark heads bent near the oil lamp. " 'The Constitution of the United States knows nothing of white or black men; makes no distinction with regard to the color or condition of free inhabitants.' "

Frederick learned to love the paper and its editor. Now he and Nathan Johnson could really talk together. Nathan found an apt pupil, and Ma Johnson took Anna under her wing.

As the days grew cooler folks began talking about Thanksgiving.

"What is it?" Anna asked, wrinkling her brow.

Then Ma Johnson told her about the Pilgrims, of their first, hard winter, of how now each year after harvest time the people of New England set aside a special feasting day in their memory, a day when they gave thanks for all the good things of the earth.

"What a beautiful idea!" Anna turned it over in her mind. "A day of thanks-giving!"

"Those poor young ones never tasted turkey." Ma conveyed this tragic information to Nathan. They decided to take a turkey to them.

"And I'll show her how to cook it." Ma was very fond of Anna.

They carried the fresh-killed bird, resplendent in all its feathers, to the little house. Frederick and Anna gazed upon it with awe.

"Hot water! Plenty of hot water!" Nathan rolled up his sleeves, and while they followed his movements like two children he plucked the fowl and handed it to Anna.

"We'll have meat all winter!" Frederick laughed, his eyes on Anna's shining face.

The little house was fairly bursting with happiness that fall. They were going to have a child—a child born on free soil.

"He'll be a free man!" Frederick made the words a hymn of praise.

And Anna smiled.

In April William Lloyd Garrison came to New Bedford.

"You must go, Frederick," Anna said, "since I can't. Look at me!"

"Not without you." The young husband shook his head, but Anna laughed and rushed supper. Frederick was one of the first to arrive at the hall.

He saw only one face that night, he heard only one voice—a face which he described as "heavenly," a voice which he said "was never loud or noisy, but calm and serene as a summer sky, and as pure."

Garrison was a young man then, with a singularly pleasing face and an earnest manner.

"The motto upon our banner has been, from the commencement of our moral warfare, 'Our country is the world—our countrymen are all mankind.' We trust it will be our only epitaph. Another motto we have chosen is 'Universal Emancipation.' Up to this time we have limited its application to those who are held in this country, by Southern taskmasters, as marketable commodities, goods and chattels, and implements of husbandry. Henceforth we shall use it in its widest latitude: the emancipation of our whole race from the dominion of man, from the thralldom of self, from the government of brute force, from the bondage of sin—and bringing them under the dominion of God, the control of an inward spirit, the government of the law of love, and into the obedience and liberty of Christ, who is the same yesterday, today, and forever."

Frederick's heart beat fast. He was breathing hard. The words came faint; for inside he was shouting, "This man is Moses! Here is the Moses who will lead my people out of bondage!" He wanted to throw himself at this man's feet. He wanted to help him.

Then they were singing—all the people in the hall were singing —and Frederick slipped out. He ran all the way home. He could not walk.

Summer came. There was more work on the wharves, when his son was born. Frederick laughed at obstacles. He'd show them! "Them" became the whole world—the white caulkers who refused to work with him, anybody who denied a place to his son because his skin was rosy brown! The young father went into an oil refinery, and then into a brass foundry where all through the next winter he worked two nights a week besides each day. Hard work, night and day, over a furnace hot enough to keep the metal running like water, might seem more favorable to action than to thought, yet while he fanned the flames Frederick dreamed dreams, saw pictures in the flames. He must get ready! He must learn more. He nailed a newspaper to the post near his bellows and read while he pushed the heavy beam up and down.

In the summer of 1841 the Massachusetts Anti-Slavery Society held its grand convention in Nantucket. Frederick decided to take a day off from work and attend a session.

The little freedom breeze was blowing up a gale. Theologians, congressmen, governors and business men had hurled invectives, abuse and legislation at the Anti-Slavery Society, at the *Liberator* and at the paper's editor, William Lloyd Garrison. But in London, Garrison had refused to sit on the floor of the World Convention of Anti-Slavery Societies because women delegates had been barred; and now the very man who had founded the movement in America was being execrated by many of those who professed to follow him.

But Frederick knew only that William Lloyd Garrison would be at Nantucket.

The boat rounded Brant Point Light and came suddenly on a gray town that rose out of the sea. Nantucket's cobbled lanes, bright with summer frocks, fanned up from the little bay where old whalers rested at anchor, slender masts of long sloops pointed to the sky, deep-sea fishing boats sprawled on the dirty waters, and discolored warehouses crowded down on the quays.

Frederick had no trouble finding his way to the big hall, for the Abolitionist convention was the main event in the town. It spilled out into the streets where groups of men stood in knots, talking excitedly. Quakers, sitting inside their covered carriages, removed their hats and talked quietly; and women, trying not to be conspicuous, stood under shade trees, but they too talked.

The morning session had been stormy. A serious rift had developed within the ranks of the antislavery movement. During his absence Garrison had been attacked by a body of clergymen for what they termed his "heresies"—the immediate charge being his "breaking of the Sabbath." Garrison, it seemed, saw no reason why anyone should "rest" from abolishing slavery any day of the week. He maintained that all days should be kept holy. He lacked forbearance and Christian patience, they charged. He "aired America's dirty linen" in Europe. He "insulted" the English brethren when he took his stand for full recognition of women in the World Anti-Slavery Convention, despite the fact that St. Paul had adjured women to silence. Garrison had made a statement in the *Liberator:* "I expressly declare that I stand upon the Bible, and the Bible alone, in regard to my views of the Sabbath, the Church, and the Ministry, and that I feel that if I can not stand triumphantly on that foundation I can stand nowhere in the universe. My arguments are all drawn from the Bible and from no other source." *

For weeks the controversy had raged—sermons were preached, columns and letters were written. Theodore Parker, young minister in Boston, was denounced by his fellow-clergymen because he sided with Garrison. Now they had all come to Nantucket—Garrisonites and anti-Garrisonites; the issue of slavery was tabled while scholars drew nice lines in the science of casuistry and ethics, and theologians chanted dogmas.

All morning Garrison sat silent. His right hand twitched nervously. Pains shot up into his arm. His face was drawn and tired. His heart was heavy. Here and there in the crowd a bewildered black face turned to him. William Lloyd Garrison lowered his eyes and shut his teeth against a groan that welled up from his heart.

And so he did not see one more dark figure push into the hall; but

* *Liberator,* Dec. 15, 1840.

William C. Coffin, a Quaker and ardent Abolitionist, did. He had met Frederick at the house of his friend, Nathan Johnson. Coffin made his way back through the crowd and laid his hand on Frederick's arm.

"Thee are well come, my friend," he said.

Frederick had been peering anxiously toward the platform. He was so far back, the crowd was so thick and the people wedged in so tightly, that he despaired of hearing or seeing anything; but he smiled a warm greeting at the Quaker.

"Follow me, there are seats up front," Friend Coffin was saying.

The older man led the way down a side aisle, and there close against the wall was a little space. Frederick gratefully slipped in beside his friend.

"This is fine," he whispered, "I hated to miss anything." He looked around at the other occupants of the side seats. He spoke worriedly. "But— But I don't belong up here."

The Quaker smiled. "This is thy place." He leaned closer, and his eyes were very earnest. "Douglass, I am asking thee to speak a few words to the convention this afternoon."

Frederick stared at him. He gasped.

"Me? Speak?"

The great hall was a vast arena packed with all the people in the world! Surely the Quaker was joking. But no, the voice was very low, but calm and sure.

"Tell them thy story, Douglass, as thee have told the men at the mill. Just tell them the truth—no matter how the words come." Frederick shook his head helplessly. He couldn't stand up there before all those people. He tried to hear what the man on the platform was saying, but the words were meaningless. The hall was stifling hot. Men were mopping their brows with damp handkerchiefs. Frederick opened his shirt at the neck and let his coat slip off his shoulders.

"Thee cannot escape thy duty, Douglass," Mr. Coffin urged quietly. "Look about you! Today, thy people need thee to speak for them." Frederick held his breath, and the Quaker added gravely, "And *he* needs thee—that good man who has worked so hard needs thy help."

Frederick followed the Quaker's eyes. He was gazing at William Lloyd Garrison, the man whom he honored and loved above all other men. How sunken and tired he looked!

"He needs thee," the Quaker said again.

Frederick's lips formed the words, though no sound came at first. "I'll try," he whispered.

How long it was after this that Frederick found himself on his feet, being gently pushed toward the platform, he could not have said. Only when he was standing up there before all those people did he realize that he had not replaced his coat. It was a clean shirt, fresh from Anna's tub and iron, but—! He fumbled with the button at his neck. His fingers were stiff and clumsy. He could not button it with the faces, a sea of faces, looking up at him, waiting. Everything was so still. They were waiting for him. He swallowed.

"Ladies and gentlemen—" a little girl, all big grave eyes, pushed her damped curls back and smiled at him, encouraging. Suddenly a mightly wave of realization lifted and supported him. These people were glad that he was free. They wanted him to be free! He began again.

"Friends, only a few short months ago I was a slave. Now I am free!" He saw them sway toward him. "I cannot tell you how I escaped because if known those who helped me would suffer terribly, *terribly*." He said the word a second time and saw some realization of what he meant reflected in their faces.

"I do not ask anything for myself. I have my hands to work—my strength. . . . All of the seas could not hold my thanksgiving to Almighty God—and to you." He was silent a moment and they saw his eyes grow darker; his face contracted as if in pain. When he began again, his voice trembled, they had to lean forward to catch his words.

"But I am only one. Where are my brothers? Where are my sisters? Their groans sound in my ears. Their voices cry out to me for help. My mother—my own mother—where is she? I hope she is dead. I hope that she has found the only peace that comes to a slave—that last, last peace in a grave. But even as I stand before you it may be— It may be that—" He stopped and covered his face with his hands. When he lifted his head, his eyes shone with resolution. "Hear me," he said, "hear me while I tell you about slavery."

And then, in a clear voice, he told them of Caroline, why she dragged her leg, and how she had risked her life to save him; he told them about Henry and John, Nada and Jeb. He told them of little children he had seen clinging to their mother as she was being sold away, of men and women whose "spirits" had to be broken, of degradation. He told them the content of human slavery.

"I am free," his voice went low; but they leaned forward, hanging on every word. "But I am branded with the marks of the lash. See!" And with one movement, he threw back his shirt. He turned, and there across the broad, young back were deep knotty ridges, where the brown flesh had been cut to the bone and healed in pink lumps. They gasped.

"I have not forgotten—I do not forget anything. Nor will I forget while, any place upon this earth, there are slaves."

He turned to leave the platform.

Then in the silence another voice, a golden voice, was heard. It was as if a trumpet called.

"Is this a thing—a chattel—or a man?"

William Lloyd Garrison stood there—his eyes flaming—his face alight. He waited for an answer, holding Frederick's hand in his, facing the audience. And from a thousand voices rose the shout.

"He is a man!"

"A man! A man!"

Garrison let the tumultuous shouts roll and reverberate. Men wept unashamed. Far down the street people heard the applause and shouting and came running. Through it all Garrison stood, holding the strong brown hand in his. At last Garrison pressed the hand gently, and Frederick stumbled to his seat. Then Garrison stepped to the edge of the platform.

Those who had heard him oftenest and known him longest were astonished by his speech that afternoon. He was the fabulous orator who could convert a vast audience into a single individuality.

"And to this cause we solemnly dedicate our strength, our minds, our spirits and our lives!"

As long as they lived men and women talked about that August afternoon on Nantucket Island.

John A. Collins, general agent of the Massachusetts Anti-Slavery Society, was at Frederick's elbow when the meeting let out.

"We want you as an agent," he was saying. "Come, Mr. Garrison told me to bring you to him."

While the crowd surged about them, the great man once more held Frederick's hand, but now he gazed searchingly at the brown face.

"Will you join us, Frederick Douglass?" he asked.

"Oh, sir, I am a member of the Society in New Bedford," Frederick answered quickly and proudly. Garrison smiled.

"Of course. But I mean more than that—a lot more. I'm asking you to leave whatever job you have and work with me. The pay is—well—uncertain. They tell me you have a family. I too have a family."

"Yes, sir. I know," Frederick said, his eyes like an adoring child's.

"I am asking you to leave your own family and work for the larger family of God."

"Yes, sir, I understand. I want to help. But I am ignorant. I was planning to go to school."

"You will learn as you walk, Frederick Douglass. Your people need your strength now. We all need you."

So Frederick left his job at the foundry and, as an agent of the Massachusetts Anti-Slavery Society, began active work to outlaw slavery in the nation.

CHAPTER SEVEN

Jobs in Washington and voting in Rhode Island

Amelia Kemp stood at her attic window. The waters of Chesapeake Bay tossed green and white and set the thick mass of trees on distant Poplar Island in motion. A boat rounded Keat Point. For a few moments Amelia could see the tips of the masts and a bit of white sail against the sky. Then it all disappeared. But the sight of a boat sailing away over the waters, of a ship going out to sea, was not at this moment depressing. She too was going away.

Lucy was dead. That morning they had laid her worn body in a grave at the edge of the pines. Covey, his Sunday suit sagging, stared stupidly while they shoveled in the hard lumps of clay. The preacher had wrung the widower's hand, reminding him that "The Lord giveth and the Lord taketh away"; and they had returned to the unpainted, sagging house. Now there was nothing further to do. She could go.

Amelia had tried to persuade her sister to leave with her before it was too late. She had dared to read her portions of Jack's letters—"Come along, there are jobs in Washington—even for women." But Lucy would have none of it. Her duty was clear. There were moments when she urged Amelia to go, others when she clung to her weakly. So the months had stretched into six years, and Amelia had stayed on.

Covey dropped into a chair on the front porch when they returned from the grave. All the lines of his body ran downward. Covey had not prospered. He knew nothing about a nationwide depression, Van Buren's bickering with the banks, wars in Texas, or gag rules in Congress; he had no idea there was any connection between the 1840 presidential election and the price of cotton. He did know he was losing ground. No matter how hard he beat the slaves, crops failed or rotted in the fields, stock died, debts piled up, markets slumped and tempers were short all around the bay.

Now, his wife was dead—*hadn't been really sick, either. Just petered out*. Here it was April, and the sun was scorching.

He had heard no sound, but Covey was suddenly aware of being watched. He sat very still and stared hard into the bushes near the corner of the porch. Two hard, bright eyes stared back. Covey spoke sharply.

"Who's that? Who's that sneakin' in them bushes?"

The eyes vanished, but the bushes did not stir. With a snarl, Covey leaned forward.

"Dammit! I'll git my shotgun!"

The leaves parted and he saw the streaked, pallid, pinched face in which the green eyes blazed—a face topped with dirty, tangled tow-colored hair. It was an old face; but the slight body with pipe-stem legs and arms was that of a child, a girl-child not more than ten years old. She wore a coarse one-piece slip. One bare foot was wrapped as if to protect some injury, the other was scratched and bruised. The child did not come forward, but crouched beside the porch giving back stare for hard stare. Then with a little cry she disappeared around the house.

Covey spat over the porch rail and settled back. It was that brat of Caroline's of course, still running about like a wild animal. Time she was helping around the house. He began to deliberate. Might be better to get rid of her right off. She'd soon be market size, and yellow gals brought good prices. He'd speak to Caroline about feeding her up. Better bring her in the house. Mustn't let Caroline suspect anything, though.

He pulled himself up and turned to go inside. Maybe Caroline had something for him to eat.

Amelia stopped him in the hallway. She was wearing a hat and carrying a suitcase. Covey frowned.

"Oh, Mr. Covey! I was looking for you." Her voice had a note of urgency.

Amelia had a way of emerging from the nondescript background with startling vividness. Months passed when he hardly saw her. Then there she was jumping out at him! What the devil did she want now? He waited for her to explain.

"I'm going away."

Just like that. No stumbling around the words. Covey let his flat eyes travel over her. Not a bad-looking woman, Amelia. More spirit than her sister. He spoke slowly.

"I ain't putting you out."

Amelia's response sounded grateful enough. "Oh, I know, Mr. Covey. It's not that. But now that poor Lucy's gone, I've no right to—to impose."

Covey remembered that he *had* been keeping a roof over her head all these years. And what had he got out of it? Nothing. His eyes narrowed.

"Where you aiming to go?"

"I'm going to Washington. A cousin of Tom's down there—his name's Jack Haley—says I can get a—a job."

Her words had started in a rush, but they faltered a little by the time she reached her incredible conclusion.

A job in Washington! Was the female crazy? In a surge of masculine protectiveness, Covey glowered at her.

"Who said you had to get out and get a job? Eh? Who said so?"

Amelia swallowed. She had not expected an argument. She did not intend to argue. She had to be getting along. She would miss her boat. She spoke firmly.

"Mr. Covey, it's all settled. I'm going. Ben told me you were sending him to town this afternoon. I want to ride with him."

Covey spoke deliberately. "The nigger's lyin'—as usual. He better not go off the place this afternoon. An' you best get those fool notions out of your head. You can stay right here and look after the house. I ain't kickin'." He strode into the kitchen. That took care of that. It was close to ten miles to St. Michaels. She'd have time to think it over. But who was this fellow in Washington—a cousin of her late husband, so she said. Um-um! Yes, Amelia had more spirit than poor Lucy.

Amelia, left standing in the hall, sighed and set down her bag. *A pretty kettle of fish!* Did Covey think he could hold her? Was she one of his slaves? Then in a flash of realization she saw the truth. She was indeed a slave—had been for all these years. And she was running away—just as much as those black slaves she read about.

Amelia picked up her suitcase, walked out onto the porch, down the steps, along the path, out to the road. She looked down the long dusty road to St. Michaels, and started walking.

It was nearly two miles to Lawson's place, and when she reached the welcome shade of his grove she sank down to rest. Not too bad:

she was making time. She rubbed her benumbed arm and wondered if there weren't something in the bag she could dump out. She was going to have blisters on her feet. Soon, now, she'd reach the highway. If she did not get a ride, she would miss the boat.

When she set out again, she stumbled and cut her foot against a hidden stone. There was no time to do anything about it, however, so she plodded along, fixing her mind firmly on the Washington boat.

Thus she did not hear the cart until it was close behind her. Then she stopped, her legs trembling. The mule stopped without any sign from the Negro driver.

It was not the same mule, driven by the old Negro who had passed Amelia one morning more than six years before. There were so many mules being driven by so many Negroes up and down the Eastern Shore. This Negro was younger and he could see quite clearly. And what he saw puzzled and disturbed him—a white woman, alone on a side road, carrying a suitcase and giving every sign of being about to ask him for a lift!

Not good. He sat, a solid cloud of gloom, waiting for her to speak.

Amelia smiled. She had to clear her throat. The mule regarded her stolidly.

"Boy," she asked, and the tone of her voice confirmed his worse fears, "are you going into St. Michaels?"

"No, *ma'm.* Jus' up da road a piece, an' right back. No, ma'm, Ah ain't goin' neah St. Michael. No, *ma'm.*"

He was too vehement. Amelia saw the confusion in his face and, because she was in the process of acquiring wisdom, she knew the cause. She must think of a way to reassure him. She spoke slowly.

"You see, I'm trying to get to St. Michaels. I want to catch a boat."

Amelia saw the man's eyes flicker. Going somewhere always aroused interest. He shook his head, but did not speak. Amelia looked away. The road seemed to quiver in the sun.

"You see, I'm starting on a journey." Now she looked full at him—she looked at him as one looks at a friend and she said softly, "I'm heading toward the north star."

Perhaps the man's hands tightened on the reins. At any rate the mule jerked up his head. The black face froze. For one instant everything stood still. Then the Negro looked up and down the road and to the right and to the left. There were only dust and fields, and here and there a tree.

He climbed down from the cart and picked up her bag. He spoke without looking at her.

"Jus' remembered, ma'm, Ah might could drive toward St. Michael. Jus' *might* could."

"Oh, thank you! Thank you so much!" The warmth in her tone forced a smile from him.

"Reckon Ah could fix up a seat for you in back."

He did fix a seat, shoving aside sacks and cords of wood. It was not an upholstered carriage, but it got her to St. Michaels. She alighted at the market, to arouse less attention. But he insisted on carrying her bag to the pier.

"Ma'm," he said, turning his hat in his hands, "hit seem mighty funny, but Ah—Ah wishes yo' luck!"

And Amelia, eyes shining, answered, "Thank you— Thank you, my friend. The same to you!"

The slave leaned lazily against a pile until the gangplank was pulled up, his eyes under the flopping straw hat darting in every direction, watching. Then, as the space of dirty water widened and the boat became a living thing, he stood up, waved his hat in the air and, after wiping the beads of sweat from his forehead, spoke fervently.

"Do Jesus!"

Washington, D. C. had become a tough problem to the Boston Abolitionists. A group was meeting one evening in the *Liberator* office to map out some course of action.

"Every road barred to us! Our papers not even delivered in the mail!" Parker Pillsbury tossed his head angrily.

"Washington is a slave city. Thee must accept facts." The Quaker, William Coffin, spoke in conciliatory tones.

"But it's our Capital, too—a city of several thousand inhabitants —and the slaveholders build high walls around it." The Reverend Wendell Phillips was impatient.

"We should hold a meeting in Washington!" William Lloyd Garrison sighed, thinking of all the uninformed people in that city.

His remark was followed by a heavy silence. An Abolitionist meeting in Washington was out of the question. Several Southern states had already put a price on Garrison's head. Frederick, sitting in the shadows, studied the glum faces and realized that, in one way or another, every man in the room was marked. They were agents of the

Anti-Slavery Society and they, no more than he, could go South. Washington was South. Then from near the door came a drawling voice.

"Gentlemen, trouble your heads no longer. I'm going home." A slender man was coming forward into the lamplight.

At the sound of the soft drawl, Frederick froze. He crouched low, hiding his face. But no alarm was sounded. There was welcome in Garrison's low greeting: "Gamaliel Bailey!"

The first voice answered, "I heard only enough to agree fully. We do need a spokesman in Washington. I would not flatter myself, gentlemen—but I am ready."

Garrison spoke with unaccustomed vehemence.

"No! We need you here."

Frederick slowly lifted his head. The man was a stranger to him. His speech proclaimed him a Southerner. Now Frederick saw an attractive, dark-haired gentleman in black broadcloth and loosely fitted gray trousers. He looked down at Garrison, his black eyes bright.

"This is the job that I alone can do," he said.

Wendell Phillips' golden voice was warm as he nodded his head.

"He's right, Garrison. Gamaliel Bailey can go to Washington. He belongs."

"Captain John Smith, himself," Pillsbury teased, but with affection.

"At your service, sir." The Southerner swept him a low bow.

"This is no laughing matter, Mr. Bailey," a stern voice interposed. "They know you have worked with us. You are a known Abolitionist!"

Gamaliel Bailey flicked a bit of non-existent dust from his waistcoat, and gave a soft laugh.

"Once a Virginia Bailey, always a Virginia Bailey! Have no fear, Mr. Hunton," he said. He caught sight of Frederick's dark face lifting itself among them. His eyes lit up. "This must be the new agent of whom I've been hearing."

"Yes," several said at once. "It's Frederick Douglass."

Their handclasp was a promise. "I go to Washington now, so that you can come later," said the Virginian.

"And I'll be along!" promised Frederick Douglass.

William Lloyd Garrison did not smile. His face was clouded with apprehension. "You'll need help," he said.

"It is best that I find my help in Washington. I know one young man whom I can count on. Jack Haley. He'll bring me all the news. You know, I think I'll publish a paper!" He grinned. "Since they won't let the *Liberator* in, we'll see if I can't get a paper out."

So it happened that Jack Haley was not on the dock to meet Amelia's boat from St. Michaels. The weekly issue of the *National Era* had hit the streets the day before, and scattered like a bomb all up and down Pennsylvania Avenue. In Congress, on the streets and in the clubs they raged! Here was heresy of the most dangerous order, printed and distributed within a stone's throw of the Capitol. It was enough to make God-fearing Americans shudder when the son of such an old and respected family as the Virginia Baileys flaunted the mongrel elements in their faces. They did shudder, some of them. And grinning reporters ran from one caucus to the other.

Jack was much younger than his cousin Tom. He remembered Tom's wife with affection. Her letters had intrigued him, and he was glad she was coming to Washington.

He found her down on the wharf, surrounded by bales of cotton, serenely rocking in a highback New England rocker!

Amelia saw him staring at her and with a little cry of joy she sprang up.

"Jack, I knew you'd get here! I wasn't worrying a bit. And kind Captain Drayton has made me quite comfortable."

The weatherbeaten Vermonter, leaning against the rail of his ship, regarded the late arrival and scowled until his thick eyebrows threatened to tangle with his heavy beard.

"Nice way to treat a female!" he boomed.

Jack held her hands in his. She was so thin, so little. The gray strands smoothed carefully behind her ears accentuated the hollows in her face; the cotton dress she wore was washed out, but the blue eyes looking up at him were young and bright.

Amelia exclaimed over the little buggy Jack had waiting. He helped her in, tucked the bag under their feet and flapped the reins.

Washington in the spring! Heavy wagon wheels bogged down in deep ruts, and hogs wallowed in the mud; but a soft green haze lay over the sprawling town and wrapped it in loveliness. They were rolling along a wide street, and Amelia was trying to see everything at once. Then she saw the Capitol lifting its glistening dome against the wide blue sky, and she caught her breath.

They circled the Capitol grounds, turned down a shaded lane and stopped before a two-story brick house which sat well back in a yard with four great elms.

"Here we are!" Jack smiled down at her.

"How nice! Is this where you live?"

"No, ma'am. This is where, I hope, you're going to live."

"But who—?" began Amelia.

"Just you wait." Jack jumped out and hitched the reins around a post. The big trees up and down the street formed an avenue of coolness. Amelia hesitated when he turned to assist her.

"Are they— Are they expecting me?"

Jack chuckled.

"Mrs. Royall, my dear, is expecting anything—at any time!"

"Jack! You don't mean Mrs. Royall—the authoress!" Amelia hung motionless over the wheel. Jack grasped her firmly by the elbow.

"Who else? There is only one Mrs. Royall. There's Her Highness now, back in the chicken yard. Come along. I'll fetch the bag later."

Amelia shook out her skirts and followed him along the path that led around the house.

The little old lady bending over a chicken coop from which spilled yellow puffs of baby chicks, might have been somebody's indulgent grandmother. The calico dress drawn in around a shapeless middle was faded; so was the bonnet from which escaped several strands of iron-gray hair.

"Good afternoon, Mrs. Royall!" There was warm deference in Jack's voice.

She stood up and her shoulders squared. There was a certain sprightliness in the movement, and in the tanned, unwrinkled face gleamed eyes of a remarkable brightness. When she spoke her voice had an unexpected crispness.

"Indeed—it's Jack Haley. And who is this female with you?"

"This is a kinswoman of mine, Mrs. Royall. I have the pleasure of presenting to you, Mrs. Amelia Kemp."

"How do ye do!" The little old lady spoke with prim formality, her eyes flashing briefly over Amelia.

"I am honored, ma'am." Amelia scarcely managed the words.

"She has come to Washington to work," Jack went on. "So I have brought her to you."

The gray eyes snapped.

"And why should you bring your kinswoman to me?"

"Because, Mrs. Royall, it's newspapers she wants to know about. And you're the best newsman in Washington, begging your pardon, ma'am." He bowed elaborately.

"You needn't!" She turned to Amelia.

"I've read one of your books, ma'am. Jack sent it to me. I learned so much about America."

Undoubtedly the gray eyes softened, but the tone did not change.

"Why don't you take her to your friend on the avenue—that infamous Abolitionist?"

"Mrs. Royall!" Jack's voice was charged with shock. "You couldn't be speaking about Editor Gamaliel Bailey?"

"He should be ashamed of himself. Selling out to those long-winded black coats!"

"But, Mrs. Royall—"

"Don't interrupt. If he'd come to me I'd tell him how to get rid of slavery. It's a curse on the land. But those psalm-singing missionaries— Bah!"

"May I remind you, Mrs. Royall," Jack spoke very softly, "that when you came back from Boston you spoke very highly of the Reverend Theodore Parker. And he's a—"

"He's *not* a black coat." The lady spoke with feeling. Her face cleared and she added sweetly, "He must be a Unitarian." Then she laughed, all shadows and restraint gone. "Forgive an old windbag, guilty of the very faults she criticizes in others." She lifted her eyes. "See how the sun shines on our Capitol. Have you ever seen anything half so beautiful?"

Amelia shook her head.

"I've never traveled any place before, ma'am. Washington is more than I can believe."

"It's too good for the people who live here. But come and rest yourself. I am a bad hostess." Her eyes twinkled as she turned to Jack. "First, does she know I'm a criminal—a convicted criminal?" She made it sound very mysterious, and Amelia stared.

Jack laughed. "You tell her, Mrs. Royall!"

" 'Tis very sad." There was mockery in her voice. "A 'common scold'—that was the finding of the jury. In England they would have ducked me in a pond; but here there was only the Potomac, and the honored judge deemed that might not be right—the waters would be contaminated. So they let me go." They were in the house now and she was setting out china cups. "You know," she frowned slightly, "the thing I really objected to was the word 'common.' That I did not like."

"I agree with you, madam. Mrs. Royall's scoldings of senators, congressmen and even presidents, of bankers and bishops, have always been in a class by themselves. 'Common' was not the word." And again he bowed.

The old lady eyed him with approval.

"Where, might I ask, did you get your good manners? They are rare enough in Washington these days." Before he could reply she had turned to Amelia—the gracious host to her guest. "Some day, my dear, I shall tell you of the Marquis de la Fayette. Ah! there were manners!"

"*Liberté, fraternité, égalité!*" Jack murmured the words half under his breath, but the old lady turned on him, her eyes flashing. Then, like an imp, she grinned.

So Amelia came to live with Anne Royall, long-time relict of Captain William Royall. He had fought beside Washington in the Revolutionary War and had been the General's lifelong friend. In her own way she waged a war too. Each week she cranked a clumsy printing press in her shed and turned out a pithy paper called the *Huntress*. It advocated free schools for children everywhere, free trade, and liberal appropriations for scientific investigation. Amelia helped her about the house and with her chickens, accompanied her on interviews, saw red-faced legislators dodge down side-streets to avoid her. Gradually she learned something of how news is gathered and dispensed, but she learned more about the ways of Washington, D. C.

Amelia had been in Washington three weeks when one evening Jack stopped by.

"I'm going up North!" he announced.

"Where? What for?"

"The boss heard something about a rebellion in New England. He's tickled pink. Said maybe that would keep Yankee noses out of other people's worries. He's sending me out to puff the scandal!"

"Do you know anything about it?" Mrs. Royall's ears were alert.

"From what I can gather, seems a lot of poor folks in Rhode Island want to vote. And the bigwigs don't like it!"

All of New England had become involved. Two state administrations were claiming the election in Rhode Island, and a clash was imminent. Until 1841 Rhode Island had operated under its colonial charter, which prohibited anyone from voting who did not own 134 acres of land. Therefore, seats in the state legislature were controlled by the older conservative villages, while the growing industrial towns, where the larger portion of the population was disfranchised, were penalized. That year Thomas Wilson Dorr, a Whig and graduate of Harvard, started a reform movement; and a new constitution was drawn up. This constitution was framed to enlarge the basis of representation and abolish the odious property requirement. But it confined the right of suffrage to white male citizens, pointedly shutting out the Negroes who had settled in Rhode Island.

Quakers were non-resistance men; they held themselves aloof from politics, but they were always on the alert to protect the black man's rights. All antislavery advocates wanted a new constitution, but they did not want a defective instrument which would require reform from the start. So they could not back Dorr. The Perry brothers, Providence manufacturers, wrote to their friend, John Brown, a wool merchant in Springfield, Massachusetts.

"The time has come when the people of Rhode Island must accept a more comprehensive gospel of human rights than has gotten itself into this Dorr constitution. We have talked to him, and while he agrees in principle he fears to go further."

John Brown sent the letter on to John Greenleaf Whittier, Secretary of the Massachusetts Anti-Slavery Society. Whittier talked it over with the Reverend Theodore Parker, who was considering making a series of speeches in Rhode Island, denouncing the color bar in what was being called a "People's Constitution."

"Why should not Negroes vote with all the other workers?" asked Whittier. "They would limit their gains in throwing out the old charter."

Theodore Parker sighed wearily.

"It's the workers who are doing this. Their own struggle has blinded them."

"Thee are right." Whittier slipped into the Quaker idiom in moments of great seriousness. "They see the black man only as a threat."

Then their eyes met, fusing in a single thought. They spoke almost in one breath.

"Frederick Douglass!"

For a moment they smiled together, congratulating themselves. Then a frown came on Whittier's face. He shook his head.

"But Friend Garrison will not consent. Thee knows his attitude toward any of us taking part in politics."

Theodore Parker was silent a moment, drumming his long, white fingers on the table. Then his black eyes flashed.

"Are we discussing politics? We are concerned here with the rights of men."

Whittier shook his head, but he grinned.

"Thee had best take care! Quoting Thomas Paine will not help."

"Fiddlesticks! Tom Paine had more religion than all the clerics of Massachusetts rolled into one." The young divine got to his feet, his thin face alight with enthusiasm. "Douglass goes to Rhode Island! I'll take care of Garrison."

It was decided, and Douglass was one of the Abolitionists' trio which invaded every town and corner of the little state. They were Stephen S. Foster of New Hampshire, Parker Pillsbury from Boston, and Frederick Douglass from some unspecified section of the slave world—two white and one black—young and strong and on fire with their purpose. The splendid vehemence of Foster, the weird and terrible denunciations of Pillsbury, and the mere presence of Douglass created a furor from one end of the state to the other. They were followed by noisy mobs, they were thrown out of taverns, they were pelted with eggs and rocks and foul words. But they kept right on talking—in schoolhouses and churches and halls, in market places, in warehouses, behind factories and on docks. Sometimes they were accompanied by Abby Kelly, who was later to become Stephen Foster's wife. Her youth and simple Quaker beauty, combined with her wonderful earnestness, her large knowledge and great logical power, bore down opposition. She stilled the wildest turmoil.

The people began to listen. They drew up a Freeman's Constitution to challenge Thomas Dorr's and called a huge mass meeting in Providence. On streamers and handbills distributed throughout the state, they listed "Frederick Douglass, Fugitive from Slavery," as the principal speaker.

Jack Haley saw the streamers when he reached Providence late in the evening. He heard talk of the meeting around the hostelry while he gulped down his supper. When he reached the crowded hall things were already under way. There was some confusion as he was pushing his way in. Someone on the floor seemed to be demanding the right to speak.

"It's Seth Luther!" whispered excited bystanders. "Thomas Dorr's right-hand man."

"Go on, Seth, have your say!" called out a loud voice in the crowd.

The young man on the platform motioned for silence. He nodded to the man standing in the aisle.

"Speak, my friend!" he said.

The man's voice was harsh.

"You philanthropists are moaning over the fate of Southern slaves. Go down there and help them! We here are concerned with equal rights for men, with the emancipation of white men, before we run out after helping blacks whether they are free or in slavery. You're meddling with what doesn't concern you!"

There was some applause. There were boos and hisses, but the man sat down amid a murmur of approval from those near him.

Then Jack saw that the chairman on the platform had stepped aside and his place had been taken by an impressive figure. Even before he said a word the vast audience settled into silence. For undoubtedly this was the "fugitive slave" they had come to hear. Jack stared: this man did not look as if he had ever been a slave. The massive shoulders, straight and shapely body, great head with bushy mane sweeping back from wide forehead, deep-set eyes and jutting jaw covered with full beard—the poise and controlled strength in every line—called forth a smothered exclamation from Jack.

"My God! What a human being!"

"Ssh-sh!" several people hissed. Frederick Douglass was speaking.

"The gentleman would have us argue more and denounce less. He speaks of men and black and slaves as if our cause can differ from his own. What is our concern except with equal rights for men? And must we argue to affirm the equal manhood of the Negro race? Is it not astonishing that, while we are plowing, planting, and reaping, using all kinds of mechanical tools, erecting houses, constructing bridges, building ships, working in metals of brass, iron, copper, silver and gold; that, while we are reading, writing and ciphering, acting as clerks and secretaries, digging gold in California, capturing the whale in the Pacific, feeding sheep and cattle on the hillside, living, moving, acting, thinking, planning, living in families as husbands, wives and children, and, above all, confessing and worshiping the Christian's God, we are called upon to prove that we are men!

"I tell you the slaveholders in the darkest jungles of the Southland concede this fact. They acknowledge it in the enactment of laws for their government; they acknowledge it when they punish disobedience on the part of the slave. There are seventy-two crimes in the state of Virginia which, if committed by a black man (no matter how ignorant he be) subject him to punishment by death; while only two of the same crimes will subject a white man to the like punishment. What is this but the acknowledgment that the slave is a moral, intellectual, and responsible being? It is admitted in fact that Southern statute books are covered with enactments forbidding, under severe fines and penalties, the teaching of the slave to read or to write. When you can point to any such laws in reference to the beasts of the field, than I may consent to argue the manhood of the black man."

Men stamped and shouted and threw their hats into the air. The hall rang. Douglass took up in a quieter mood. He talked of the meaning of constitutional government, he talked of what could be gained if exploited people stood together and what they lost by battling among themselves.

"The slaveholders, with a craftiness peculiar to themselves, encourage enmity of the poor labouring white man against the blacks, and succeed in making the white man almost as much a slave as the black slave himself. The difference is this: the latter belongs to one slaveholder, the former belongs to the slaveholders collectively. Both are plundered, and by the same plunderers."

Afterward Jack tried to go forward and ask some questions of the amazing orator, but the press of the crowd stopped him. He gave up and returned to the inn. And the next day they had gone back to Boston, he was told. Thomas Dorr, through his timidity and caution, had lost the people.

When the new Rhode Island constitution was finally adopted the word *white* had been struck out.

Jack Haley returned to Washington and handed in his account of the "rebellion." The editor blue-penciled most of it. He said they had thrown away money on a wild-goose chase.

But Gamaliel Bailey studied the closely written pages Jack laid on his desk. True, he could not now publish the material in his *National Era*; but he drew a circle around the name "Frederick Douglass" and slipped the sheets into his file for future reference.

Every drop of blood slowly drained from Amelia's face while Jack talked. Mrs. Royall dropped the stick of type she had been clutching —Jack had interrupted them at work in the shed—and stared at her helper.

"She's sick!"

But Amelia shook her head. She leaned against the board, struggling to speak while into her white face there came a glow which changed her blue eyes into dancing stars.

"You said his name was Frederick, didn't you? About how old would you say he was?"

"What?" asked Mrs. Royall.

"*How old?*" asked Jack.

"Yes." Amelia was a little impatient. "The one you're talking about—that slave who spoke. I'm sure I know who he is!"

"Oh, my goodness, Amelia! That's impossible!" The idea made Jack frown. Mrs. Royall snorted.

"Describe him to me, Jack," Amelia insisted, "every detail."

She kept nodding her head while Jack rather grudgingly complied with her request. It seemed such a waste of time. He shook his head as he finished.

"There couldn't possibly have been such an extraordinary slave around any place where you've been. All of us would have heard of him!"

Amelia smiled.

"I remember how he came walking up the road that day in a swirl of dust. He was little more than a boy then. Now he's a man. It is the same."

Then she told how that morning at dawn she had leaned from her attic window and watched a young buck slave defy a slave-breaker, how he had sent the overseer moaning to one side with his kick, how he had thrown the master to the ground. This was the first time she had ever told the story, but she told it very well.

"His name was Frederick—the same color, the same powerful shoulders and the same big head."

"But this man—he looked older—he's educated! If you had heard him!" Jack could not believe this thing.

Amelia only smiled.

"I found out afterward that even then he could read and write. Mr. Covey had him help with the accounts."

"It's just too incredible. That man from the Eastern Shore!"

Mrs. Royall spoke precisely. "Young man, when you're my age you'll know that it's the incredible things which make life wonderful."

And Amelia added, "There couldn't be two Fredericks—turned from the same mold!"

CHAPTER EIGHT

On two sides of the Atlantic

MANY PEOPLE would have shared Jack's reluctance to believe Amelia's story. As time passed the Massachusetts Anti-Slavery Society found itself caught in a dilemma. The committee knew all the facts of Frederick's case; but for his protection the members took every precaution, withholding the name of the state and county from which he had come, his master's name and any other detail which might lead to his capture. Even so they realized that they must be constantly on guard. But the audiences began to murmur that this Frederick Douglass could not be a "fugitive from slavery."

During the first three or four months Frederick's speeches had been almost exclusively made up of narrations of his own personal experiences as a slave.

"Give us the facts," said Secretary Collins. "We'll take care of the philosophy."

"Tell your story, Frederick," Garrison would whisper as his protégé stepped upon the platform. And Frederick, smiling his devotion to the older man, always followed the injunction.

But Frederick was growing in stature. Scholars' libraries were thrown open to him. Theodore Parker had sixteen thousand volumes; his library covered the entire third floor of his house.

"Come up any time, Frederick. Books, my boy, were written to be read."

And Frederick reveled in Thomas Jefferson, Carlyle, Edmund Burke, Tom Paine, John Quincy Adams, Jonathan Swift, William Godwin. He became drunk on books; staggering home late at night, his eyes red, he would fall heavily across his bed. He pored over the newspapers from all parts of the country which Garrison gathered in the *Liberator* office; he sat at the feet of the greatest orators of the day —Wendell Phillips, Charles Redmond, Theodore Parker among them. He munched sandwiches and listened, while John Whittier read his verses; and always the young fugitive from slavery followed in the wake of William Lloyd Garrison, devouring his words, tapping his sources of wisdom, attuning his ears to every pitch of the loved voice.

Frederick's speeches began to expand in content, logic and delivery.

"People won't believe you ever were a slave, Frederick, if you keep on this way," cautioned Collins. But Garrison shook his head.

"Let him alone!" he said.

The year 1843 was one of remarkable antislavery activity. The New England Anti-Slavery Society mapped out a series of one hundred conventions. The territory covered in the schedule included all of New England, New York, Pennsylvania, Ohio and Indiana. Under Garrison's leadership it was a real campaign, taking more than six months to complete. Frederick Douglass was chosen as one of the agents to tour the country.

The first convention was held in Middlebury, Vermont, home of William Slade, for years co-worked with John Quincy Adams in Congress. Yet in this town the opposition to the antislavery convention was intensely bitter and violent. Vermont boasted that within her borders no slave had ever been delivered up to a master, but the towns did not wish to be involved in "agitation."

What was in this respect true of the Green Mountain State was most discouragingly true of New York, the next state they visited. All along the Erie canal, from Albany to Buffalo, they met with apathy, indifference, and sometimes the mob spirit. Syracuse refused to furnish church, market, house, or hall in which to hold the meetings. Mr. Stephen Smith, who had received the little group of speakers in his home, was sick with distress. Frederick, standing beside a wide window, looked out upon a park covered with young trees. He turned to his unhappy host.

"Don't worry, my friend," he said. "We'll have our meeting."

The next morning he took his stand under a tree in the southeast corner of this park and began to speak to an audience of five persons. Before the close of the afternoon he had before him not less than five hundred. In the evening he was waited upon by the officers of the Congregational church and tendered the use of an old wooden building which they had deserted for a better. Here the convention continued for three days.

In the growing city of Rochester their reception was more cordial. Gerrit Smith, Myron Holly, William Goodell and Samuel Porter were influential Abolitionists in the section. Frederick was to know the eccentric, learned and wealthy Gerrit Smith much better. Now he argued with him, upholding Garrison's moral persuasion against Gerrit Smith's ballot-box, as the weapon for abolishing slavery. From Rochester, Frederick and William Bradburn made their way to Buffalo, a rising city of steamboats, business and bustle. The Friends there had been able to secure for the convention only an old dilapidated and deserted room on a side-street, formerly used as a post-office. They went at the time appointed and found seated a few cabmen in their coarse, wrinkled clothes, whips in hand, while their teams were standing on the street waiting for a job.

Bradburn was disgusted. After an hour of what he considered futile talk and haranguing, he left. That evening he took the steamer to Cleveland. But Frederick stayed on. For nearly a week he spoke every day in the old post-office to constantly increasing audiences. Then a Baptist church was thrown open to him. The following Sunday he spoke in an open park to an assembly of several thousand persons.

In Richmond, Indiana, their meeting was broken up, and their clothes ruined with evil-smelling eggs. In Pendleton, Indiana, Frederick's speaking schedule suffered a delay.

It had been found impossible to obtain a building in Pendleton in which to hold the convention. So a platform was erected in the woods at the edge of town. Here a large audience assembled and Frederick and his companion speaker, William A. White, were in high spirits. But hardly had they climbed to the stand when they were attacked by a mob of about sixty persons who, armed with clubs, picks and bricks, had come out to "kill the nigger!"

It was a furious but uneven fight. The Friends tried to protect Frederick, but they had no defense. White, standing his ground, pleaded with the ruffians and got a ferocious blow on the head, which cut his scalp and knocked him to the ground. Frederick had caught up a stick, and he fought with all his strength; but the mob beat him down, leaving him, they supposed, dead on the ground. Then they mounted their horses and rode to Anderson where, it was said, most of them lived.

Frederick lay on the ground at the edge of the woods, bleeding and unconscious. Neal Hardy, a Quaker, carried him to his cart and took him home. There he was bandaged and nursed. His right hand had been broken and never recovered its natural strength and dexterity. But within a few days he was up and on his way. His arm was in a sling but, as he remarked, the rest of him "little the worse for the tussle."

"A complete history of these hundred conventions would fill a volume far larger than the one in which this simple reference is to find place," Frederick Douglass wrote many years later. "It would be a grateful duty to speak of the noble young men who forsook ease and pleasure, as did White, Gay and Monroe, and endured all manner of privations in the cause of the enslaved and down-trodden of my race. . . . Mr. Monroe was for many years consul to Brazil, and has since been a faithful member of Congress from Oberlin District, Ohio, and has filled other important positions in his state. Mr. Gay was managing editor of the *National Anti-Slavery Standard*, and afterward of the *New York Tribune*, and still later of the *New York Evening Post*." *

The following winter, against the advice of his friends, Douglass decided on an independent course of action.

"*Your word* is being doubted," he said to Garrison and Phillips. "That I cannot endure. They are saying that I am an impostor. I shall write out the facts connected with my experience in slavery, giving names, places and dates."

"It will be a powerful story!" said Garrison, his eyes watching the glow of light from the fireplace.

Theodore Parker spoke impatiently. "So powerful that it will bring the pack on his heels. And neither the people nor the laws of Massachusetts will be able to protect him."

"He's mad!" Wendell Phillips' golden voice was hard. "When he has finished I shall advise him to throw the manuscript in the fire!"

But Garrison smiled.

"Gentlemen," he said, "we'll find a way. God will not lose such a man as Frederick Douglass!"

They looked at him sitting there in the dusk, with the firelight playing over his calm face. There were times when Garrison's quiet faith confounded the two divines.

A way did reveal itself. In May, 1845, the *Narrative of the Life*

* Douglass, *Life and Times of Frederick Douglass,* chap. v, p. 288.

of Frederick Douglass, prefaced by letters by Garrison and Phillips, made its appearance. Priced at fifty cents, it ran through a large edition. In August, Douglass, with a purse of two hundred and fifty dollars raised by his friends in Boston, boarded the British ship *Cambria* for England, in company with the Hutchinsons, a family of Abolitionist singers, and James Buffum, vice-president of the Massachusetts Anti-Slavery Society.

Anna stood on the dock and waved goodbye. She smiled, though the ship was blurred and she could not distinguish his dear face at the rail. A blast of the whistle made little Freddie clutch her skirts and bury his face in alarm. He wanted to go home. Close by her side, straight and unmoved, stood six-year-old Lewis, holding the hand of his weeping sister, Rosetta.

"Look after Mother and the children, Son. I'm depending on you!" Lewis was turning over his father's parting words. Now he would be the man of the house. Girls, of course, could cry. He watched his mother's face.

A few final shouts, a last flutter of handkerchiefs, some stifled sobs, and the relatives and friends of the voyagers began to disperse. Anna felt a light touch on her arm.

"Come, Mrs. Douglass"—it was Mrs. Wendell Phillips—"we're going to drive you home."

Friends surrounded her—comforting, solicitous.

"You can depend upon us, Mrs. Douglass. You know that."

Anna smiled. She had wanted him to go, to get out of harm's reach. She could not continue to live in the terror that had gripped her ever since Frederick had returned from the western trip. He had made light of the "Indiana incident," but his broken hand could not be hidden. Each time he left her after that, she knew what *might* happen. So she had urged him to go; she had smiled and said, "Don't worry about us, Frederick. You must go!"

"My salary will be paid direct to you."

"I'll manage. Now that we're in our home, it will be easy." Nothing but confidence and assurances for him.

The summer before they had bought a lot in Lynn, Massachusetts. They had planned the house together; and in the fall—between trips and with the help of several friends—Douglass had built a cottage.

Anna hated to leave New Bedford—"a city of friends," she called it.

"But you see," she explained to them ruefully, "the Douglass family has simply rent the seams of this little house. We have to have more room."

They had chosen Lynn because it was more on the path for Frederick's work and because the town had a thriving Anti-Slavery Society. Came the day when they moved into their cottage. Anna washed windows and woodwork, and Lewis followed his father around, "chunking up all the holes" so that when the cold weather came they would be snug and warm.

The highway was good and the May day pleasant as the Reverend Wendell Phillips drove Douglass' family back to their home.

"How long do you think he'll have to stay away, Mr. Phillips?"

They were nearly there, before Anna dared ask the question she had been avoiding.

Wendell Phillips flicked his whip. It was a moment before he answered.

"It's impossible to say, Mrs. Douglass. We're certain he'll render valuable service to the cause of freedom among peoples who do not know the realy horrors of American slavery. Meanwhile, we'll do what we can to see that his own return may be safe."

"Pray God the time will not be long!" Mrs. Phillips laid her hand over that of the woman by her side.

Then they were at the gate and goodbyes were said. The children climbed down nimbly and rushed up the path. Anna moved more slowly.

She smiled at the sight of moist, chubby Charlie in the neighbor woman's arms. This was their youngest son—hers and Frederick's. Poor little fellow! Anna felt her heart contract. *He* didn't know his father was going so far away.

"Hasn't whimpered a mite," the neighbor had kept him during the family's absence. "So I mixed up a pot of soup for you. It's on the stove all ready. I knew you'd all be starved."

Anna's voice choked when she tried to thank the good soul. The woman patted her arm and hurried homeward across the vacant lot.

Small Charlie was quite happy, so Anna left him with the other children and went to the room she shared with her husband. It was very small. The wardrobe door, left swinging open, bumped against the washstand crowding the bed. Anna took off her hat, placed it on the shelf and closed the door. Moving mechanically, she emptied the half-filled bowl of water on the stand and hung up an old alpaca coat.

Frederick had discarded it at the last moment. Then she stood motionless, just thinking.

She had not told him she was going to have another baby: he might not have gone. But she knew she needed more money than that tiny salary. She could not leave the children. There must be something she could do. She must manage. Suddenly her face lighted. Lynn, Massachusetts, had one industry which in the early 1840's spilled over into every section. Lynn had developed like a guild town in England; and that evening Anna made up her mind that she could do what was being done in many households in the town—she would make shoes.

In time she learned to turn a sole with the best of them.

Meanwhile a ship was going out to sea. And all was not smooth sailing.

"We should have taken one of the French boats—even if they are slower!" Mrs. Hutchinson regarded the apologetic purser scornfully.

"I'll see the Captain at once." And James Buffum stalked away in search of him.

No cabin had been assigned to Frederick Douglass. Though the tickets had been purchased together, the party was being separated— the Hutchinsons and Mr. Buffum sent to cabins, Frederick Douglass to the steerage.

Douglass took no part in the angry discussion that ensued. It was an old story to him. Negroes who had the temerity to travel about the United States were subject to insults and indignities. On the Sound between New York and Stonington no colored man was allowed abaft the wheel. In all seasons of the year, hot or cold, wet or dry, the deck was his only place. Douglass had been in many fights—had been beaten by conductors and brakemen. He smiled now remembering the time six men ejected him from a car on the Eastern Line between Boston and Portland. He had managed to tear away several seats and break a couple of windows.

But this morning, as the *Cambria* nosed her way out of the bay and started back to the Old Country which so many had left in their search for freedom, Douglass shrugged his shoulders.

"Let it go!" he said. "We'll all reach England together. If I cannot go to the cabins, you can come to me in the steerage."

"Oh, yes, Mr. Douglass," Captain Judkins quickly intervened.

"There is only the formality of an invitation. You can visit your friends at any time."

"Thank you, sir!" Douglass bowed gravely.

But Mrs. Hutchinson would not be quieted. "It's ridiculous!"

Her husband sighed and slipped his arm through Frederick's.

"Let's go now and see that our friend is properly settled," he said.

So they all went first to the steerage. And here, to the edification of the steerage passengers, they spent most of their time. But, as always happens within a small world, word got around, and during the long afternoons and evenings other first-class passengers began visiting the steerage.

The Hutchinsons, celebrated vocalists, sang their sweetest songs, and groups gathered on the rude forecastle-deck in spirited conversation with Frederick Douglass.

"Always thought Abolitionists were crackpots!" The man from Indiana frowned.

"Wouldn't think any—er—a black could talk like that!" The speaker, who came from Delaware, certainly had never heard such talk before.

"This man—he is not black." The tinge of foreign accent in the words caused the Americans to glance up sharply. Perhaps the immaculate swarthy passenger was from Quebec. A Washingtonian eyed him coolly and rose to his feet.

"He's a nigger just the same!" he said, and walked away from the group.

They fell silent after that. But some time afterward several of the passengers approached the Captain with the request that he invite this unusual character to deliver a lecture in the salon. Captain Judkins, who had been unhappy about the matter, gladly complied. He himself went to the steerage and sat chatting with the ex-slave. The dark man's manners captivated him.

Announcement was made of the scheduled lecture. News of the Captain's visit to the steerage got around. In one of the most expensive suites on the ship three young men faced each other. They were trembling with rage.

"By God, suh," said one, thumping the table with his fist, "we won't stand for it!"

"Invited to the salon!" said another.

"By the Captain!"

The pampered son of a Louisiana planter tore his silk cravat as he loosened it.

"Dog of a runaway slave—flaunted in our faces!" His voice choked in his throat. His cousin quickly assented.

"Fool Captain ought to be horsewhipped!"

The fair-haired boy from Georgia emptied his glass of brandy and waved his hand drunkenly.

"Just a minute, gentlemen. No rash talk! Gotta plan—that's it—gotta plan!"

"Plan—hell!" The dark face of the Louisianian flushed dangerously. "We'll just throw the nigger overboard if he dares show his impertinent face!"

"Yes," agreed his cousin. "That'll show the damned Yankees!"

They did not really believe he would come. But, of course, they did not know Frederick Douglass.

On the appointed evening the salon filled up early. Few of the ladies had dared to go to the steerage, and now flowered ruffles and curls fluttered with excitement as they settled into the cushioned seats. Promptly on the hour the imposing figure appeared in the doorway. At a sign from the Captain, who had risen, Douglass walked toward the front of the room.

Then it happened.

The three young men were now five. At Douglass' appearance the two who were inside the salon sprang quickly to their feet, the three who had been watching from the deck came running in.

"We'll stop him!"

"Get the nigger!"

"Throw him overboard!"

Ladies screamed, men jumped up, but Frederick only stood still while they closed in on him. Perhaps he had expected something like this. At any rate, his face did not change. The clamor increased as, cursing, the young men knocked aside any opposition.

But they had reckoned without the Captain. The stern old Britisher's voice thundered out. His shipmen came running, and before the rioters could realize what had happened, they were struggling in the firm grasp of British seamen, who looked toward the Captain for further orders.

Captain Judkins was outraged. He glared at the offenders who, utterly bewildered by the turn of events, were stuttering their objections. The Captain chose to ignore everything except one obvious fact.

"Put these young drunks in irons until they sober up!" He turned away, leaving his competent crewmen to execute the order.

The Louisianian's face paled. He stared about stupidly, expecting the whole roomful of people to rise in protest. But they did not. The faces swam before his eyes crazily as, stumbling a little, he was led away. Later he heard them applauding on the upper deck.

The next day they sighted land. A mist between the ocean and the sky turned green, took shape. The man beside Frederick gripped the rail with his broken nails.

" 'Tis Ireland," he repeated softly. And there was pain and heartache in his voice.

Frederick did not sleep that night. He was one of the huddled group that stayed on deck. They talked together in low voices, watching the distant flicker of an occasional light, straining their ears to catch some sound. Some of them had failed in the bewildering New World, and they were going back. Others had succeeded and now were returning for parents or wives and children.

But Frederick was breaking through the horizon. He was getting on the other side. He had sailed through the sky. America and all that it had meant to him lay far behind. How would Europe receive this dark-skinned fugitive from slavery?

The ship docked at Liverpool, but certain preliminaries prevented the passengers from going ashore immediately. Baltimore, New Bedford, not even New York, had prepared Frederick for the port of Liverpool. It was rapidly becoming Britain's monstrous spider of commerce, flinging its sticky filaments to the far corners of the world and drawing into its net all that the earth yields up to men.

Just inside the bottleneck entrance to the Mersey River, kept relatively free from silt by tidal scour, Liverpool was once a shelter for fishing vessels which built up a comfortable coastal trade with Ireland. Medieval sailors gave little thought to the sandstone hill that lay beyond the marshy fringe. The Dee River silted up and trade with America grew; and it was found that Liverpool was well situated to meet the change. The mouth of the old pool was converted into wet docks, the marshes were hollowed out, and railroads tunneled through the sandstone hill with ease. The British Empire was expanding.

Now all along the wharves rode merchant ships of every variety, ships laden with iron and salt, timber and coal, grains, silks and woollens, tobacco and, most of all, raw cotton from America.

Frederick saw them unloading the cotton and piling it high on the docks. He knew it was going to the weavers of Lancashire. He wondered if those weavers knew how cotton was planted and chopped and picked.

The Hutchinsons had been in Liverpool before, so they all went to a small hotel not far from the wide Quadrant. Frederick stood in the square gazing up at the great columned building fashioned after the Greek Parthenon and for a moment he forgot about the cotton. He liked the quiet, solid strength of that building. He resolved to visit it to feel the stone and measure the columns.

Quite unexpectedly Liverpool became aware of Frederick Douglass.

The young men who had been so rudely halted in their premeditated violence, went immediately to the police demanding the arrest of the "runaway slave" and of the ship's Captain! They were not prepared for the calm detachment of British justice. Never doubting the outcome, the young men repaired to the newspapers, where they told of their "outrageous treatment," denounced the Captain and all his crew and heaped abuse upon the insolent instigator of this "crime against society."

British curiosity is not easily aroused. But the young men's language pricked both the authorities and the newspapermen. They did not like it. They dropped in on Captain Judkins. His words were few, brusque and pointed. The police asked politely if he wished them to lock the young men up. The Captain considered their proposal coolly and decided he had no interest in the young men. He *was* going to take his Missus to hear the black American speak. She would enjoy it. And now, if the inspector was finished, his Missus was waiting. The Captain hurried away, rolling a little on his sea legs; and the newspapermen decided they would visit the "black American."

The Honorable William Gladstone, down from London for a few days, re-read a certain column in his paper over a late and solitary breakfast. The new Colonial Secretary spent most of his time in London; but Liverpool remained his home. It was a lovely house, well out of town, away from the dirt and noise of warehouses and docks. Well back from the graveled road, behind high fences and undulating greens, sat the residences of England's merchant princes. Gladstone had represented his neighbors in the government since he was twenty-three years old, first as vice-president and then president of the Board of Trade. Now, at thirty-six, he had been made Colonial Secretary. It took a man who knew trade and the proper restrictions for its protection to handle the affairs of Egypt, Australia and fabulously rich India.

The young man frowned and crumpled his paper.

"Nevins!" he called.

"Yes, sir!"

"Nevins, have you been in town this week?"

Nevins considered before answering. There must be no mistake about this matter.

"Not this week, sir.

"Well, have you heard any talk of a British India Society meeting?"

"I beg your pardon, sir?"

"India Society," the Colonial Secretary explained, "or anything at all about India. I understand there have been meetings in the provinces—talk about starving India—Indian independence—some sort of agitation."

"We've had nothing of that kind in these parts." Nevins spoke with a touch of disapproval.

The Colonial Secretary picked up his paper. He frowned at it a moment.

"I was wondering if there were any connection. Any connection at all. Might well be, you know."

"I don't understand, sir."

"There's something here about a runaway slave from America speaking in town tonight—at one of those workers' halls. They're springing up all over England." He added the last thoughtfully.

"Did you say a slave, sir, perhaps an African cannibal?"

"Exactly. This gives a most extraordinary account of the fellow on shipboard. Ship's Captain says he's educated."

"I can't believe it, sir."

"Um—would be very strange, if true. But who would be bringing him over here?" The American Revolution had not yet become a mellowed memory. Americans—white *or* black—would bear watching.

"Nevins!"

"Yes, sir."

"I should like you to attend this meeting."

"I, sir?"

"Find out what this slave has to say and what's behind him."

It had really been planned by the Hutchinsons as a concert. The Anti-Slavery Society had asked Mr. Buffum to say a few words. Douglass was merely to be presented and to say that he was glad to be in England. But the newspapers had played up Frederick Douglass' story so much that at the last moment they decided to seize the opportunity and feature him. When, long before dark the hall began to fill, it was obvious that they had come to hear "the black man."

While the crowd listened respectfully to the Hutchinsons, Frederick studied his first British audience. Somehow it was different. He realized it bore out what he had witnessed in two days of wandering about Liverpool. For the first time in his life he had seen white people whose lot might well be compared with that of the black slave in America. Here in Liverpool they could indeed leave their jobs, he thought grimly; but their children would starve. He saw them living in unbelievable squalor, several families herded together in two or three rooms, or in a single dirty cellar, sleeping on straw and shavings.

He sat on the platform and studied their faces. There was something in their eyes, something in the stolid set of their chins, something hard and unyielding, some strength which could not be destroyed—something to join with his strength. And so when he rose he did not fumble for words. He told them that he was glad that here on British soil he was truly free, that no slave-hunter could drag him from the platform, no arm, however long, turn him over to a master. Here he stood a free man, among other free men!

They cheered him lustily. And when they had quieted down he began to talk to them about cotton. He talked to them of the cotton piled high on the docks of Liverpool and how it got there. He talked to them of black hands picking cotton and blood soaking into soil around the cotton stalks.

"Because British manufacturers need cotton, American slavery can defy the opinions of the civilized world and block Abolitionists in America and England. If England bought free cotton from some other part of the world, if she stopped buying slave-grown cotton, American slavery would die out."

Graphically, he added up the horrors of slavery. He told how the labor of the slave in chains cheapened and degraded labor everywhere. They listened, leaning forward in their seats, their eyes fixed.

"Cotton can be grown by free labor, at a fair cost and in far greater abundance, in India. England, as a matter of self-interest as well as on the score of humanity, should without delay redress the wrongs of India, give protection and encouragement to its oppressed and suf-fering population, and thus obtain a permanent and abundant supply of free cotton produced by free men."

"A powerful speech, sir!" Nevins reported the next morning.

The Colonial Secretary looked at his man with some impatience.

"Well, really, Nevins! Let's be a bit more specific. A black make a powerful speech—something of an exaggeration, surely!"

"He's not really a black, sir," Nevins answered surprisingly.

"Good Lord! What is he then?"

"I couldn't rightly say, sir." There was a dogged stubbornness about Nevins this morning. The Colonial Secretary shrugged his shoulders.

"Well, well. What did he talk about?"

A lucid thought flashed across Nevins' mind.

"He talked about cotton, sir."

"About cotton?" The Colonial Secretary stared. "What on earth did he say about cotton?"

"He said that better cotton could be raised in India than in America."

The lucid moment passed, and Nevins could tell no more. But the young Colonial Secretary saw the newspaper accounts of Douglass's talk before he returned to London. He took out his notebook and on a clean, fresh page he wrote a name, "Frederick Douglass." Then he thoughtfully drew a circle around it. William Gladstone's mind had projected itself into the future, when there might be no more cheap cotton coming from America. The Colonial Secretary was a solid young man with no nonsense about him.

Across the narrow strip of water, in Dublin, Daniel O'Connell sat in a ruby-brick house off Rutland Square, while the dusk of a Septem-ber evening closed about him. He held a letter in his hand—a letter he had been re-reading while he waited. From far-off America his friend, William Lloyd Garrison, had written:

I send him to you, O'Connell, because you of all men have most to teach him. He is a young lion, not yet fully come into his strength, but all the latent power is there. I tremble for him! I am not a learned man. When confronted with clever phrasing of long words I am like to be confused. Scholars well versed in theology say I am a perfectionist. . . . As Christians, I believe we must convert the human race. Yet, God forgive me, doubts assail my heart. Here is a man, a few short years ago a slave. I stand condemned each time I look into his face. I am ashamed of being identified with a race of men who have done him so much injustice, who yet retain his people in horrible bondage. I try to make amends. But who am I to shape this young man's course? I have no marks of a lash across my back; I've had the comforts of a mother's tender care; I speak my father's name with pride. I am a free white man in a land shaped and designed for free white men. But you, O'Connell, know of slavery! Your people are not free. Poor and naked, they are governed by laws which combine all the vices of civilization with those of primitive life. The masses of Ireland enjoy neither the freedom of the savage, left to roam his own forests and draw fish from his rivers, nor the bread of servitude. . . . From you, Frederick Douglass can learn. I commend him to you, with my love. He will strengthen your great heart. He will renew your faith and hope for all mankind.

The old man sat, turning the letter in his hand. The years lay heavy along his massive frame. His own voice came back to him: *Sons of Ireland! Agitate, agitate, agitate!*

Yet the evictions of starving tenants went on. The great castle in its circle of wretched cabins, stripped the surrounding country of food and fuel. People were ignorant because they could not go to school, slothful because there was nothing they could do. Drunkards because they were cold. Ireland had long been in subjection harsh enough to embitter, yet not complete enough to subdue. But the failure of the potato crop this year had brought a deadening apathy. The Irish cottier was saying he could never be worse off or better off by any act of his own. And everywhere there were the gendarmes, sodden with drink and armed with carbines, bayonets and handcuffs.

Daniel O'Connell had been thirty-six years old when, in 1812, Robert Peel came to Dublin. To O'Connell the twenty-four-year-old Secretary for Ireland was the embodiment of everything English. The Irishman had been destined and educated for the priesthood, had taken up law instead, and risen as rapidly as a Catholic could in a Protestant government. An Irish Catholic could vote, but could not sit in Parliament; he could enter the army, navy or professions, but could not rise to the higher ranks. The universities and all the important posts in the Civil Service were closed to him.

As an advocate, Daniel O'Connell had been greatly in demand. In those days he stood six feet tall, with a head of fox-red curls and a face that had irregular, almost ugly features. They said his voice could be heard a mile off and was like music strained through honey. Reckless, cunning, generous and vindictive, O'Connell had fought for Ireland. They threw him in jail when he challenged Robert Peel to a duel. It never came off. He finally apologized, thinking to propitiate the Englishman in the matter of his Catholic Relief Bill that was up before Parliament.

Now Robert Peel was Prime Minister of England, and misery still lay like a shroud over all Ireland. O'Connell shook his head. Garrison was mistaken. There was nothing he could teach his young man. At seventy, one's work is finished, and he, Daniel O'Connell, had failed.

After a while the girl brought in a lighted lamp and set it on the table. O'Connell said nothing. He was waiting.

Then he heard voices in the hall and he stood up, his keen eyes fixed on the door. It opened to admit Frederick Douglass. The dark man stood a moment where the lamplight fell on him; then he smiled. And something in the Irishman's tired heart ran out to meet that smile. O'Connell strode across the room. He placed his two hands on the younger man's shoulders and looked deep into his eyes.

"My son, I'm glad you've come," he said.

So Frederick Douglass saw Ireland and came to know its people. He learned why women's faces beneath their shawls aged so quickly. He watched children claw the débris on the coal-quays of Cork. He saw the rich grasslands of the Golden Vale where fine, fat cattle fed while babies died for milk. Looking out over the Lakes of Killarney, he saw on the one side uncultivated tracts, marshy wastes studded with patches of heather, with here and there a stunted fir tree; and on the other, along the foot of the mountains beside the lovely lakes, green, smiling fields and woods of almost tropical vegetation. He learned that in Ireland there were only rich and poor, only palaces and hovels.

"Misrule is due to ignorance and ignorance is due to misrule." O'Connell tapped the short stem of his pipe on the table. "Few Englishmen ever visit Ireland. When they do they drive in a carriage from country house to country house. The swarms of beggars in Dublin only fill them with disgust."

"But— But why don't these beggars work?"

"There are no industries in Ireland. Our wool and wheat go into English mills. In Ireland, in order to work, one must have a plot of land."

Frowning, Douglass grappled with the problem. Oppression then was not confined to black folks! There was some common reason for it all.

O'Connell nodded his head.

"Possession of the land! This is the struggle, whether we're talking about the Gaels of Scotland and Ireland, the brown peoples of India, or the blacks of South Africa. Indeed, where are your red men in America?"

The young man's face showed something of horror. Was the earth so small then that men must destroy each other to have their little bit?

"Not at all. But there have always been those who would share nothing. Conquest has come to be a glorious thing. Our heroes are the men who take, not those who give!"

The old man was in fine form that fall. The young man with his vibrant personality and searching questions inspired him. Earlier in the year he had vetoed plans for a huge rally at the great Conciliation Hall. The place held twenty thousand people and O'Connell had not felt equal to it. But now he announced a change of mind: he and Douglass would speak there together.

It was an event talked of many a long winter evening afterward. "Dan—Our Dan," they said, outdid himself. The massive stooped shoulders were squared, the white head high. Once more the magnificent voice pealed forth.

"Until I heard this man that day," Douglass himself wrote, "I had thought that the story of his oratory and power was exaggerated. I did not see how a man could speak to twenty or thirty thousand people at one time and be heard by any considerable portion of them, but the mystery was solved when I saw his ample person and heard his musical voice. His eloquence came down upon the vast assembly like a summer thunder-shower upon a dusty road. At will he stirred the multitude to a tempest of wrath or reduced it to the silence with which a mother leaves the cradle-side of her sleeping babe. Such tenderness, such pathos, such world-embracing love! And, on the other hand, such indigation, such fiery and thunderous denunciation, such wit and humor, I never heard surpassed, if equaled, at home or abroad." *

A piece on O'Connell came out in *Brownson's Review*. Mr. O. A. Brownson, recently become a Catholic, took issue with the "Liberator" of Ireland for having attacked American institutions. O'Connell gave another speech.

"I am charged with attacking American institutions, as slavery is called," he began. "I am not ashamed. . . . My sympathy is not confined to the narrow limits of my own green Ireland; my spirit walks abroad upon sea and land, and wherever there is sorrow and suffering, there is my spirit to succor and relieve."

The striking pair toured Ireland together. O'Connell talked about the antislavery movement and why the people of Ireland should take part in it; Douglass preached O'Connell's doctrines of full participation of all peoples in government and legislative independence.

"There must be government," said O'Connell. They were talking together quietly in the old man's rooms. "And the people must take part, must learn to vote and take responsibility. You have a fine Constitution in the United States of America. I have studied it carefully."

"I have never read it," confessed the dark man, very much ashamed.

"No?" O'Connell studied the somber face. "But you have read the Declaration of Independence. A glorious thing!"

"Yes." And now there was deep bitterness. "And I find it only words!"

The Irishman leaned over and placed his hand upon the young man's knee. He spoke softly.

"Aye, lad—words! But words that can come alive! And that's worth working and even fighting for!"

* Douglass, *Life and Times of Frederick Douglass*, chap. vi, p. 249.

"To be henceforth free, manumitted and discharged from all manner of servitude to me . . ."

THE TWO LETTERS reached them in the same mail. One came from James Buffum to Frederick; the other was for Daniel O'Connell from George Thompson, the English Abolitionist. Thompson, who had been stoned from his platform in Boston on his last trip to America, had not met Frederick. However, he had heard from William Lloyd Garrison.

Their letters said substantially the same thing: "We need Douglass in Scotland."

The facts were brief. It had been proved that the Free Church of Scotland, under the leadership of the great Doctors Cunningham, Candlish and Chalmers, had taken money from slave-dealers to build churches and to pay church ministers for preaching the gospel. John Murray of Bowlien Bay and other antislavery men of Glasgow had called it a disgrace. The leading divines had thereupon undertaken to defend, in the name of God and the Bible, not only the principle of taking money from slavers, but also of holding fellowship with these traffickers in human beings. The people of Scotland were thoroughly aroused. Meetings were being called and strong speakers were needed. Buffum and Thompson were already on their way to Edinburgh.

"You'll come back, Frederick?" O'Connell's voice was wistful. It was like parting with a son.

"Come with us!" Frederick urged. But the "Liberator" shook his head.

"Our people are threatened with starvation. First our potatoes. And now the wheat crop has failed in England. There is no longer time. Richard Cobden writes that the Prime Minister may be with us. A shallow hope, but I must be on hand if needed."

"Perhaps then I shall see you in London?" The thought that he might not see the old man again was unbearable.

"Perhaps, Frederick. God bless you!"

Frederick found the famous old city of Edinburgh literally plastered with banners. *Send Back the Money* stared at him from street corners. Every square and crescent carried the signs. They had scribbled it on the sidewalks and painted it in large white letters on the side of the rocky hill which stands like some Gibraltar, guarding the city: *Send Back the Money*.

For several days George Thompson, James Buffum and another American, Henry C. Wright, had been holding antislavery meetings in the city. As soon as Douglass arrived, they hurried him off to the most beautiful hall he had ever seen. The audience was already assembled and greeted him with cheers. Without taking time to remove the dust and grime of travel, he mounted the platform and told his story.

After that, excitement mounted in the town. *Send Back the Money* appeared in a banner across the top of Edinburgh's leading newspapers. Somebody wrote a popular street song, with *Send Back the Money* in the chorus. Wherever Douglass went, crowds gathered. It was as if he had become the symbol of the people's demand.

At last the general assembly of the Free Church rose to the bait and announced they would hold an open session at Cannon Mills. Doctors Cunningham and Candlish would defend the Free Church of Scotland's relations with slavery in America. The great Dr. Chalmers was in feeble health at the time. "Besides," Douglass wrote afterward,* "he had spoken his word on this question; and it had not silenced the clamor without nor stilled the anxious heavings within." As it turned out, the whole weight of the business fell on Cunningham.

The quartet of Abolitionists made it their business to go to this meeting of the opposition. So did the rest of Edinburgh. The building held about twenty-five hundred persons. Long ahead of time, the crowd gathered outside and stood waiting for the doors to open.

Douglass always remembered the meeting at Cannon Mills with relish.

* Douglass, *My Bondage and My Freedom*, chap. xxiv, p. 385.

Dr. Cunningham rose to tumultuous applause and began his learned address. With logic and eloquence he built up his argument, the high point of which was that neither Jesus Christ nor his holy apostles had looked upon slaveholding as a sin.

Just as the divine reached this climax, George Thompson called out, in a clear, sonorous, but rebuking voice, "Hear! Hear! Hear!" Speaker and audience were brought to a dead silence.

"The effect of this common exclamation was almost incredible," Douglass reported.* "It was as if a granite wall had been suddenly flung up against the advancing current of a river. . . . Both the Doctor and his hearers seemed appalled by the audacity as well as the fitness of the rebuke."

After a moment the speaker cleared his throat and continued. But his words stuck in his throat—the flow of language was dammed. The speech dragged on for several minutes, and then the Doctor stumbled to his seat to scattered patting of hands.

The Free Church of Scotland held on to its blood-stained money, and the people bowed their heads in shame.

"Ours is a long history," said Andrew Paton, sadly, "of incompetent leadership and blind, unquestioning following by the ranks."

"But this time you did protest. The people of Scotland know what slavery means now," George Thompson assured him.

Thompson, Buffum and Douglass traveled back to London together. They went by stagecoach, stopping each night at some inn. It was like a holiday. Frederick thought the soft mist that lay over all the land was very lovely. And there was something comforting and homelike about the way the stark grandeur of Scotland's rugged crags gave way to rounded hills, wide valleys and gently rolling moors. The roads of Ireland had been bad, the occasional inns wretched and dirty. Now, for the most part, they rolled along in state; and, when night came, lights from an inn twinkled a jolly welcome, the dinner was hot and filling, the innkeeper genial. Undoubtedly, thought Frederick, life is pleasanter in England.

The three Abolitionists were teetotalers—temperance men on principle. But Frederick could not stifle a desire to taste of the foamy ale which he saw being tossed off with such gusto.

"Are you *sure* it's alcoholic?" he asked.

Thompson threw back his head with a hearty laugh.

"If you mean will a bit of our ale with your dinner make you

* *Ibid., loc. cit.*

drunk, I'll say no." He eyed him with a quizzical twinkle. "You'd like some?"

"Frederick!" Buffum frowned his disapproval. He was three-fourths Massachusetts Puritan and he felt an older man's responsibility.

But the Englishman spread his hands and reasoned.

"This is a test, Friend Buffum. Here is a newcomer to England. He observes that ale is a national drink. He asks why?" He leaned forward. "How can he speak of the temptations of any kind of drink if he has never even tasted ale? Be logical, man!" Frederick was certain that one eye winked. He grinned and look anxiously at the Secretary of the Massachusetts Anti-Slavery Society. By now he really *wanted* some ale. Buffum had to laugh, if weakly. He clucked his tongue and shook his head.

"Frederick, Frederick! What would the folks at home say?"

Thompson was signaling to the waiter to bring them a large ale.

"That," he said sagely, as he turned back to his companions, "is something history will not record!" He looked at Frederick's broad, rather solemn face and raised his eyebrows. "But I am of the opinion that a single wild oat sown by our young friend will do him no great harm."

The boy came up, bearing three huge, foaming mugs, having interpreted the order as he thought right. He set the mugs down with a thump, scattering the suds in every direction, and departed before anyone could say "Jack Robinson!"

"Well"—Thompson shook with laughter—"it seems our young friend here is not going to sow his oats alone. So be it!" He raised his mug high in the air and led off.

"Gentlemen! To the Queen! God bless her!"

As they neared London they talked plans.

"First," said Thompson, "our distinguished visitor must have some clothes."

Frederick wondered whom he was talking about, but Buffum, his eyes on Frederick, nodded his head thoughtfully.

"Yes, I suppose so," he murmured. Then they both looked at Frederick and he shifted uneasily. Answering the unspoken question in his face, Thompson explained.

"You are becoming something of a celebrity. You will be going to dinners and teas. You must have proper apparel."

"But—" Frederick began, flushed and downcast.

"You are now in the employ of the World Anti-Slavery Society," Thompson went on, "our chief and most effective spokesman. In the interest of the entire cause you must make what the French call the good impression."

Now Frederick's apprehensions began to mount. How could he go into English "society"?

"Clothes do not make a gentleman," he said, shaking his head violently. "I am a workingman. I will speak—yes—anywhere. I will tell the meaning of slavery, I will do anything, but I have no manners or ways for society."

Thompson regarded the young man a long moment before answering.

"You are right, Frederick," he said quietly. "Clothes do not make a gentleman. They only serve to render him less conspicuous." He placed the tips of his fingers together and continued. "It will interest you to know that our word aristocracy comes from the Greek *aristokratia*, which is to say 'the best workman.'" He leaned forward. "Someday we'll recognize that. Meanwhile, Frederick Douglass, make no mistake about it—*you* belong!"

Came the evening when the swaying stagecoach drew up before the Golden Cross Hostelry on Charing Cross. The thick fog gave Frederick a feeling of unreality. He could see nothing but dim lights and looming shadows, but he was surrounded by a kind of muffled, intermittent rumbling. He stood in the drizzling rain listening.

"Come," said Thompson, taking him by the arm. "Let's get inside. You'll be drenched before you realize it."

Thompson lived in Dulwich, a suburb of London, but he was going to stay in town a few days until his friends had found suitable lodging and until, as he put it, chuckling, Frederick was "launched."

The next few days were busy ones. They found lodgings in Tavistock Square, not far from the Tavistock House, where Dickens lived for ten years. London would be Douglass' headquarters. From there he would make trips throughout England and in the spring would go to Wales. He was waited upon by the British India Committee, the Society of Friends, the African Colonial Society and by a group working for the repeal of the Corn Laws.

"It is the poor man's fight," they said.

The newcomer listened carefully, read newspapers morning and night and asked questions. He spoke at the Freemason's Hall, taking as his theme the right of every workman to have bread. Douglass spoke well, for he had only to step outside his rooms in London to see the pinch of poverty. Then, just as Thompson had warned him, the writers William and Mary Howitt sent a charming note asking him for a week-end in the country. Fortunately Frederick had managed to see a good tailor.

"Go, Frederick," his co-workers urged him. "They are Quakers. They have influence. You will come back rested."

Fall was closing around London like a shroud, but Clapham was delightful. The Howitts greeted him warmly.

"We have read your *Narrative*, so you are an old friend."

This was Frederick's initiation into English country life. He walked out into the beautiful garden where, rounding a smilax, he almost stepped on Hans Christian Andersen!

It was Mary and William Howitt who had translated the Danish writer's works into English. Andersen was very fond of them, and their home in Clapham was his haven. When they had guests he could always putter about in the garden. He knew that the famous ex-slave was coming that afternoon, but he would meet him after the tea party was over. Now, on his knees, trowel in hand, a smudge of mud on his nose, he stared with amazement. *So much of darkness and beard— and what a head!*

A peal of musical laughter behind him caused Frederick to turn. The funny little man scrambled to his feet and Mary Howitt, who had followed Frederick into the garden, was saying, "It is our dear Hans."

Andersen knew very little English and Frederick had never before heard Danish, so they could do very little more than grin at each other. But later, before an open fire, Frederick read Hans Christian Andersen's fairy stories, while Andersen, sipping his brandy, watched the expressive dark face. Their eyes met, and they were friends.

The next day Douglass asked the Howitts about their translations and what it meant to study languages other than one's native tongue. Then the writer of fairy tales began to talk. He spoke in Danish, and Mary interpreted. He talked of languages, of their background and history. He told Frederick about words and their symbolic magic. And another corner of Frederick's brain unfolded itself.

There was too much rain the summer and fall of 1845. Robert Peel, Prime Minister of Great Britain, stood at his window and watched it beat down on the slippery stones of the court. But he was not seeing the paving stones, he was not seeing the dripping walls. He was seeing unripened spikes of wheat rotting in the mud. He knew he had a crisis on his hands and he was not ready.

Robert Peel was a Tory. His background and education, his administration as Secretary of Ireland, his avowed policies, all had been those of the Conservative party. In appearance he was cold and proud. But he was an honest man, and he grew in wisdom.

Until the 1840's, despite the vast industrial changes of the previous half-century, some balance had been maintained between industry and agriculture. British farmers had been able to feed most of the workers in the new towns and factories and mines. But population had increased, villages had dwindled, and whole networks of manufacturing towns had sprung into being. When Peel took office the country was already in serious straits. The problem was economic, he knew. He listened to the speeches of John Bright, a Quaker cotton-spinner from Lancashire and he received Richard Cobden.

"There are thousands of houses in England at this moment where wives, mothers, and children are dying of hunger. Come with me and you will never rest until you give them bread," Cobden said.

Cobden backed his facts with logic. High tariffs kept out food-stuffs and essential commodities; landowners were keeping up the price of wheat while workingmen starved. Britain was on the verge of social revolution.

So Robert Peel, the Conservative, began to reduce customs. In 1842 he set a gradually lowering scale for corn duties. He sought to shift the burden of taxation from the poor to the wealthier classes and to cheapen the necessities of life. He saw that reforms were necessary, but he wished to avoid hasty changes. And in this caution lay his undoing.

His own party fell away. The Whigs distrusted the haughty, gray-eyed Minister. What did he, a Tory, mean by "seeming" to favor lower tariffs? The Irish still hated him because he stood firm against Repeal of the Union. The Catholics opposed him because he had backed nonsectarian schools.

But the enemy who kept closest watch was Disraeli. Not for a day did this ambitious member of Parliament forget that he had been left out of the new Prime Minister's cabinet. He took this omission as a personal slight. Hatred for Peel distorted his every move. Cleverly, coolly, calculatingly, Disraeli widened the cleavage in party ranks; he drew young aristocrats about him; he flattered them with his wit and charm, and whispered that Robert Peel, *their* Robert Peel, was betraying them. He was pushing the country into Free Trade. He would open the gates to a deluge that would destroy England.

In the spring of 1845 Richard Cobden had risen in the House of Commons and called for Repeal of the Corn Laws. He said that Free Trade ought to be applied to agriculture and pointed to what it had done for British manufacturing. He decried the old fallacy that wages vary with the price of bread. He thundered that there was no truth in the contention that wages were high when bread is dear and low when bread is cheap. The Conservatives drew together, their faces hardening.

But Robert Peel no longer backed the Corn Laws. He wanted the drawbridges around Britain lowered forever. But he wondered how could he, leader of the Conservative party, carry through such a revolutionary change? He decided to let the present Parliament run its course. In the next election he would appeal to the country: he would carry the fight to the people. Then they could send him back, free of all party ties and obligations, as a Free Trader.

But the weather is no respecter of parliamentary elections! The wheat crop failed in England, like the potato crop in Ireland. People were starving, and the Corn Laws locked out food. Peel called a meeting of his Cabinet, and the storm broke.

The Cobden forces were ready. They held great mass meetings, with Cobden and Bright enlisting every available speaker. Frederick Douglass addressed crowds in Piccadilly, on the docks, and in Hyde Park. He and John Bright went down into Lancashire. They talked in Birmingham and other towns and cities about the worker's right to have bread.

Then one morning a week before Christmas, Bright burst into the rooms on Tavistock Square, waving a newspaper.

"We've won! We've won!" he shouted. "The Cabinet's intact, the Prime Minister is back, the Repeal stands! We've won!"

James Buffum rolled out of bed and reached for the paper. Frederick, partly dressed, emerged from behind a curtained cubicle and clapped the little man on the shoulder. John Bright had watched his wife die of starvation while he sat at his spindles. But he could not fill enough spools. He could not spin fast enough. She had died. So John Bright had left his loom and joined Richard Cobden. Now there would be more food in England. He stood clinging to the dark man's hand—this new friend who knew so much about suffering.

"I'm going home," he said in his rich rolling Lancashire brogue.

"I'm going down to tell the folks myself. Come with me. We'll be glad together!"

So it happened that Frederick spent the Christmas in a spinner's shack in Lancaster. On Christmas Eve he wrote Anna.

The baby's crying in the next room and here in the corner sleeps a little lad just about Freddie's age. He's curled in a tight knot and his hair is falling over his face. It's not as round as I remember Freddie's, nor are his legs as plump. This house isn't as big as our little place in New Bedford and there are four children! But tonight they're all happy. The weavers carried on as if John and I had given them the world! My hand shakes as I think of it. We brought a goose and a few toys for the children. You should have seen their eyes! Tomorrow we will feast! How I wish you could share this with me. They're letting me borrow their little ones. But my heart cannot but be anxious for my own. Are you well and are the children well? I enclose some money. Enough, I hope, for your most urgent needs. But my real Christmas present to you is news that will make you very happy. Friends here are raising money to purchase my freedom—seven hundred and fifty dollars! The Misses Richardson, sweet sisters in Newcastle, have written to Mr. Walter Forward of Philadelphia, who will seek out Captain Auld and ask what he will accept for my person. He will tell my former master that I am now in England and that there is no possibility of my being taken. There can be little doubt that under the circumstances the Captain will name his price—and be very glad to get it! So, dear Anna, soon this separation will be at an end. I will return to you and to my dear children, in fact and before the law, a free man.

The writer sat for a few moments regarding that last line. Anna's eyes would shine when she read it. For an instant her face was there. Then the child stirred in his sleep. Frederick rose and straightened the little limbs on the cot. His hands were very tender.

"Frederick! I believe you've grown," Garrison beamed. He had just arrived in London from America.

John Bright nodded. "He is a big man," he said.

Garrison whisked Frederick away to Sir John Bowring's castle where they had been asked for over New Year's.

Sir John had represented England as Minister to China. He was a brilliant talker and drew about himself a circle of literary friends. On New Year's Eve, Douglass stood at a table covered with fine linen and old silver. He held in his hand a crystal glass and drank another toast: "The Queen! God bless her!"

They were all back in London for the opening of Parliament. Robert Peel on the side of the people! A great day for England!

As if to honor the auspicious occasion the fog blew away during the night, and January 22, 1846, dawned clear and bright like a spring day. People poured into the streets and lined Pall Mall. The Queen was coming! They crowded into Cannon Row and Parliament Street and surrounded Westminster Hall and Parliament. The Queen was coming!

Cobden had secured seats for them in the gallery, but Garrison and Douglass lingered in the crowd, craning their necks. The bobbies were forcing them back to keep the way clear when a modest, closed carriage drew up and a tall figure in a high silk hat stepped out.

"It's Peel! It's Robert Peel!" shouted Garrison and that started the crowd cheering. They had not recognized the Prime Minister. But the tall, pale man looked neither to the right or left. He walked straight ahead, unsmiling, and disappeared. The people were disappointed. They wanted to know him. They wanted to be friends.

The cheers had not gone unheeded. In the great, open carriage with prancing horses that now turned into the square, Disraeli tightened his lips. The carriage stopped with a clatter, the footman sprang down and threw open the door. Disraeli stepped out, his head high, his silken cape enveloping him with majesty. The crowd pressed forwar.

"Who is it?"

"Who is that man?"

"Disraeli!" someone answered.

"The Jew!" another voice added.

They drew back then, and let him pass in silence. Frederick Douglass followed him with his eyes. There was something painful in the defiant swagger. As he disappeared Frederick caught his breath sharply. He felt a hurt in his chest.

"I'm sorry for that man," he said, in a heavy tone.

"Why?" asked Garrison coolly. "He would spit upon you!"

Frederick shook his head. "Let's go in." Suddenly, he was very tired.

Inside he forgot his singular depression when, from the throne of

England, Queen Victoria declared the session of Parliament open. She was only thirty-one years old at that time, not beautiful perhaps, but a radiantly happy woman. Prince Albert was at her side. She was adored by her people. None of their hardships were laid at her door. Now she felt that a crisis had been successfully averted. Her voice rang with confidence and pride as she addressed her trusted Prime Minister.

And all the Lords and Ministers of the realm bowed low. The royal couple took their leave, and the business of running an empire was resumed. Every eye turned toward Robert Peel.

The Prime Minister rose, very pale, and began to state his case. He had the facts. Step by step, he unfolded his plan for combating the economic stalemate: cheap raw materials for the manufacturer, no protection against fair foreign competition, cheaper seed for the farmer, the open door for foreign meat and corn; for all, cheaper living.

No longer was his face cold and remote. The fires of deep conviction glowed in his eyes, and there was passion in his final declaration of independence.

"I will not, sirs," he concluded, "undertake to direct the course of the vessel by observations which have been taken in 1842." His words rang. "I do not wish to be Minister of England, but while I have the high honor of holding that office, I am determined to hold it by no servile tenure. I will only hold that office upon the condition of being unshackled by any other obligation than those of consulting the public interests, and of providing for the public safety."

He bowed and took his seat. Douglass wet his dry lips. What did the heavy silence mean? He wanted to blister his hands with applause. Garrison laid his hand on the younger man's arm.

There was a slight stir of movement, and Sir John Russell was on his feet. He commended the Prime Minister's speech and quietly backed it up with the authentic statement of Whig disasters. Some of the tenseness relaxed. There was polite applause when Sir John ended and a bit of parliamentary phrasing by the clerk. Men moved restlessly, wondering what to do next.

Then, like an actor carefully choosing his entrance Disraeli rose. Slowly his eyes swept the chamber. There was a sneering smile on his lips. It was as if he scorned their cowardly silence. Disraeli knew his time had come.

He stepped forth as defender of everything sacred! He talked of all the fine traditions of Great Britain. Englishmen, he said, must be protected without and within, from those who would undermine her power. The Prime Minister had given a "glorious example of egotistical rhetoric," and his policy was a "gross betrayal of the principles which had put him in power and of the party which kept him there."

The brilliance of his style held them spellbound. His defense of England thrilled them and his attack on Peel justified their selfishness. Disraeli took his seat to thunderous applause.

Douglass was shaking as though ill.

"What does it mean?" he asked, when they had got away.

"It means," said Richard Cobden, grimly, "that we'll have to fight every inch of the way all over again. We have won nothing. Except that now Disraeli will stop at nothing to ruin Peel."

"But how can Disraeli oppose the cause of poor people? I thought he knew of oppression and suffering from his own experience." Douglass' distress was very real. John Bright tried to explain.

"Suffering and oppression often only embitter men, Frederick, embitter and harden them. They close in upon themselves. They are so determined to be safe that they are ruthless and cruel. Undoubtedly Disraeli has suffered, but he has suffered selfishly—he has refused to see the sufferings of other people. He will sacrifice anything for power."

Frederick Douglass was learning what it takes to make men free. In the spring he went up into Wales. He traveled, as he said in a letter which was published in the *Liberator,* "from the Hill of Howth to the Giant's Causeway, and from the Giant's Causeway to Cape Clear." On May 12 he made a speech at Finsbury Chapel, Moorfields, which was published throughout England. William Gladstone addressed a note to him, inviting him to call.

Douglass heard that Daniel O'Connell was in London, that the Irish and Catholics were joined in the coalition against Peel. Yet the Prime Minister carried his Corn Bill through the House of Commons with comparative ease. It began to look as if, in spite of Lord Bentinck and Disraeli, it would get through the House of Lords. Then they attacked Peel's character.

Returning to London in May, Douglass immediately sought out O'Connell. The old man greeted him warmly, but he was haggard and shaken. Also, he was on the defensive. They could not avoid the subject which was uppermost in both their minds.

"He's a lifelong enemy of Ireland, lad." O'Connell studied Frederick's troubled face anxiously.

"But Richard Cobden proves that Peel will listen to reason. Cobden has won him so far along the way. His enemies are using the Irish question now to destroy him."

"He would tie Ireland to England forever!" The old man rose defiantly, shaking his white hair.

On June 25 the Corn Bill passed in the House of Lords, but the same day the Commons repudiated the Minister's Life Preservation bill for Ireland by a majority of seventy-three. Once more his enemies could say that Peel had betrayed his principles and fooled his followers. Three days later Peel tendered his resignation to the Queen.

That evening Douglass, accompanied by O'Connell, made his way to the Parliament.

"He will speak tonight—for the last time," John Bright had told them.

The members sat in their seats, strangely subdued. The contest between Peel and Disraeli was over. True, the Corn Laws were repealed—the gates were down. But Disraeli had forced Robert Peel out. He was finished.

Yet the grimness which had marked his pale face in the past months was gone, and in his final words there was a sense of peace that seemed to reach beyond that time and place.

"When Ministers appear to change their course, and lay themselves open to the charge of inconsistency, it were better perhaps for this country and for the general character of public men that they be punished by expulsion from office." He did not blame them, then. There was no word of bitterness. Moreover, the credit for his reforms, he said, should not go to him. "The name which ought to be chiefly associated with the success of these measures is the name of Richard Cobden," one who has achieved his disinterested purpose by "appeals to our reason."

There was a slight rustle throughout the chamber. It was as if the very shadows were listening.

"In relinquishing power, I shall leave a name censured by many who deeply regret the severance of party ties, by others, who, from no selfish interest adhere to the principles of Protection, considering its maintenance essential to the welfare and interests of the country; I shall leave a name execrated by every monopolist, who clamors for Protection because it conduces to his own individual benefit. But it may be that I shall leave a name sometimes remembered with expressions of goodwill in the abodes of those whose lot it is to labor, and to earn their bread by the sweat of their brow. Perhaps they too will call my name when they shall recruit their exhausted strength with abundant and untaxed food, the sweeter because it is not leavened by a sense of injustice."

It was all over in a few minutes. Frederick turned at a sound beside him. O'Connell had covered his face with his two hands. Frederick slipped his arm through his, pressing against him. The grand old man of Ireland was weeping.

It was the Reverend Samuel Hanson Cox who now decided that London had had just about enough of Frederick Douglass!

Sixty or seventy American divines had arrived in London that summer for the double purpose of attending the World Evangelical Alliance and the World Temperance Convention. It was the avowed purpose of a group of these ministers, under the leadership of the Reverend Cox, to procure a blanket endorsement for the Christian character of slaveholders. The matter was becoming a little ticklish in certain quarters, and these churchmen were determined to establish the Biblical and divine status of the "sons of Ham" whom—they agreed—God had designated "hewers of wood and drawers of water."

What was their dismay, therefore, to find one of the slaves running around at large in England, speaking from platforms, and being invited to the homes of respectable, but utterly misguided, Englishmen *and* Englishwomen—*God save us!*

The divines set about enlightening the English people. Before they realized it, the question of slavery became a burning issue in the Evangelical Alliance. And things did not go well. By far the larger crowds were attracted to the Temperance Convention, which was being held in huge Covent Garden. The Abolitionists planned carefully. One afternoon when the Garden was packed, Frederick Douglass was called from the audience to "address a few words" to the Convention. The slavers' advocates were thunderstruck! They could not believe that such treachery existed within their own ranks. As, amid clamorous applause, Douglass made his way to the platform, Reverend Cox leaped to his feet and shouted his protests. But he was yelled down.

"Let him speak!"

"Hear him!"

"Douglass! Frederick Douglass!"

They shouted until the livid little divine sank helpless into his seat.

Frederick Douglass, "the young lion," had come into his full strength. He stood facing the audience which filled every corner of Covent Garden, and felt power coursing all along his veins. He resolved that no man or woman within the sound of his voice that afternoon should ever be able to say "I did not know!"

According to the account written by the Reverend Cox that appeared in his denominational paper, the *New York Evangelist,* Douglass' speech was "a perversion, an abuse, and an iniquity against the law of reciprocal righteousness—inspired, I believe, from beneath, and not from above. This Douglass," said Reverend Cox, "denounced American temperance societies and churches as a community of enemies of his people. He talked to the American delegates as if he had been our schoolmaster and we his docile and devoted pupils."

And Covent Garden rocked as it seldom had in all its history.

"We all wanted to reply," the account concluded, "but it was too late. The whole theater seemed taken with the spirit of the Ephesian uproar; they were boisterous in the extreme, and poor Mr. Kirk could hardly obtain a moment to say a few well-chosen words."

The applause was like thunder. When Douglass bowed and tried to leave the platform, people rushed forward to seize his hand. They blocked his path. Men and women wept. They shouted until they were hoarse. Nobody heard or heeded "poor Mr. Kirk." Douglass left the theater at the head of a procession of Londoners, who continued to cheer him as they came out on the street. Curious passersby swelled the ranks. They followed him down Bow Street to Russell and past the Drury Lane Theater. But just beyond the theater Frederick stopped. He faced the crowd and at a motion from him they closed in around him.

"My friends," he told them, "never in my life have people been so good to me. But I have spoken not to arouse you to cheers, but to move you to action. I have told you of slavery, of oppression, of wrongdoing which is going on in this world. I tell you now that this is true not only of black slaves in America, but of white slaves here in Europe. My friends, these are not times for cheering. Go to your homes, to your shops and to your offices! Pass my words along and find the job that you can do to bring about the freedom of all peoples. Go now, quickly!"

He stood facing them until they had dispersed, looking back over their shoulders, talking excitedly.

Then, with a sigh of deep satisfaction, Frederick Douglass went walking on down Russell Street. He turned into Drury Lane and half an hour later was rolling along Fulham Road.

Tavistock Square no longer claimed him as a lodger. When James Buffum returned to America and Douglass set out on his northern tour the attic rooms were given up. Upon his return to London he had been invited to make his home with friends in Chelsea where, in the rare periods between strenuous rounds, he could enjoy a haven from the noise and dirt of the city. He remembered that summer with pleasure—no fog, a mild sun, long walks over the Heath, across Albert Bridge and down by the river. Hours of undisturbed reading in a little arbor behind the cottage continually opened new vistas and broadened his understanding. More than the scars on his back, he deplored his lack of education. Now he seized every opportunity to learn.

Back in America the Mexican War was arousing people. The possibility of more slave states being added to the Union speeded up the Abolitionists. Word was rushed to the Anti-Slavery Society in England to enlist the people of Great Britain, to let the workers of Britain know how slavery in America threatened all their hard-bought gains, and perhaps get them to boycott slave-grown cotton.

Frederick Douglass rose to the need. Thousands packed into the Free Trade Hall in London to hear him; workers in Manchester and Birmingham learned how cotton was produced; merchants and dock hands rubbed shoulders at Concert Hall in Liverpool.

Frederick Douglass spoke to men and women in every walk of life. William Gladstone listened and learned from the black American. In Edinburgh he was entertained by George Combe, and the eminent philosopher listened as well as talked. Together they discussed the Corn Laws, reduction of hours of labor, and what black slavery was doing to the world. During this time Douglass was urged to remain in Europe. He was offered important posts in Ireland and in Scotland.

"Send for your family, Douglass!" they said. "There is work here for you to do."

But he shook his head. In spite of all his activities, he was growing restless that winter. True, he was presenting the case of the slave to Britain. In a few months he had become famous; but within himself he felt that all this had only been a period of preparation. He was like an athlete who, trained to the pink of condition, was only going through preliminary skirmishes. For Frederick Douglass knew his real work lay ahead—in America.

They were still waiting for the final settlement with Captain Auld. He had asked one hundred and fifty pounds sterling for his slave. The money had been promptly sent.

Then, one morning, a letter reached Douglass in Darlington. It was from George Thompson.

"Your papers have arrived. Come down with us for two or three days before you go to Wales. There is so much to talk about and I know this means an early farewell."

This was the beginning of his last days in Britain. He was invited to dinners, receptions, teas, scheduled for "farewell" speeches.

"What will you do?" they asked.

"I should like to establish a paper, a paper in which I can speak directly to my people, a paper that will prove whether or not a Negro has mind, the tongue of reason, and can present facts and arguments clearly."

They placed twenty-five hundred dollars in his hands—as a start toward this enterprise.

"You will come back!" They made it both a question and an affirmation.

"When we have won our fight!" He nodded.

A crowd accompanied him to the boat at Liverpool and stood waving him goodbye. John Bright's eyes were wet.

"We'll miss you, Douglass!" said the little spinner from Lancaster.

The shores and wharves and people blurred as he stood on the deck. They had been so good. He reached in his pocket and once more took out the precious papers that declared him free.

The transaction had to be in two parts. Thomas Auld first sold him to his brother Hugh, and then the Philadelphia lawyer had secured the final manumission paper through the Baltimore authorities. It was this second and final sheet that Frederick unfolded—the paper for which the people of England had paid seven hundred and fifty dollars.

To all whom it may concern: Be it known, that I, Hugh Auld, of the city of Baltimore, in Baltimore county, in the state of Maryland, for divers good causes and considerations, me thereunto moving, have released from slavery, liberated, manumitted, and set free, and by these presents do hereby release from slavery, liberate, manumit, and set free, My Negro Man, named Frederick Bailey, otherwise called Douglass, being of the age of twenty-eight years, or thereabouts, and able to work and gain a sufficient livelihood and maintenance; and him the said negro man, named Frederick Bailey, otherwise called Frederick Douglass, I do declare to be henceforth free, manumitted, and discharged from all manner of servitude to me, my executors, and administrators forever.

In witness whereof, I, the said Hugh Auld, have hereunto set my hand and seal, the fifth of December, in the year one thousand eight hundred and forty-six.

Signed HUGH AULD.

Sealed and delivered in presence of T. HANSON BELT.*

He looked out across the waters. He had been away nearly two years. It was spring, and he was going home.

* Douglass, *My Bondage and My Freedom,* chap. xxiv, p. 373.

CHAPTER TEN

A light is set on the road

MASSACHUSETTS hung out her fairest garlands that spring. The fruit trees were in bloom. Dandelions a foot tall framed the winding roads in gold; across the meadows lay Queen Anne's lace and white daisies; the lake shallows were covered with dark, green rushes; and alders, growing at the water's edge, stood between white and yellow water-lilies. There was sweetness in the air.

Behind the little house between two cedar trees the line of white clothes waved merrily in the breeze. Mrs. Walker from the other side of the fence, stood in the doorway and admired the scrubbed and polished kitchen.

"Land sakes, Mis' Douglass, you *are* smart this morning!"

The dark woman, her sleeves tucked up, was kneading a batch of dough. She did not stop. There was still so much to do, and her breasts were heavy with milk. She must set these loaves before she nursed the baby. But she smiled at her neighbor, her eyes shining.

"My husband's coming home!"

Mrs. Walker laughed sympathetically.

"I know, but not today. Body'd think he was walkin' in this minute."

In the next room little Rosetta filled an earthen jar with buttercups and violets she had picked down by the river. It spilled over and she began to cry.

"Never mind," comforted Lewis. He spoke with masculine superiority, reinforced by his eight years. "Pa's got no time for flowers anyhow."

But Miss Abigail always kept flowers on the table. She had taught Rosetta how to arrange them, and now the little girl wiped her eyes and returned to her task. She had only that week been brought back to the cottage in Lynn for her father's homecoming. Shortly before the baby was born the Misses Abigail and Lydia Mott had taken the child to live with them in Albany. To this extent the Quaker ladies had lightened Anna's responsibilities. They had cared for and taught Frederick Douglass' little daughter carefully. Now she was home for a visit, they said: they wanted her back.

"Don't touch!" Rosetta climbed down from the chair and eyed her centerpiece with satisfaction. She spoke to three-year-old Charlie, whose round face was also turned toward the flowers. Freddie, all of his six years intent on mending a hole in the fence, had sent his "baby brother" into the house with a terse "Get outta my way!"

Charlie's plump legs carried him hither and yon obeying orders. Now he was wondering what he could do on his own. Pa was coming —and he wanted to do something special. All at once he yelled, "I'll show him the baby!"

Two days later he clung, ecstatic with joy, to the big man's coat when for the first time the father held his new daughter in his arms. It was love at first sight. Perhaps because she was called Annie, or perhaps it was the very special way she wrapped her fist about his thumb.

Over the heads of their children, Anna and Frederick smiled at each other. The months had put lines on her face; he knew the days and nights had not been easy. He had yet to rub the rough callouses on her hands and find out about the shoes! Anna saw that her husband had grown, that he had gone far. He had walked in high places. But now he was home again. They were together.

They feasted that evening. The children tumbled over themselves being useful. They emptied their plates and then sat listening, wide-eyed. He talked and then he too asked questions.

"Say nothing about the shoes. We'll surprise him," she had cautioned.

A joke on Pa! They hugged their secret gleefully, as children will. At last the house was still and she lay down beside him.

"Everything's gone fine, hasn't it, dear?" He spoke with deep contentment. "The children are well. The house looks better than it did when I went away. How did you do it?"

Her body touched his in the old bed.

"I managed," she murmured. The shoes had made her hands rough and hard. His skin was warm and smooth.

"Have you missed me?" he asked.

Her sigh of response came from a heart at peace.

Washington read of Frederick Douglass' return in the *National Era*. Gamaliel Bailey had been printing short accounts of his activities in Great Britain. Many of the Abolitionists had protested against Douglass' purchase by English friends. They declared it a violation of antislavery principles and a wasteful expenditure of money. The *National Era* took up the issue.

"Our English friends are wise," Bailey's editorial commented. "Maryland's slave laws still stand. Frederick Douglass is now free anywhere in the United States, only because he carries manumission papers on his person. The Eastern Shore can no longer claim him."

The slaveholding power, it seemed, was stronger than ever. Texas with its millions of acres had been admitted to the Union, and President Polk was negotiating a treaty that favored the slave oligarchy. Abolitionists had split over political matters and had weakened themselves. But the sparks had fallen and were lighting fires in unexpected places. Charles Sumner, emerging from the State Legislature in Massachusetts, was moving toward the United States Senate. From Pennsylvania came David Wilmot with his amendment of the proposed treaty saying "neither slavery nor involuntary servitude shall ever exist in any part" of the territory acquired as a result of the Mexican War. Longfellow, most popular author in America, was writing thunderously on slavery; *The Biglow Papers* were circulating, and petitions, signed by tens of thousands, were gathered and delivered in Washington by Henry Wilson and John Greenleaf Whittier. Inside Congress, the aged John Quincy Adams laid the petitions before the House. The House tabled them—but the sparks continued to fly.

On an evening late in May a group of people responded to invitations sent out by the Reverend Theodore Parker and gathered at his house in Boston. He had called them together to discuss further strategy. Among those present were Bronson Alcott, Ralph Waldo Emerson, William Ellery Channing,* Walter Channing,* Wendell Phillips, James Russell Lowell, James and Lucretia Mott, Charles Sumner, Joshua Blanchard, William Lloyd Garrison and Frederick Douglass.

* Nephews of Garrison's old detractor.

These men and women had not agreed on every issue in the past, but now they united their efforts toward one single end: Slavery must be stopped. If it could not now be abolished, at least it must not spread. The *Wilmot Proviso* must be carried to the country.

And who was better equipped to carry out such a mandate than William Lloyd Garrison and their newly returned co-worker, who had been hailed throughout Great Britain? The man who bore his "diploma" on his back, Frederick Douglass. So it was decided.

Douglass' reputation no longer rested on the warm word of his personal friends. Not only had accounts of him been printed in the *Liberator,* but the *Standard* and the *Pennsylvania Freeman* had told of his speeches and reception abroad. Every antislavery paper in the country had picked up the stories. Horace Greeley had told New York about him. Nor was the opposition unaware of him. The advocates and supporters of slavery pointed to him as "a horrible example" of what "could happen."

"Douglass!" The name was whispered in cabins and in tobacco and rice fields. It traveled up and down the Eastern Shore. A tall black girl, dragging logs through the marsh, heard it and resolved to run away. She became "Sojourner Truth" of the Underground Railroad—the fearless agent who time after time returned to the Deep South to organize bands of slaves and lead them out.

In Boston and Albany and New York they clamored to see and hear Douglass. And in clubs and offices and behind stone-fronts they muttered angry words.

During the first week in August the Anti-Slavery Society held a three-day convention in Morristown, Pennsylvania, with hundreds of people coming by train from Philadelphia. Lucretia Mott, the foremost woman Abolitionist of her day, fired the crowd with enthusiasm. Douglass did not arrive until the second day. His name was on everyone's lips, the trainmen craned their necks to see him, and he was pointed out wherever he went.

The evening of the closing day of the convention, Garrison and Douglass were to speak together at a church. It was packed when they arrived. Garrison spoke first. All went well until Douglass rose, when there came a sound of breaking glass and large stones flew through the windows. The men in the audience rushed out. There was the sound of shouting and running outside. The rowdies fled, and in a short while the meeting continued.

In Philadelphia there were a large number of educated and extremely active Negro Abolitionists. Douglass was particularly happy to spend some time with them, and they were eager to heed and honor him. William Grant Still, secretary of the Philadelphia Vigilance Committee, saw to it that they met Douglass.

On Saturday morning Garrison and Douglass said goodbye to their friends and hurried to the station. At the last moment Garrison recalled an errand.

"Go ahead and get the tickets, Douglass," he said. "I'll be along in time."

Douglass complied with his request, but Garrison had not arrived when the train pulled in. Douglass boarded one of the last cars and, sitting down close to a window, watched rather anxiously for his traveling companion.

He did not notice the man who came up to the seat until he heard: "You there! Get out of that seat!"

It came like the old-remembered sting of a whip. He had not heard that tone for so long. He looked up. The speaker was a big man. He had evidently been drinking. His face was flushed.

"Get along up front where you belong!"

"I have a first-class ticket which entitles me to this seat," Douglass said quietly. The muscles along his back were tightening.

"Why, you impudent darky!"

"Oh, John, please!"

Then Douglass saw that behind the man and, until that moment hidden by him, was a little woman, the thin, gray strands of her hair partly concealed by a poke bonnet, her blue eyes now wide with alarm.

"Oh," said Douglass, rising, "excuse me, madam. Would you like my seat?"

The bully's mouth dropped open. For a moment the unexpected words struck him dumb.

"Why—why— I—" the woman stammered.

"Shut up!" The man had recovered his breath. "Don't talk to that nigger. I'll knock his teeth down his black throat if he says another word."

Frederick smiled at the woman.

"As I said, I have my ticket. But there are plenty of seats. I'll gladly vacate this one for a lady."

He moved quickly, catching his assailant's blow with a swing of his arm, and brushed past before the man could recover himself. Douglass went on down the aisle. Behind him the man cursed.

"Oh, please, John!" the little lady protested.

Out on the platform, Douglass walked into Garrison. They hurried into another car and the train moved off.

"We'll report the man when we reach the station," said Garrison.

Douglass shrugged his shoulders. "He was drunk!" was his only comment.

The train pulled into Harrisburg about three o'clock in the afternoon. At the depot they found Dr. Rutherford, long-time subscriber to the *Liberator*, his sister-in-law, Agnes Crane, and several colored people awaiting them. One of the latter, a Mr. Wolf, proudly bore off Frederick Douglass to his home, while Dr. Rutherford took Mr. Garrison in tow.

Harrisburg, capital of Pennsylvania, was very much under the influence of slavery. The little group of Abolitionists had struggled valiantly against odds. They had obtained the Court House for the Saturday and Sunday evening presentations of their two speakers. Heretofore, antislavery lecturers had drawn only a few anxious listeners. This Saturday evening the Court House was filled to overflowing, and crowds had gathered in the street in front of the building.

Mischief was brewing. Outside, mounted horsemen mingled with the crowd, and inside the hall seethed with tense expectancy.

The chairman for the evening rose and introduced Mr. Garrison first. He spoke briefly, merely to open the meeting. Everybody knew that whatever happened would be aimed at Douglass. The dark speaker came forward, and someone in the back yelled, "Sit down, nigger!"

It was the signal. Through the windows came hurtling stones, bricks and pieces of Harrisburg pottery. From the back of the hall people threw stones and rotten eggs, ripe tomatoes and other missiles. Several men armed with clubs leaped for the platform.

The hall had become a bedlam: shrieks, shattering glass, and shouts of "Out with the damned nigger!" "Kill him!" "Break his head!" Douglass, recalling the mob in Indiana, seized a chair and laid about him with a will. A flying stone struck him just above the eye, and a brickbat grazed his head; but no one could get near him. It turned into a free-for-all. Garrison from his place on the platform thundered denunciations and rallied the people to their own defense. Gradually, they routed the disturbers and peace was restored.

One might suppose that the exhausted audience would have called it quits. But not so with this crowd which had come out to hear Frederick Douglass. Scratches and wounds and broken heads were hurriedly tended; cold cloths were applied. And finally, holding a damp handkerchief to his head to stay the flow of blood, Douglass told his story. Far down the street the would-be "nigger killers" heard the cheers.

Sunday morning and afternoon they spoke at Negro churches. White people attended both times, and the meetings were unmolested. The Sunday evening crowd at the Court House was doubled. There was no trouble.

"Always heared tell them nigger-loving Abolitionists was chicken-hearted!" a man in a tavern complained morosely. "It's a damn lie!" He rubbed his aching head thoughtfully.

Monday morning they left for Pittsburgh, going by train as far as Chambersburg, where they had to change to the stage. Here they were told that there had been some mistake about the tickets. The one Douglass held enabled him to go directly through on the two o'clock stage, but Garrison would have to wait until eight in the evening. Garrison told Douglas they would be expected and he might as well go ahead.

The route over the Alleghenies was beautiful, but slow and difficult. The stage was crowded, and it was a melting-hot day. When they drew up at the taverns for meals, Douglass was not allowed to eat in the dining room. He was told he might eat, if he stood outside. He preferred to go hungry—for the better part of two days.

On arriving at Pittsburgh the stage was met by a committee of twenty white and colored friends, with a brass band of colored men playing for all they were worth! The stage was late. It pulled in at three o'clock in the morning, but both committee and band had waited.

Douglass could not help relishing the consternation of his fellow-travelers when, to the accompaniment of deafening blasts from tuba and trumpet, he was literally lifted from the stage. How could they have known that the quiet, dark man whom they had seen humiliated and pushed aside, was a celebrity?

There was much about the dingy, smoke-covered city of Pittsburgh which reminded Douglass and Garrison of manufacturing towns in England. These people were down to bare necessities. They knew life and death could be hard and violent. They wanted no part of slavery.

"No more slave states!" they shouted.

Their enthusiasm was in the English style. They expressed approval without stint. At the close of the final meeting, they gave three tremendous cheers—one for Garrison, one for Douglass, and one for the local worker who had brought the speakers, A. K. Foster.

On Friday Garrison and Douglass took a steamer down the Ohio River. They stopped off at New Brighton, a village of about eight hundred people. They spoke in a barn, where, from barrels of flour piled on the beams over their heads, specks sifted down, whitening their clothes. They left aboard a canal boat, in the company of a young Negro named Peck, a future graduate of Rush Medical College at Chicago.

The next stop was Youngstown, where they were the guests of a jovial tavern keeper. He always took in Abolitionist lecturers free of charge. There they spoke three times in a huge grove. By evening Douglass was without voice. His throat was throbbing and he could not speak above a whisper. Garrison carried on. New Lyme, Painesville, Munson, Twinsburg—every town and hamlet on the way—in churches, halls, barns, tents, in groves and on hillsides. Oberlin, which come next, was a milestone for them both.

"You know that from the commencement of the Institution in Oberlin," Garrison wrote his wife, "I took a lively interest in its welfare, particularly on account of its springing up in a wilderness, only thirteen years since, through the indomitable and sublime spirit of freedom by which the seceding students of Lane Seminary were actuated. . . .

"Oberlin has done much for the relief of the flying fugitives from the Southern prison-house, multitudes of whom have found it a refuge from their pursuers, and been fed, clad, sheltered, comforted, and kindly assisted on their way out of this horrible land to Canada. It has also promoted the cause of emancipation in various ways, and its church refuses to be connected with any slaveholding or pro-slavery church by religious fellowship. . . .

"I think our visit was an important one. . . . Douglass and I have been hospitably entertained by Hamilton Hill, the Treasurer of the Institution, an English gentleman, who formerly resided in London, and is well acquainted with George Thompson and other antislavery friends. . . . Among others who called was Miss Lucy Stone, who has just graduated, and who yesterday left for her home in Brookfield, Massachusetts. . . . She is a very superior young woman, and has a soul as free as air, and is preparing to go forth as

a lecturer, particularly in vindication of the rights of woman. . . .
But I must throw down my pen, as the carriage is at the door to take
us to Richfield, where we are to have a large meeting today under the
Oberlin tent, which is capable of holding four thousand persons." *

It was Garrison who finally broke down.

Their first meeting in Cleveland was held in Advent Chapel.
Hundreds were turned away, and in the afternoon they moved out
into a grove in order to accommodate the crowd. It sprinkled occasionally during the meeting, but no one seemed to mind. The next
morning, however, Garrison opened his eyes in pain. He closed them
again and tried to move. He sat up, dizzy and swaying. Douglass,
seeing his face, rushed to his side.

The doctor ordered him to stay in bed for a few days. They were
scheduled to leave for Buffalo within the hour, and once more Garrison urged Douglass to go on ahead.

"I'll be along," he said weakly.

Garrison did not join him at Buffalo. Douglass held the meetings
alone and it was the same at Waterloo and West Winfield. By the
time he reached Syracuse on September 24, Douglass had begun to
worry. There, however, he found word. Garrison had been very ill.
He was now recovering and would soon be in Buffalo. Somewhat
relieved, Douglass went on to Rochester, where he held large and
enthusiastic meetings.

For a few days he visited with Gerrit Smith on his estate at
Peterboro. Only then did he realize how tired he was. The high-
ceilinged, paneled rooms of the fine old manor offered the perfect
refuge from the rush and noise and turmoil of the past weeks.
Douglass stretched out in an easy chair before an open fire and rested.

Something was bothering Douglass. Now that the cheering
crowds were far away he frowned. Gerrit Smith fingered a long-
stemmed glass of sherry and waited.

"They listened eagerly," Douglass said at last, "they filled the
halls and afterward they cheered." He stopped and Gerit Smith
nodded his head.

"And what then?" Smith's voice had asked the question in
Douglass' mind.

Douglass was silent a long moment. He spoke slowly.

"They did not need convincing. The people know that slavery is

* Letter dated August 28, 1847. Garrison, *William Lloyd Garrison*, Vol. III,
chap. vii, p. 202.

wrong." Again Smith nodded his head. Douglass frowned. "Is it that convictions are not enough?"

Then Gerrit Smith leaned forward.

"Convictions are the final end we seek," he said. "But even you dare not pit your convictions against the slaveholder's property. Slave holders are not concerned or bothered about cheering crowds north of the Ohio river. They can laugh at them! But they will not laugh long if the cheering crowds go marching to the ballot box. Convictions need votes to back them up!"

The shadows in the room deepened. For a long time there was only silence.

"There's a man in Springfield you ought to know," Gerrit Smith spoke quietly. "His name is John Brown."

And so Douglass first heard of John Brown, in whose plans he would be involved for many years to come.

Upon the establishment of Oberlin College in 1839, Gerrit Smith had given the school a large tract of land in Virginia. The small group in Ohio hardly knew what to do with his gift until, in 1840, young John Brown, son of one of the Oberlin trustees, wrote proposing to survey the lands for a nominal price if he could buy some of it himself and establish his family there.

"He said," continued Smith, "that he planned to set up there a school for both the Negroes and poor whites of the region."

Titles to the Virginia lands were not clear because squatters were in possession, and the Oberlin trustees welcomed Brown's plan. Thus John Brown first saw Virginia and looked over the rich and heavy lands which rolls westward to the misty Blue Ridge. The Oberlin lands lay about two hundred miles west of Harpers Ferry in the foothills and along the valley of the Ohio.

"He wrote that he liked the country as well as he had expected and its inhabitants even better," Smith chuckled.

By the summer of 1840 the job was done, and Brown had picked out his ground. It was good hill land on the right branch of a valuable spring, with a growth of good timber and a sugar orchard. In August the Oberlin trustees voted "that the Prudential Committee be authorized to perfect negotiations and convey by deed to Brother John Brown of Hudson, one thousand acres of our Virginia land on the conditions suggested in the correspondence which has already transpired between him and the Committee." *

* Du Bois, *John Brown*, chap. iv, p. 55. (Origin: *Records of the Board of Trustees*, Oberlin College, Aug. 28, 1840.)

"But then"—Gerrit Smith's voice took on new urgency—"all negotiations stopped. The panic overthrew everybody's calculations. Brown's wool business collapsed, and two years later he was bankrupt. He had endorsed notes for a friend, and they sent him to jail. Then he entered into partnership with a man named Perkins, with a view to carrying on the sheep business extensively. Perkins was to furnish all the feed and shelter for wintering, and Brown was to take care of the flock." Smith was silent for a few minutes, puffing on his pipe. "I think he loved being a shepherd. Anyway, during those long, solitary days and nights he developed a plan for furnishing cheap wool direct to consumers.

"He has a large store now in Springfield, Massachusetts. They say his bales are firm, round, hard and true, almost as if they had been turned out in a lathe. But the New England manufacturers are boycotting him. He's not playing according to the rules and he's being squeezed out. The truth of the matter is that John Brown has his own set of rules. He says he has a mission to perform." There was another long silence. Then Gerrit Smith spoke and his voice was sad. "I wish I had it in my power to give him that tract of land protected by the Blue Ridge Mountains. I think that land lies at the core of all his planning."

Gerrit Smith was right. John Brown had a plan. One thing alone reconciled him to his Springfield sojourn and that was the Negroes whom he met there. He had met black men singly here and there before. He was consumed with an intense hatred of slavery, and in Springfield he found a group of Negroes working manfully for full freedom. It was a small body without conspicuous leadership. On that account it more nearly approximated the great mass of their enslaved race. Brown sought them in home, in church and on the street; he hired them in his business. While Garrison and Douglass were touring Ohio, John Brown was saying to his black porter and friend, "Come early in the morning so that we'll have time to talk."

And so before the store was swept or the windows wiped, they carefully reviewed their plans for the "Subterranean Pass Way."

Amelia and Mrs. Royall did not make the trip north. Amelia's disappointment was tempered because she knew Frederick Douglass was somewhere out West. Jack Haley laughed and said that was the reason the old lady did not go. But Anne Royall said no newspaper woman could leave Washington when news was fairly bristling in the air.

That last was true. Had not the South fought and paid for the gold fields of California? Now the scratch of President Polk's pen as he signed the treaty with Mexico reverberated through the halls of Congress. Tempers were short.

"And manners have been tossed out the window," said Anne Royall.

Then Jefferson Davis was sent up from Mississippi. Mrs. Royall was immediately intrigued by the tall, handsome war hero.

"Careful, Mrs. Royall!" warned Jack Haley, shaking his finger.

"Attend your own affairs, young man," snapped the old lady. "Jefferson Davis brings charm into this nest of cawing crows!"

Foreign consulates were rocking, too. Ambassadors dared not talk. For this was a year of change—kings being overthrown; Garibaldi, Mazzini, Kossuth emerging as heroes. Freedom had become an explosive word—to be handled with care. They smashed the windows of the *National Era* office and talked of running Gamaliel Bailey out of town. But it was difficult to call out a mob within sight of the Capitol building. And Gamaliel Bailey—facing his critics with that dazzling, supercilious, knowing smile of his—sent them away gnashing their teeth but helpless.

The time had come for action. Oratory was not enough. Convictions, however sound and pure, were not enough. Time was running out.

Frederick Douglass wrote a letter to John Brown in Springfield, Massachusetts. Douglass told the wool merchant of his recent visit with Gerrit Smith.

"I'd like to talk with you," he wrote. And John Brown answered, "Come."

Of that first visit with John Brown, Douglass says:

"At the time to which I now refer this man was a respectable merchant in a populous and thriving city, and our first meeting was at his store. This was a substantial brick building on a prominent, busy street. A glance at the interior, as well as at the massive walls without, gave me the impression that the owner must be a man of considerable wealth. My welcome was all that I could have asked. Every member of the family, young and old, seemed glad to see me, and I was made much at home in a very little while. I was, however, surprised with the appearance of the house and its location. After seeing the fine store I was prepared to see a fine residence in an eligible locality. . . . In fact, the house was neither commodious nor elegant, nor its situation desirable. It was a small wooden building on a back street, in a neighborhood chiefly occupied by laboring men and mechanics. Respectable enough, to be sure, but not quite the place where one would look for the residence of a flourishing and successful merchant. Plain as was the outside of this man's house, the inside was plainer. Its furniture would have satisfied a Spartan. It would take longer to tell what was not in this house than what was in it. There was an air of plainness about it which almost suggested destitution.

"My first meal passed under the misnomer of tea. . . . It consisted of beef-soup, cabbage, and potatoes—a meal such as a man might relish after following the plow all day or performing a forced march of a dozen miles over a rough road in frosty weather. Innocent of paint, veneering, varnish, or table-cloth, the table announced itself unmistakably of pine and of the plainest workmanship. There was no hired help visible. The mother, daughters, and sons did the serving, and did it well. They were evidently used to it, and had no thought of any impropriety or degradation in being their own servants. It is said that a house in some measure reflects the character of its occupants; this one certainly did. In it there were no disguises, no illusions, no make-believes. Everything implied stern truth, solid purpose, and rigid economy. I was not long in company with the master of this house before I discovered that he was indeed the master of it, and was likely to become mine too if I stayed long enough with him. . . .

"In person he was lean, strong and sinewy, of the best New England mold, built for times of trouble and fitted to grapple with the flintiest hardships. Clad in plain American woolen, shod in boots of cowhide leather, and wearing a cravat of the same substantial material, under six feet high, less than one hundred and fifty pounds in weight, aged about fifty, he presented a figure straight and symmetrical as a mountain pine. His bearing was singularly impressive. His head was not large, but compact and high. His hair was coarse, strong, slightly gray and closely trimmed, and grew low on his forehead. His face was smoothly shaved, and revealed a strong, square mouth, supported by a broad and prominent chin. His eyes were bluish-gray, and in conversation they were full of light and fire. When on the street, he moved with a long, springing, race-horse step, absorbed by his own reflections, neither seeking nor shunning observation.

"After the strong meal already described, Captain Brown cautiously approached the subject which he wished to bring to my attention; for he seemed to apprehend opposition to his views. He denounced slavery in look and language fierce and bitter, thought that slaveholders had forfeited their right to live, that the slaves had the right to gain their liberty in any way they could, did not believe that moral suasion would ever liberate the slave, or that political action would abolish the system.

"He said that he had long had a plan which could accomplish this end, and he had invited me to his house to lay that plan before me. He had observed my course at home and abroad and he wanted my co-operation. His plan as it then lay in his mind had much to commend it. It did not, as some suppose, contemplate a general rising among the slaves, and a general slaughter of the slave-masters. An insurrection, he thought, would only defeat the object; but his plan did contemplate the creating of an armed force which should act in the very heart of the South. He was not averse to the shedding of blood, and thought the practice of carrying arms would be a good one for the colored people to adopt, as it would give them a sense of manhood. No people, he said, could have self-respect, or be respected, who would not fight for their freedom. He called my attention to a map of the United States, and pointed out to me the far-reaching Alleghenies, which stretch away from the borders of New York into the Southern states. 'These mountains,' he said, 'are the basis of my plan. God has given the strength of the hills to freedom; they were placed there for the emancipation of the Negro race; they are full of natural forts, where one man for defense will be equal to a hundred for attack; they are full also of good hiding-places, where large numbers of brave men could be concealed, and baffle and elude pursuit for a long time. I know these mountains well, and could take a body of men into them and keep them there desepite of all the efforts of Virginia to dislodge them. The true object to be sought is first of all to destroy the money value of slave property; and that can only be done by rendering such property insecure. My plan, then, is to take at first about twenty-five picked men, and begin on a small scale; supply them with arms and ammunition and post them in squads of five on a line of twenty-five miles. The most persuasive and judicious of these shall go down to the fields from time to time, as opportunity offers, and induce the slaves to join them, seeking and selecting the most restless and daring.'

"When I asked him how he would support these men, he said

emphatically that he would subsist them upon the enemy. Slavery was a state of war, and the slave had a right to anything necessary to his freedom. . . . 'But you might be surrounded and cut off from your provisions or means of subsistence.' He thought this could not be done so they could not cut their way out; but even if the worst came he could but be killed, and he had no better use for his life than to lay it down in the cause of the slave. When I suggested that we might convert the slaveholders, he became much excited, and said that could never be. He knew their proud hearts, and they would never be induced to give up their slaves, until they felt a big stick about their heads.

"He observed that I might have noticed the simple manner in which he lived, adding that he had adopted this method in order to save money to carry out his purpose. This was said in no boastful tone, for he felt that he had delayed already too long, and had no room to boast either his zeal or his self-denial. Had some men made such display of rigid virtue, I should have rejected it as affected, false and hypocritical; but in John Brown, I felt it to be real as iron or granite. From this night spent with John Brown in Springfield in 1847, while I continued to write and speak against slavery, I became all the same less hopeful of its peaceful abolition." *

Soon after this visit with John Brown, Frederick Douglass decided on a definite step. He would move to Rochester, New York, and there he would set up his contemplated newspaper.

He had been dissuaded from starting a newspaper by two things. First, as soon as he returned from England he had been called upon to exercise to the fullest extent all his abilities as a speaker. Friends told him that in this field he could render the best and most needed service. They had discouraged the idea of his becoming an editor. Such an undertaking took training and experience. Douglass, always quick to acknowledge his own deficiencies, began to think his project far too ambitious.

Second, William Lloyd Garrison needed whatever newspaper gifts Douglass had for the *Liberator*. Garrison felt that a second anti-slavery paper in the same region was not needed. He pointed out that the way of the *Liberator* was hard enough as it was. He did not think of Douglass as a rival. But, quite frankly, he wanted the younger man to remain under his wing. There was nothing more selfish here than what a father might feel for his own son.

* Douglass, *Life and Times of Frederick Douglass*, chap. vii, pp. 337–39.

But Douglass was no longer a fledgling. The time had come for him to strike out for himself.

Rochester was a young, new city. It was ideally located in the Genesee valley, where the Genesee River flowed into Lake Ontario; it was a terminus of the Erie Canal. Here was an ideal set-up for getting slaves safely across into Canada! Day and night action—more action—was what Douglass wanted now. There was already an intelligent and highly respected group of Abolitionists in Rochester. It was composed of both Negroes and whites. They would, he knew, gather round him. He would not be working alone. In western New York his paper would in no way interfere with the circulation of the *Liberator*.

And so on December 3, 1847, appeared in Rochester, New York, a new paper—the *North Star*. Its editor was Frederick Douglass, its assistant editor Martin R. Delaney, and its object "to attack slavery in all its forms and aspects; advance Universal Emancipation; exact the standard of public morality, promote the moral and intellectual improvement of the colored people; and to hasten the day of freedom to our three million enslaved fellow-countrymen."

"Politics is an evil thing—it is not for us. We address ourselves to men's conscience!" Garrison had often said. But Frederick Douglass went into politics.

The Free Soil party, formed in 1848, did not become a positive political force under that name. But, assembling in August as the election of 1852 drew near, it borrowed the name of "Free Democracy" from the Cleveland Convention of May 2, 1849, and drew to itself both Free Soilers and the remnants of the independent Liberty party. Frederick Douglass, on motion of Lewis Tappan, was made one of the secretaries. The platform declared for "no more slave states, no slave territory, no nationalized slavery, and no national legislation for the extradition of slaves."

The most aggressive speech of the convention was made by Frederick Douglass, who was for exterminating slavery everywhere. The lion had held himself in rein for some time. The duties of editor and printer of his paper had chained him to his desk. He had built onto his house to make room for the fugitive slaves who now came in a steady stream to Rochester, directed to "Douglass," agent of the Underground Railroad, who handled the difficult and dangerous job of getting the runaway slaves into Canada.

Douglass was still a young man, yet that night as he stood with the long, heavy bush of crinkly hair flowing back from his head like a mane—thick, full beard and flashing eyes—there was about him a timeless quality, embracing a long sweep of years, decades of suffering and much accumulated wisdom.

"Americans! Your republican politics, not less than your republican religion, are flagrantly inconsistent. You boast of your love of liberty, your superior civilization, and your pure Christianity, while the whole political power of the nation (as embodied in the two great political parties) is solemnly pledged to support and perpetuate the enslavement of three million of your countrymen. You hurl your anathemas at the crowned headed tyrants of Russia and Austria and pride yourselves on your democratic institutions, while you yourselves consent to be the mere tools and bodyguards of the tyrants of Virginia and Carolina. You invite to your shores fugitives of oppression from abroad . . . and pour out your money to them like water; but the fugitives from your own land you advertise, hunt, arrest, shoot and kill. . . . You shed tears over fallen Hungary, and make the sad story of her wrongs the theme of your poets, statesmen and orators. . . . Your gallant sons are ready to fly to arms to vindicate her cause against the oppressor; but, in regard to the ten thousand wrongs of the American slave, you would enforce the strictest silence. . . . You are all on fire at the mention of liberty for France or for Ireland; but are as cold as an iceberg at the thought of liberty for the enslaved of America!"

The people went out along the streets of Pittsburgh repeating his words. The convention delegates scattered to their states.

And out in Illinois a homely state legislator named Abraham Lincoln was saying that it is "the sacred right of the people . . . to rise up and shake off the existing government, and form a new one that suits them better. . . . It is the quality of revolutions not to go by old lines or old laws, but to break up both and make new ones."

Part III

THE STORM

When the measure of their tears shall be full—when their groans shall have involved heaven itself in darkness—doubtless a God of justice will awaken to their distress, and by his exterminating thunder manifest his attention to the things of this world, and that they are not left to the guidance of a blind fatality.

—Thomas Jefferson

The storm came up in the West and birds flew North

THERE NEVER HAD been such a time for cotton. All over the South the cotton foamed in great white flakes under the sun. Black workers staggered beneath its weight. Up and down the roads straining mules pulled wagons loaded with bubbling masses of whiteness. The gins spat flames and smoke; the presses creaked and groaned, as closer and closer they packed the quivering mass until, dead and still, it lay in hard, square bundles on river wharves, beside steel rails and on rotting piers. Shiploads were on their way to the hungry looms of England and the crawling harbors of China. Prosperity lay like a fragrant mist upon the Southland in 1854.

William Freeland rode over his acres with satisfaction. True, they had diminished in number; but if cotton prices continued to rise, the master of Freelands could see years of ease stretching ahead. Since his mother's death Freeland had left the running of the plantation pretty much to hired overseers. He had not interfered. He spent a lot of time in Baltimore, Washington and Richmond. With his dark brooding face and wavy, gray-streaked hair, the master of Freelands enjoyed much popularity with the ladies. He remained a bachelor.

It was Sunday morning, and the slight chill in the air was stimulating. Dead leaves rustled beneath his horse's hoofs as he pulled up just inside the wrought-iron gates, where the graveled drive was guarded by the old sycamore. Time was beginning to tell on the big house far up the drive, but it still stood firm and substantial, though the Old Missus no longer tapped her cane through its halls. William Freeland sighed. He wished his mother had lived to see the last two good years at Freelands. For things falling to piece had made her unhappy. "A strong hand was lacking," she said. The Mistress had grieved when old Caleb died and Aunt Lou, crippled with rheumatism and wheezing with asthma had to be sent away to a cabin at the edge of the fields. Henry had taken Caleb's place, of course. But in this, she had acknowledged, her son had been right: Henry was stupid and incompetent. It was evident he would never master the job of being a good butler. On the other hand she used to remind William of the "bad-blood rascal" he had brought in to plant wicked seeds of rebellion at Freelands. Grumbling and sullen faces multiplied. In the old days, she had said, Freeland slaves never tried to run away.

The overseers came, had tightened up on things. The last runaway had been a young filly with her baby. The dogs had caught her down by the river and torn her to pieces. Freeland had gone away for a while afterward.

He went on up the drive slowly, chuckling when he spied the queer figure bent double under the hedge, scooping at the dirt with his bare hands. The inevitable butterfly net and mesh bag lay close by on the ground, though everybody knew that fall was no time to chase butterflies. William Freeland shook his head. What some men did to get famous! For that funny little figure under his hedge was Dr. Alexander Ross, entomologist, ornithologist, and ichthyologist, whose discoveries of rare specimen of bugs were spread out on beautifully colored plates in expensive books! He had met the scientist at the home of Colonel Drake in Richmond. The daughter of the house, who had been sent North to school, had simply babbled about him. She had displayed an autographed copy of one of those books, as if it were worth its weight in gold. When the funny little man had murmured he might be able to find a *Croton Alabameses* on the Eastern Shore of Maryland, the master of Freelands had invited him to his plantation where, he had said with a laugh, there were sure to be some very rare bugs indeed. Later Freeland learned that a *Croton Alabameses* was not a bug, but a plant. It was the first evening when they were sitting on the veranda, and Dr. Ross had remarked on the charm of the old garden with its sweeping mosses, overgrown walks and thick hedges.

"It is lovely!" The little man had screwed up his eyes behind his thick glasses and blinked with delight.

After that he had been up before dawn and out all day, net and bag in hand. He tramped great distances through woods and river mud. He talked with the slaves, who, his host was certain, thought the little man was crazy. Freeland thought it well to warn him about lonely, unused lanes and river lowlands.

"Time was," he added, "when I'd never think of cautioning a visitor at Freelands. Crime used to be unknown in these parts. But now there are many bad blacks about. It's dangerous!" The little man was not listening. He was measuring the wing spread of a moth. Freeland became more insistent.

"Just a few weeks ago," he said, "a poor farmer named Covey was found in his own back yard with his head crushed in. Most of the slaves were caught before they got away, but the authorities are still looking for his housekeeper, whom they really suspect of the crime. It's horrible!"

The scientist was frowning, a puzzled expression on his round face.

"But why— Why should they think his housekeeper did this awful thing?"

William Freeland shrugged his shoulders. "It seems a dealer in the village told how this woman carried on like mad when Covey sold some girl off the place. I don't know the details. But the man says he heard the woman say she'd kill her master."

"Tck! Tck!" The little man shook his head.

"So you see, Doctor," continued his host, judiciously, "that woman is at large and *you'd* never be able to cope with her."

"Why, is she in the neighborhood?" Now Dr. Ross seemed interested.

"It would be very hard for her to get through the cordon they've laid around that neck of land. In your long tramps you might easily wander into the section without knowing it. So I wouldn't get too far off the place if I were you."

The little man nodded his head. Next evening, however, he did not return to the house until long after dark. He was bespattered with mud. He said he had stumbled and lost his specimens for the day. The mesh bag hung limp at his side.

But no harm had befallen him. There he was, looking like one of his own bugs, under the hedge. William Freeland swung off his horse and went into the house.

"Tell the Doctor breakfast is ready," he said to Henry, who came forward.

"Dat dirty old man!" grumbled Henry, as he shuffled away on his errand. The master had to laugh.

No yellow canary sang in the alcove, but breakfast hour in the high-ceiled, paneled room passed very pleasantly. In the rare intervals when Dr. Ross was not squinting through his microscope or chasing through the woods, he was an interesting talker. This morning he compared the plant and insect life of this section of the Eastern Shore to a little strip of land in southern France on the Mediterranean.

"Nature has scattered her bounties lavishly here in the South," he said. And because it was a happy subject William Freeland began to tell the scientist about cotton.

"The new state of Texas added thousands of acres. They're starting to raise cotton in California, and now," his voice showed excitement, "they find cotton can be raised in the Nebraska Territory."

"A marvelous plant!" Dr. Ross was really interested.

A shadow crossed Freeland's face.

"There is just one drawback. There aren't enough slaves to raise cotton on all this land. The Yankees fear our cotton. They know that, if they let us alone, cotton will become the deciding factor throughout the country. Because they have no cotton lands, they try to throttle us. They tie our hands by trying to limit slavery. They know that cotton and slavery expand together."

"But if slavery becomes illegal—as it did in Great Britain—in the West Indies?" The little man leaned forward. William smiled indulgently. He took a long draw on his pipe before answering.

"The United States is only a federation of states—nothing more. Where slavery was not needed it was abolished. But we need slaves here in the South, now more than ever. So"—and he waved his pipe —"we'll keep them!"

"I'm reversing my schedule today," Dr. Ross said as they rose from the table. "This afternoon I shall take a nap, because tonight I'm going out after *Lepidoptera*. I saw signs of him down by the creek yesterday, but they only fly after dark. I may be out all night."

His host frowned.

"I'd better send one of the boys with you." The little man shook his head.

"No need at all, sir. I doubt if I go off your grounds. I'll trap one down in the bottoms below the meadow."

William Freeland thought about the doctor that night when he went to bed—out chasing moths in the dark. Freeland took another sip of brandy before he put out his light.

Nine young men met Alexander Ross that night in the woods. To all of them, through devious channels, had come the word that "riders" on the Underground Railroad could be accommodated.

Dr. Ross sorted them into three groups and gave each one a set of directions. At such and such a place in the woods, the first trio would find a man waiting. Half a mile up the river bank, the second contingent were to look for an empty skiff tied to a willow: it wasn't empty. The others had a wagon waiting for them on a nearby back road.

They had come supplied with as much food as they could conveniently carry. Ross handed each slave a few dollars, a pocket compass, a knife and pistol.

Then they scattered. Ross went a few miles with the group heading inland through the woods and then doubled back toward Freelands. He even caught a rare moth, which he carefully placed in his mesh bag.

A few days later the quiet little scientist shook hands with his host and took his departure.

Such was Alexander Ross before he was knighted by several kings for his scientific discoveries and honored by the French Academy. Wherever he went in Virginia, Maryland, South Carolina, Georgia, Alabama or Mississippi, he talked of birds and plants. Equipped with shotgun and preservatives, he roamed nonchalantly into field and wood. The slave disappearances were never related to him.

Along the Underground Railroad they called him "the Birdman." Through him, Jeb, the boy Frederick had left behind in Baltimore, got away to freedom. And there were others along the Eastern Shore to whom Frederick had said, "I'll not be forgetting!" Douglass sent Alexander Ross back along the way he had come and made good his promises.

Cotton and slavery—by 1854 the two words became synonymous. The Cotton Empire was straining its borders. More land was needed for the "silver fleece," and slaves must break the land and plant the seed and pick the delicate soft pods. There was no other way.

Then a shrewd bidder for the presidency made an offer to the South—western territory for their votes—and they sprang at the bribe. Passage of the Nebraska Bill stacked the ammunition for civil war dangerously high.

This scrapping of the Missouri Compromise struck antislavery men all in a heap. The line against slavery had been so clear—no slaves above the line. It should have run to the Pacific, stretching west with the course of empire. But now, by means of the clever wording of the Nebraska (Territory) Bill—"to leave the people . . . free to form and regulate their domestic institutions in their own way" —a vast tract embracing upward of four hundred thousand square miles was being thrown open to slavery. Stephen Douglas drove the Bill through Congress. It was his moment of triumph.

The North reacted. Harriet Beecher Stowe led eleven hundred women marching through the streets in protest. Great mass meetings assembled. They hanged Stephen Douglas in effigy. State legislatures met in special sessions and sent manifests to Congress. William Lloyd Garrison, Frederick Douglass, Wendell Phillips, Henry Highland Garnet, and Henry Ward Beecher raised their voices like mighty trumpets; they filled the air with oratory.

The five sons of John Brown set out for Kansas.

They were among the less important people who saw that if "the domestic institutions" were to be left to those who lived there to decide, it was going to be necessary for antislavery men to settle on the land. The brothers' combined property consisted of eleven head of cattle and three horses. Ten of this number were fine breeds. Thinking of their value in a new country, Owen, Frederick and Salmon took them by way of the Lakes to Chicago and thence to Meridosia where they were wintered. When spring came, they drove them into Kansas to a place about eight miles west of the town of Osawatomie, which the brothers had selected as a likely spot to settle.

Seven hundred and fifty men set out that summer under the auspices of the Massachusetts Emigrant Aid Society. Some traveled by wagon over lonely trails. Others sailed down the Ohio River, their farm implements lashed to the decks of the boats.

They found a lovely land—wide open spaces, rolling prairies and wooded streams under a great blue dome. They set up their tents and went about breaking soil. They dreamed of cattle herds, waving fields of corn and wheat, orchards and vineyards. There was so much of the good, rich earth in Kansas.

Election Day—when members for the first territorial legislature were chosen—came on March 30, 1855. Horace Greeley himself went out to Kansas to cover the election for his paper, the *New York Tribune.*

Slaveholders poured into the territory from Missouri by the thousands and took over the polls.

"On the evening before and the day of the election," Greeley wrote, "nearly a thousand Missourians arrived in Lawrence in wagons and on horseback, well armed with rifles, pistols and bowie-knives." According to his account, they made no pretense of legality, one contingent bringing up two pieces of cannon loaded with musket balls. It was the same everywhere in the territory: the invaders elected all the members of the legislature, with a single exception in either house. These were two Free Soilers from a remote district which the Missourians overlooked. "Although only 831 legal electors in the territory voted, there were no less than 6,320 votes polled."

The people of Kansas repudiated this election and refused to obey the laws passed. Ruffians were called in "to aid in enforcing laws." Then it was that the sons of John Brown wrote their father asking him to procure and send them arms and ammunition to defend themselves and their neighbors.

John Brown had given up his store in Springfield, Massachusetts, and moved to a small farm in the hills of North Elba, New York. Just before the trek West, he had written his son John: "If you or any of my family are disposed to go to Kansas or Nebraska with a view to help defeat Satan and his legions in that direction, I have not a word to say; but I feel committed to operate in another part of the field." *

He had not heard from Kansas for many months, when he got the request for arms.

John Brown held his sons' letter in his hands. He went outside and stood looking up at the Adirondacks, his hacked-out frame and wrinkled, yellow face hard against the sky. Then he strode to the barn and saddled his horse.

"I'm going to Rochester," he told his wife. "I want to talk this over with Douglass."

She stood in the narrow door and watched him riding down the trail. He did not look back. John Brown never looked back.

In Rochester people had already begun pointing out Frederick Douglass' house to strangers. Until Douglass came and moved his family into the unpretentious two-story frame dwelling, Alexander Street had been one of many shady side-streets in a quiet section of the city. The dark-skinned new arrivals caused a lot of talk, but no open antagonism.

Famous folk from Boston and New York and Philadelphia began appearing on Alexander Street. Somebody said he'd recognized

* Du Bois, *John Brown*, chap. vi, p. 126.

Horace Greeley, editor of a newspaper in New York; and somebody else was sure he saw the great preacher, Wendell Phillips. The neighbors grew accustomed to seeing Mr. Daniel Anthony's huge carryall drive up of a Sunday afternoon and stop in front of the house, while all the Douglass family piled in. Mr. Anthony's big place with its rows of fruit trees was several miles out in the country. Evidently that was where they went. Then they talked about Mr. Anthony's daughter, Susan B. Anthony. She was pretty famous herself—what with going around the country and getting her name in all the papers. Some of the men shook their heads over this. But the women bit off the threads of their sewing cotton with a snap and eyed each other significantly. They reminded their men folks that the Woman's State Temperance Convention had been a pretty important affair.

"Temperance conventions is one thing," said the men, "but this talk about women voting is something else!"

Then one lady spoke up and said she'd heard their neighbor Frederick Douglass make a speech about women voting. "And it was wonderful!" she added.

"Seems like he'd have enough on his hands trying to free slaves!" grumbled one man, snapping his suspenders.

Douglass did have a lot on his hands. The *North Star* was a large sheet, published weekly, and it cost eighty dollars a week to issue. Everybody rejoiced when the circulation hit three thousand. There were many times when Douglass was hard pressed for money, and the mechanical work of getting out the paper was arduous. The entire family was drafted. Lewis and Frederick learned typesetting, and both boys delivered papers. The two little fellows soon became a familiar sight on Rochester streets, papers under their arms and schoolbooks strapped to their backs.

But the paper was only part of Douglass' work. One whole winter he lectured evenings at Corinthian Hall. Other seasons he would take an evening train to Victor, Farmington, Canandaigua, Geneva, Waterloo, Buffalo, Syracuse or elsewhere. He would speak in some hall or church, returning home the same night. In the morning Martin Delaney would find him at his desk, writing or mailing papers.

Sleep in his house was an irregular business. At any hour of the day or night Underground "passengers" arrived. They came sometimes in carriages, with Quaker capes thrown about their shoulders; or they came under loads of wheat or lumber or sacks of flour. Some of them rode in boldly on the train, and more than once a packing-box arrived, marked *Open with Care.*

Every agent of the Underground Railroad risked fine and imprisonment. They realized they were bailing out the ocean with a teaspoon, yet the joy of freeing one more slave was recompense enough. One time Douglass had eleven fugitives under his roof. And there they had to remain until Douglass could collect enough money to send them on to Canada. His wife cooked numerous pots of food which quickly vanished. "Passengers" slept in the attic and barn loft.

Many people in Rochester became involved. One evening after dark a well-dressed, middle-aged man knocked at Douglass' door and introduced himself as the law partner of the United States commissioner of that city. He would not sit down.

"I have come to tell you," he said, "that an hour ago the owner of three slaves who have escaped from Maryland was in our office. He says he has traced them to Rochester. He has papers for their arrest, and he is coming to your house!"

Douglass stared at the man in amazement. He had recognized his name as that of a distinguished Democrat, perhaps the last person in Rochester from whom he would have expected assistance. He tried to say something, but the gentleman waved him aside.

"I bid you good evening, Mr. Douglass. There is not a moment to lose!" And he disappeared down Alexander Street.

One of the fugitives was at that moment in the hayloft, the other two were on the farm of Asa Anthony, just outside the city limits. That night two black horses rode swiftly through the night. Then Asa Anthony's farm wagon rumbled down to the docks, and in the morning the three young men were on the free waves of Lake Ontario, bound for Canada.

Douglass and the *North Star* formed the pivot about which revolved much of the work of other Negro Abolitionists, whom Douglass now met for the first time. Henry Highland Garnet, well-educated grandson of an African chief, had never been closely associated with William Lloyd Garrison. From the first he had gravitated toward political action. There were Dr. James McCune Smith, who had studied medicine at Glasgow; James W. Pennington, with his degree from Heidelberg; Henry Bibb, Charles L. Redmond, and Samuel Ringgold Ward, Garnet's cousin, who attracted Douglass in a very special manner. Ward was very black and of magnificent physique.

They were all older than Douglass. But they strengthened his hand; and he, in his turn, was proud of them.

Then in 1850 the Fugitive Slave Law was passed, and no Negro, regardless of his education, ability, or means, was safe anywhere in the United States. Douglass had his manumission papers. His freedom had been bought. But Henry Highland Garnet and Samuel Ringgold Ward knew it was best that they leave the country.

Until Ward died the two men traveled in Europe, where Henry Highland Garnet came to be called the "Negro Tom Paine." Douglass felt most deeply the loss of Ringgold Ward, whom he considered vastly superior to any of them, both as an orator and a thinker.

"In depth of thought," he wrote, "fluency of speech, readiness of wit, logical exactness, and general intelligence, Samuel Ringgold Ward has left no successor among colored men amongst us."

Meanwhile Douglass squared his shoulders and took on more responsibility. He saw former slaves who had lived for years safely and securely in western New York and elsewhere—who had worked hard, saved money and acquired homes—now forced to flee to Canada. Many died during the first harsh winter. Bishop Daniel A. Payne of the African Methodist Episcopal Church consulted Douglass as to the advisability of both of them fleeing.

"We are whipped, we are whipped," moaned Payne, "and we might as well retreat in order.

Douglass shook his head. "We must stand!"

It was the spring of 1855, and never had the huge mills and factories and tanneries of Rochester been busier. Great logs of Allegheny pine rode down the Genesee River and lay in clean, shining tiers of lumber in the yards. Up and down the Erie Canal went the flatboats, mules straining at the heavy loads; and on the docks of Rochester Port the goods lay piled waiting for lake steamers to go westward. Rochester boasted that it was the most important station on the newly completed New York Central Railroad.

The vigorous young city waxed fat. Sleek, trim "city fathers" began considering the "cultural aspects" of their town. Rochester's Gallery of Fine Arts was established; plans were drawn up for an Academy of Music. "Causes" became less popular than they had been. There were those who gave an embarrassed laugh when Susan B. Anthony's name came up, and some wondered if so much antislavery agitation was good for their city.

Slaveholders, vacationing in Saratoga Springs, dropped in on Rochester. They admired its wide, clean streets and fine buildings, but they shuddered at the sight of well-dressed Negroes in the streets. The Southerners spent money freely and talked about new cotton mills; and more than one wondered aloud why Frederick Douglass was allowed to remain in such a fine city.

But the hardy, true strain of the people ran deep. When Frederick Douglass was prevented from speaking in nearby Homer by a barrage of missiles, Oren Carvath resigned as deacon of the Congregational Church, sold his farm and moved to Oberlin. His son, Erastus, made Negro education the work of his life and became the first president of Fisk University.

There was scarcely any moon the night Douglass rode his horse homeward along Ridge Road. He had spoken in Genesee on the Nebaska Bill and politics for Abolitionists.

He enjoyed these solitary rides. They cleared his brain. But tonight he kept thinking about an angry letter he had received that day—a letter in which the writer had accused Douglass of having deserted his friend Garrison "in the time of his greatest need." Douglass loved William Lloyd Garrison and the complete unselfish sincerity of the New Englander's every utterance.

"If there is a *good* man walking on this earth today, that man is Garrison!" Douglass spoke the words aloud and then he sighed.

For he knew that the *North Star* was diverging more and more from Garrison's *Liberator*. Douglass took a different stand on the Constitution of the United States.

Garrison had come to consider the Constitution as a slaveholding instrument. Now as the clashes were becoming more bitter in Boston and New York, he was raising the slogan "No Union with Slaveholders."

Douglass, with the Abolitionists in western New York, accepted the fact that the Constitution of the United States was inaugurated to "form a more perfect union, establish justice, insure domestic tranquility, provide for common defense, promote the general welfare, and secure the blessings of liberty." They therefore repudiated the idea that it could at the same time support human slavery. Douglass held the Constitution as the surest warrant for the abolition of slavery in every state in the Union. He urged the people to implement the Constitution through political action.

And so the former teacher and pupil were being pushed farther and farther apart. Douglass knew that Garrison's health was poor. He thought, *I must go to Boston, I must see him.* And then his mind reverted to the low state of his funds. He rode along sunk in dejection.

He did not heed the horses' hoofs beating the road until they came close behind him. He looked back—three riders were just topping the hill. They slowed up there and seemed to draw together. And suddenly Douglass felt that familiar stiffening of his spine. At the moment he was in the shadow of a grove; but just ahead the road lifted and he would be completely exposed. He walked his horse. Perhaps he was mistaken. They were coming forward at a slower pace and would most certainly see him any moment now. As he left the shadow of the trees he touched his horse and shot forward. He heard a shout and bent over as a bullet whizzed by!

It was to be a chase, but they were armed and he could not outrun their bullets. The road was a winding ribbon now, and he was gaining. He saw a clump of trees ahead. Yes, there was a little lane. As he turned off sharply, he felt a sear of pain across his head. He leaned forward and let his horse find its own way through the trees. Once a low hanging branch nearly swept him off, and several times the animal stumbled. Then they came out into a field, and ahead on a slight knoll was a big house. He could hear them behind him, and that open field meant more exposure; but the house was his only hope. He thought of the unfinished editorial lying on his desk.

"I've got to finish it!" he thought desperately, and gritted his teeth to keep from fainting.

Horse and rider were panting when they pulled up at the steps of the wide porch. No lights showed anywhere. Naturally, Douglass thought, everybody was sound asleep. His head felt very queer. He wanted to giggle—*What on earth am I doing pounding at this heavy door in the middle of the night?*

Gideon Pitts heard the pounding. He got up and started down in his bare feet.

"You'll catch your death of cold, Gideon!" his wife called after him. But she herself was fumbling for her wrapper. She lit the lamp and holding it in her hand followed her husband to the head of the stairs. Down below in the dark he was fumbling with the heavy bolt. It shot back at last and the great door swung in. A big man filled the doorway. He was gasping for breath. He took one step inside and said, "I'm— I'm Frederick Douglass." Then he collapsed on the floor at Gideon Pitts's bare feet.

Gideon stood staring out. Through the open door he was sure he saw a couple of horsemen down at the edge of the field. He slammed the door.

Mrs. Pitts was hurrying down, the lamp casting grotesque shadows on the wall.

"What is it, Gideon? What is it? Did he say—?"

"Hush! It's Frederick Douglass. He's been hurt. Somebody's after him!" Her husband's words were hurried and low. He was bending over the man on the floor.

"I'll call—" Mrs. Pitts began. Her husband caught her robe.

"Don't call anyone. Pray God the servants heard nothing. He's coming to!"

Mrs. Pitts was suddenly the efficient housewife.

"Some warm water," she said, setting the lamp down, "and then we'll get him upstairs." She disappeared in the shadows of the hall.

There was a patter of feet on the stairway.

"What's the matter, papa?" a child's voice asked. "Oh!"

"Go back to bed, Helen! Mr. Douglass, are you all right?" Gideon Pitts bent over his unexpected visitor anxiously. Douglass sat up and put his hand to his head. It came away sticky. He looked around him and knew he was safe.

"I'm fine, thank you!" he smiled.

"Lie quiet, Mr. Douglass. Your head is hurt. My wife's gone for warm water."

"You are very kind, sir." Douglass' head was clearing now. "I've been shot."

He heard a gasp and both men looked up. The little girl in her trailing white nightgown was leaning over the banister just above them, her blue eyes wide with excitement.

"Helen," her father spoke sharply. "I told you to go back to bed!"

"Oh, father, can't I help? The poor man is hurt!"

"Don't worry, honey," Douglass smiled up at her.

Now Mrs. Pitts was back with bowl and towels. She wiped away the blood, and Gideon Pitts declared that Douglass' head had only been grazed. Douglass told what had happened, while they bandaged and fussed over him. Then Mrs. Pitts hurried away to get the guest-room ready.

"We'll be honored if you'd stay the night!" Pitts said. There was nothing else to do. "I'll drive you in town first thing in the morning," his host assured him, helping him upstairs and into a great four-poster bed.

Everybody got up to see him off. Mrs. Pitts insisted that he have a "bite of breakfast." The hired man had rubbed down and fed his horse.

Holding the bridle reins in his hand Douglass climbed into the buggy with Mr. Pitts.

"Better that I go in with you," said his host. "Those ruffians might be lingering somewhere along the road."

It was a fresh, sweet morning in May. The Pitts orchard was in bloom. Everywhere was peace and growing things. Douglass smiled at the little girl standing on the wide porch, and Helen Pitts waved her hand.

"Goodbye, Mr. Douglass. Do come back again!"

She felt important, waving at the great Frederick Douglass.

So it happened that the next day John Brown found Douglass with a bandage fastened about his head.

"It's Captain John Brown!" called Charles, ushering the visitor in.

Anna Douglass came in from the kitchen and greeted him warmly.

"We're just sitting down to breakfast, Captain Brown. You are just in time."

Little Annie set another plate, smiling shyly at the old man. His hand smoothered her soft hair.

"We'll take a ride," he promised and Annie's eyes shone.

"They've attacked you!" John Brown exclaimed when Douglass came in with the bandage on his head.

"It was nothing, a mere scratch." Douglass shrugged away the incident. "And how are you, my good friend? Something important brings you here."

"Let him eat his breakfast first," begged the wife.

Afterward Douglass read the letter from Kansas.

"Perhaps God directs me to Kansas," said Brown earnestly. "Perhaps my path to Virginia lies through Kansas. What do you think?"

Douglass shook his head.

"I do not know." He was silent a moment, then his eyes lighted. "I'm leaving tomorrow for our convention in Syracuse. Come with me. Lay this letter from Kansas before all the Abolitionists. You'll need money. Kansas is our concern."

A few days later John Brown wrote his wife:

DEAR WIFE AND CHILDREN:

I reached here on the first day of the convention, and I have reason to bless God that I came; for I have met with a most warm reception from all, so far as I know, and—except by a few sincere, honest, peace Friends—a most hearty approval of my intention of arming my sons and other friends in Kansas. I received today donations amounting to a little over sixty dollars—twenty from Gerrit Smith, five from an old British officer; others giving smaller sums with such earnest and affectionate expression of their good wishes as did me more good than money even. John's two letters were introduced, and read with such effect by Gerrit Smith as to draw tears from numerous eyes in the great collection of people present. The convention has been one of the most interesting meetings I ever attended in my life; and I made a great addition to the number of warm-hearted and honest friends.

The die was cast: John Brown left for Kansas. Instead of sending the money and arms, says his son John, "he came on with them himself, accompanied by his brother-in-law, Henry Thompson, and my brother Oliver. In Iowa he bought a horse and covered wagon; concealing the arms in this and conspicuously displaying his surveying implements, he crossed into Missouri near Waverly, and at that place disinterred the body of his grandson, and brought all safely through to our settlement, arriving there about the 6th of October, 1855.*

* Du Bois, *John Brown*, chap. vi, p. 133.

CHAPTER TWELVE

An Avenging Angel brings the fury of the storm

"DID YOU GO out under the auspices of the Emigrant Aid Society?" they asked John Brown at the trial four years after.

"No, sir," he answered grimly, "I went out under the auspices of John Brown, directed by God."

The settlement was a romantic place. Red men gliding by in their swift canoes had seen stately birds in the reedy lowlands of eastern Kansas and called the marsh the "swamp of the swan." Here, on the good lands that rose up from the dark sluggish rivers, John Brown and his youngest son, Oliver, drove into the Brown colony.

"We found our folks in a most uncomfortable situation, with no houses to shelter one of them, no hay or corn fodder of any account secured, shivering over their little fires, all exposed to the dreadful cutting winds, morning, evening and stormy days."

On November 23, 1855, Brown wrote to his wife:

"We have got both families so sheltered that they need not suffer hereafter; have got part of the hay secured, made some progress in preparation to build a house for John and Owen; and Salmon has caught a prairie wolf in a steel trap. We continue to have a good deal of stormy weather—rains with severe winds, and forming into ice as they fall, together with cold nights that freeze the ground considerably. Still God has not forsaken us." * He did not tell her he had been down with fever.

Thus it was that John Brown came to Kansas and stood ready to fight for freedom. But no sooner had he arrived than it was plain to him that the cause for which he was fighting was far different from

* Du Bois, *John Brown*, chap. vii, p. 147.

that for which most of the settlers were willing to risk life and property. John Brown publicly protested the resolution already drawn up, excluding all Negroes—slave or free! His words were coldly received.

From Frederick Douglass came more money and a letter.

"We are directing the eyes of the country toward Kansas," Douglass wrote. "Charles Sumner in the Senate is speaking as no man ever spoke there before; Henry Ward Beecher has turned his pulpit into an auction block from which he sells slaves to freedom; Gerrit Smith and George L. Sterns have pledged their money; Lewis Tappan and Garrison have laid aside all former differences. Garrison is no longer bitter about my politics. He can see that we are accomplishing something. Free Soilers, Whigs, Liberals and antislavery Democrats are uniting. The state-wide party which we initiated some time ago has grown into a national movement. . . . We have adopted the name Republican, which was, you may recall, the original name of Thomas Jefferson's party. Our candidate is John C. Frémont. His enemies say he is a dreamer who knows nothing of politics. If the people gather round in full strength we will show them."

John Brown folded the letter. There was an unusual flush on his seared face.

"What is it, father?" Owen asked.

"From Douglass," Brown replied. "God moves in mysterious ways!" That was all he said, but the sound of prairie winds was in his voice.

It was in December when rumor that the governor and his proslavery followers planned to surround Lawrence came to the Browns. On getting this news, they at once agreed to break camp and go to Lawrence. The band, approaching the town at sunset, loomed strangely on the horizon: an old horse, a homely wagon, and seven stalwart men armed with pikes, swords, pistols and guns. John Brown was immediately put in command of a company. Negotiations had commenced between Governor Shannon and the principal leaders of the free-state men. They had a force of some five hundred men to defend Lawrence. Night and day they were busy fortifying the town with embankments and circular earthworks. On Sunday Governor Shannon entered the town, and after some parley a treaty was announced. The terms of the treaty were kept secret, but Brown wrote jubilantly to New York that the Kansas invasion was over. The Missourians had been sent home without fighting any battles, burning any infant towns, or smashing a single Abolitionist press. "Free-state men," he said, "have only hereafter to retain the footing they have gained, and Kansas is free."

Developments in Kansas did not please the powerful slavocracy. Furious representatives hurried to Washington. And President Pierce, who had once sent a battleship to Boston to bring back one trembling, manacled slave, denounced the free-state men of Kansas as lawless revolutionists, deprived them of all support from the Federal government, and threatened them with the penalty for "treasonable insurrection." Regular troops were put into the hands of the Kansas slave power, and armed bands from the South appeared, one from Georgia encamping on the "swamp of the swan" near the Brown settlement.

Surveying instruments in hand and followed by his "helpers"— chain carriers, axman and marker—John Brown sauntered into their camp one May morning. He was taken for a government surveyor and consequently "sound." The Georgians talked freely.

"We've come to stay," they said. "We won't make no war on them as minds their own business. But all the Abolitionists, such as them damned Browns over there, we're going to whip, drive out, or kill— any way to get shut of them, by God!" *

They mentioned their intended victims by name, and John Brown calmly wrote down every word they said in his surveyor's book.

On May 21 the pro-slavery forces swooped down on Lawrence, burned and sacked it. Its citizens stood by trembling and raised no hand in defense.

The gutted, burning town sent a wave of anger across the country. It struck the Senate with full force. Only an aisle separated men whose eyes blazed with hate. Charles Sumner lifted his huge frame and in a voice that resounded like thunder denounced "a crime without example in the history of the past." He did not hesitate to name names —calling Stephen Douglas, Senator from Illinois, and Matthew Butler from South Carolina murderers of the men of Lawrence. The next day, while Sumner sat writing at his seat, young Preston Brooks, representative from South Carolina, came up behind the Massachusetts legislator and beat him over the head with a heavy walking stick. Charles Sumner, lying bleeding and unconscious in the aisle, reduced the whole vast struggle to simple terms.

Out West, John Brown hurried to Lawrence. He sat down by the smoldering ashes in tight-lipped anger. He was indignant that there had been no resistance.

---

* Du Bois, *John Brown*, chap. vii, p. 153.

"What were they doing?" he raged.

Someone mentioned the word "caution."

"Caution, caution, sir!" he sneered. "I am eternally tired of hearing the word caution. It is nothing but the word of cowardice."

Yet there seemed to be nothing to do now; and he was about to leave, when a boy came riding up. The gang at Dutch Henry's, he said, had told the women in Brown settlement that all free-state folks must get out by Saturday or Sunday, else they would be driven out. Two houses and a store in the nearby German settlement had been burned.

Then John Brown arose.

"I will attend to those fellows." He spoke quietly. Here was something to do. He called four of his sons—Watson, Frederick, Owen and Oliver—and a neighbor with a wagon and horses offered to carry the band. They began carefully sharpening cutlasses. An uneasy feeling crept over the onlookers. They all knew that John Brown was going to strike a blow for freedom in Kansas, but they did not understand just what that blow would be. As the wagon moved off, a cheer arose from the company left behind.

He loosed a civil war. Everything that came after was only powder for the hungry cannon. Freedom is a hard-bought thing! John Brown knew. He already knew on that terrible night when he rode down with his sons into "the shadows of the Swamp of the Swan—that long, low-winding and somber stream fringed everywhere with woods and dark with bloody memory. Forty-eight hours they lingered there, and then of a pale May morning rode up to the world again. Behind them lay five twisted, red and mangled corpses. Behind them rose the stifled wailing of widows and little children. Behind them the fearful driver gazed and shuddered. But before them rode a man, tall, dark, grim-faced and awful. His hands were red and his name was John Brown. Such was the cost of freedom." *

John Brown became a hunted outlaw.

They burned his house, destroyed everything he and his sons had garnered. But he had only begun his war upon the slavers. Out of the night he came, time after time, and always he left death behind.

"He's mad! Mad!" they said, but pro-slavery men began to leave Kansas.

"Da freedom's comin'!" Black men lifted their hands in silent ecstasy. They slipped across the borders and looked for John Brown.

* Du Bois, *John Brown*, chap. iv, p. 144.

Tabor, a tiny prairie Iowa town of thirty homesteads, became the most important Underground Railroad station on the western frontier. For here John Brown set up camp, and began to organize for his "march." Strength had come up in the old man, charging his whole being with power.

"We should not have given him money!" the folks back East were saying.

Douglass, moving back and forth from Rochester to Boston—to New York, Syracuse and Cleveland—grew thin and haggard. He had stood like a bulwark of strength, even when the Supreme Court had handed down its Dred Scott decision. People found clarion words in the *North Star*.

"The Supreme Court of the United States is not the only power in this world," Douglass wrote. "We, the Abolitionists and colored people, should meet this decision, unlooked for and monstrous as it appears, in a cheerful spirit. This very attempt to blot out forever the hopes of an enslaved people may be one necessary link in the chain of events preparatory to the complete overthrow of the whole slave system."

Months passed, and all he heard from Kansas were the awful reports of John Brown's riding abroad. He could not argue the right or wrong of this thing. Condemnation of John Brown left him cold. But was John Brown destroying all they had built up? This was war! Was John Brown's way the only way? They had lost the election. The new party's fine words fell back upon them like chilling drops of rain. Then out in Kansas the Governor declared the state free! There was peace in Kansas.

One night in January, 1858, Douglass was working late in the shop. The house was still, locked in the hard fastness of a winter night. Outside, great slow white flakes were falling, erasing the contours of the street beneath a blanket that rounded every eave, leveled fences and walks, and muffled every sound. But he heard the light tapping on the window pane and instantly put out the light. There must be no light to throw shadows when he opened the door upon one of his fugitives. But even without a light he recognized the muffled figure.

"John Brown!" Douglass' low voice sang a welcome.

He drew him in and brushed the snowflakes off. He lit the lamp with hands that trembled. Then he turned and looked at this man who had proved that he hated slavery more than he loved his life, his good name, or his sons. Even the little flesh he used to have was burned away. Yet one could see that all his bones were granite, and bright within the chalice of his mortal frame his spirit shone, unquenchable.

"You're safe, John Brown!" It was a ridiculous thing to say, and John Brown rewarded him with one of his rare smiles—the smile few people knew he had, with which he always won a child.

"Yes, Douglass, now I am free to carry out my mission."

Douglass' heart missed a beat. John Brown had not sought him out as a fugitive, he had not come to his house to hide away—not John Brown!

"Frederick is dead."

The words came with blunt finality, but a spasm of pain distorted the old man's face.

"Oh, John! John!"

Douglass gently pushed him into the armchair, knelt at his feet, pulled off the heavy boots, then hurried away to bring him food. He ate as one does whose body is starving, gulping down unchewed mouthfuls with the warm milk.

"I come direct from the National Kansas Committee in Chicago. They will perhaps equip a company. I have letters from Governor Chase and Governor Robinson. They endorse my plan."

Douglass expressed his pleased surprise. Brown wiped his shaggy beard. Something like a grin flickered on his face.

"Kansas is free and the good people are glad to be rid of me," he said dryly.

Douglass understood: they dared not jail the man.

Brown's plan was now complete. He spread out maps and papers and, as he talked, traced the lines of his march with a blunt pencil.

"God has established the Allegheny Mountains from the foundation of the world that they might one day be a refuge for the slaves. We march into these mountains, set up our stations about five miles apart, send out our call; and, as the slaves flock to us, we sustain them in this natural fortress."

Douglass followed the line of his pencil.

"Each group will be well armed," the old man continued, "but will avoid violence except in self-defense. In that case, they will make it as costly as possible to the assailing parties—whether they be citizens or soldiers. We will break the backbone of slavery by rendering slave property insecure. Men will not invest their money in a species of property likely to take legs and walk off with itself!" His eyes were shining.

"I do not grudge the money or energy I have spent in Kansas," he went on, "but now my funds are gone. We must have arms, ammunition, food and clothing. Later we will subsist upon the country roundabout. I now have the nucleus of my band." Shadows crossed his face. "Already they have gone to hell and back with me."

He talked on—three military schools to be set up, one in Iowa, one in northern Ohio and one in Canada. It would be a permanent community in Canada. "Finally the escaped slaves will pass on to Canada, each doing his share to strengthen the route," he explained.

"But won't it take years to free the slaves this way?" his friend asked.

"Indeed not! Each month our line of fortresses will extend farther south." His pencil moved across Tennessee, Georgia, Alabama, to Mississippi. "To the delta itself! The slaves will free themselves."

Pale dawn showed in the sky before they went upstairs.

"You must sleep now, John Brown."

But before lying down, the old man looked hard into the broad, dark face. Douglass nodded his head.

"I'm with you, John Brown. Rest a little. Then we'll talk," Douglass said and tiptoed from the room.

When John Brown left the house in Alexander Street several days later, he was expected in many quarters. He went first to Boston, George L. Sterns, the Massachusetts antislavery leader, paying his expenses. Sterns, who had never met "Osawatomie Brown," had written to Rochester offering to introduce him to friends of freedom in Boston. They met on the street outside the committee rooms in Nilis' Block, with a Kansas man doing the honors; and Brown went along to Sterns' home.

Coming into the parlor to greet the man who had become a household word during the summer of 1856, Mrs. Sterns heard her guest saying, "Gentlemen, I consider the Golden Rule and the Declaration of Independence one and inseparable."

"I felt," she said later, writing about the profound impression of moral magnetism Brown made on everybody who saw him in those days, "that some old Cromwellian hero had dropped down among us."

Emerson, she remembered, called him "the most ideal of men, for he wanted to put all his ideas into action." Yet Mrs. Sterns was struck by his modest estimate of the work he had in hand. After several efforts to bring together their friends to meet Captain Brown in his home, Sterns found that Sunday was the only day that would serve everybody's convenience. Being a little uncertain how this might strike their guest's ideas of religious propriety, Sterns prefaced his invitation with something like an apology.

"Mr. Sterns," came the prompt reply, "I have a little ewe-lamb that I want to pull out of the ditch, and the Sabbath will be as good a day as any to do it."

Over in Concord he went to see Henry David Thoreau. They sat at a table covered with lichens, ferns, birds' nests and arrowheads. They dipped their fingers into a large trencher of nuts, cracked the shells between their teeth, and talked as kindred souls. Thoreau, lean and narrow-chested, thrust his big ugly nose forward and, with his searching gray eyes, probed the twisted steel of John Brown. The hermit believed then what he said afterward, when he served his term in jail:

"When one-sixth of a people who are come to the land of liberty are enslaved, it is time for free men to rebel."

The secretary of the Massachusetts State Kansas Committee received Captain Brown with cautious respect. Half an hour later he was saying, "By God, I'll *make* them give him money!" But the Committee warned, "We must know how he will use the money."

Kind-hearted, genial Gerrit Smith was glad to have his old friend with him for a few days.

"Be sure of your men," he advised.

"My men need not be questioned, sir." John Brown spoke a little stiffly.

Gerrit Smith stifled a sigh. *His faith in God and man is sublime!* he thought a little sadly.

Swarthy, bearded Thomas W. Higginson, young Unitarian minister, set out immediately to raise funds on his own. He was hissed at Harvard, his Alma Mater, but he was not swayed from his course.

At a meeting at the Astor House in New York the National Kansas Committee voted "in aid of Captain Brown . . . 12 boxes of clothing, sufficient for 60 persons, 25 Colt revolvers, five thousand dollars to be used in any defense measures that may become necessary." But only five hundred dollars was paid out.

John Brown was disappointed. He had hoped to obtain the means of arming and thoroughly equipping a regular outfit of minutemen.

He had left his men suffering hunger, cold, nakedness, and some of them sickness and wounds. He had engaged the services of one Hugh Forbes, who claimed to have been a lieutenant of Garibaldi. Forbes was to take over the military tactics. He had demanded six hundred dollars for his expenses. John Brown had given it to him.

"I am going back," Brown said to Douglass, when he stopped overnight in Rochester. "You must keep up the work here—solicit funds, keep the issue before them. I have no baggage wagons, tents, camp equipage, tools . . . or a sufficient supply of ammunition. I have left my family poorly supplied with common necessaries."

"I do not like what you tell me about this Hugh Forbes," said Douglass.

Brown was a little impatient.

"He is a trained man in military affairs. I know nothing about maneuvers. We need him!"

It was John Brown's intention to leave the actual training of his men to Forbes, so that he might be free for larger matters. Nor did he want to spend time raising funds. He wanted to organize Negroes for the job ahead.

Perhaps better than any other white man of his time John Brown knew what Negroes in every part of North America were doing. He knew their newspapers, their churches and their schools. To most Americans of the time all black men were slaves or fugitives. But from the beginning John Brown sought to know Negroes personally and individually. He went into their homes, sought them out in business, talked to them, listened to the stories of their trials, harkened to their dreams, advised, and took advice from them. He set out to enlist the boldest and most daring spirits for his plan.

In March, Brown and his eldest son met with Henry Highland Garnet and William Still, Negro Secretary of the Philadelphia Anti-Slavery Society, in the home of Stephen Smith, a Philadelphia Negro lumber merchant. Brown remained in Philadelphia a week or ten days, holding long conferences in Negro churches.

Meanwhile, his black lieutenant, Kagi, ragged, stooped, insignificant-looking, shrewd and cunning, was traveling over the Allegheny Mountains, surveying the land, marking sites and making useful contacts. Kagi had some schooling and, when he desired, could speak clearly and to the point. He knew in detail the vast extent of Brown's plan. He lived and breathed it. He had been wounded with John

Brown in Kansas, and unswerving he walked to his death with him. For Kagi believed that John Brown was making a mistake to attack Harpers Ferry when he did, but the little black man held the bridge until his riddled body plunged into the icy waters below.

In the spring of 1858 Brown went to Canada to set up personal contacts with the nearly fifty thousand Negroes there. Chatham, chief town of Kent County, had a large Negro population with several churches, a newspaper and a private school. Here on May 10 the Captain addressed a convention called together on the pretext of organizing a Masonic lodge. And at this convention they drew up and adopted the constitution of forty-eight articles that stunned the authorities when they found it in the hide-away farmhouse near Harper's Ferry.

Up to this time Frederick Douglass was fully cognizant of all John Brown's plans. The Douglass home in Rochester was his headquarters. (He had insisted that he pay board, and Douglass charged him three dollars a week.)

"While here, he spent most of his time in correspondence," Douglass wrote later. "When he was not writing letters, he was writing and revising a constitution which he meant to put in operation by means of the men who should go with him into the mountains. He said that, to avoid anarchy and confusion, there should be a regularly-constituted government, which each man who came with him should be sworn to honor and support. I have a copy of this constitution in Captain Brown's own handwriting, as prepared by himself at my house.

"He called his friends from Chatham to come together, that he might lay his constitution before them for their approval and adoption. His whole time and thought were given to this subject. It was the first thing in the morning and the last thing at night. Once in a while he would say he could, with a few resolute men, capture Harpers Ferry, and supply himself with arms belonging to the government at that place; but he never announced his intention to do so. It was, however . . . in his mind as a thing he might do. I paid little attention to such remarks, though I never doubted that he thought just what he said. Soon after his coming to me, he asked me to get for him two smoothly planed boards, upon which he could illustrate, with a pair of dividers, by a drawing, the plan of fortification which he meant to adopt in the mountains.

"These forts were to be so arranged as to connect one with the other, by secret passages, so that if one was carried another could easily be fallen back upon, and be the means of dealing death to the enemy at the very moment when he might think himself victorious. I was less interested in these drawings than my children were, but they showed that the old man had an eye to the means as to the end, and was giving his best thought to the work he was about to take in hand." *

The month of May, 1859, John Brown spent in Boston collecting funds, and in New York consulting his Negro friends, with a trip to Connecticut to hurry the making of his thousand pikes. Sickness intervened, but at last on June 20, the advance guard of five— Brown and two of his sons, Jerry Anderson and Kagi—started southward.

Many times during these months Frederick Douglass wondered whether or not John Brown did not have the only possible plan for freeing the black man. The antislavery fight had worn very thin. The North knew of the moral and physical horror of slavery. The South knew also, but cotton prices continued to rise. Logic would not separate cotton growers from their slaves. Many of the old, staunch Abolitionists were gone. Theodore Parker had burned himself out in the cause. Down with tuberculosis, he was on a ship bound for southern Italy where, in spite of the warm sunshine, he was to die.

Daily the South grew more defiant. When the doctrine of popular sovereignty failed to make Kansas a slave state, Southern statesmen abandoned it for firmer ground. They had lost faith in the rights, powers and wisdom of the people and took refuge in the Constitution. Henceforth the favorite doctrine of the South was that the people of a territory had no voice in the matter of slavery. The Constitution of the United States, they claimed, of its own force and effect, carried slavery safely into any territory of the United States and protected the system there until it should cease to be a territory and became a state. In practical operation, this doctrine would make all future new states slaveholding states; for slavery, once planted and nursed for years, could easily strengthen itself against the evil day of eradication.

In a rage, Garrison publicly burned a copy of the Constitution denouncing it as a "covenant with Satan." Douglass went away heartsick.

* Douglass, *Life and Times of Frederick Douglass*, chap. x, p. 385.

In the heart of the Alleghenies, halfway between Maine and Florida, opens a mighty gateway. From the south comes the Shenandoah, a restless silver thread gleaming in the sun; from the west the Potomac moves placidly between wide banks. But at their junction they are cramped. The two rivers rush together against the mountains, rend it asunder and tear a passage to the sea. And here is Harpers Ferry.

Why did John Brown choose this particular point for his attack upon American slavery? Was it the act of a madman? A visionary fool? What was his crime?

John Brown did not tell them at the trial. His lieutenant, Kagi, was dead. Green, Coppoc, Stevens, Copeland, Cook and Hazlett followed their captain to the gallows without a word. Perhaps only one man went on living who knew the full answers. His name was Frederick Douglass.

Douglass has been attacked because he did not go with John Brown to Harpers Ferry, because he did not testify in Brown's defense, because he put himself outside the reach of pursuers who would drag him to the trial. He could not have saved John Brown and his brave followers. Every word of the truth would have drawn the noose tighter about their necks. It would have hanged Douglass!

It was on a pleasant day in September when the letter came from John Brown. It was very short.

"I am forced to move sooner than I had planned. Before going forward I want to see you."

Brown, under the guise of a farmer interested only in developing a recently purchased piece of land, was living under an assumed name with his two "daughters"—actually a daughter and young Oliver's wife. His men were keeping under cover. They made every effort to keep the farm normal-looking. Brown asked Douglass to come to Chambersburg. There he would find a Negro barber named Watson, who would conduct him to the place of meeting. A last line was added: "Bring along the Emperor. Tell him the time has come."

Douglass knew that he referred to Shields Green, a fugitive slave, whom the old man had met in his house. Green, a powerful black, had escaped from South Carolina. He was nicknamed "the Emperor" because of his size and majestic carriage. Brown had seized upon him immediately, confiding to him his plan, and Green had promised to go with him when Brown was ready to move.

They set out together, stopping over in New York City with a Reverend James Glocester. Upon hearing where they were going, Mrs. Glocester pressed ten dollars into Douglass' hand.

"Give it to Captain Brown, with my best wishes," she said.

They sped southward past the waving, green fields and big, white farms of prosperous Dutch farmers. Douglass sat by the window with his massive head sunk forward, not looking out. Then the train curved into the Blue Ridge Mountains where the pine-covered hills begin, and stopped at Chambersburg, Pennsylvania. The first man at the depot whom they asked directed them to Watson, the barber.

He stood looking after the two Negroes as they strode down the platform.

"Damned if they don't walk like they own the earth!" he grunted.

Watson called to his boy when they stepped into his shop. He took them to his house, where his wife greeted the great Frederick Douglass and his friend with much fluttering.

"Make yourselves at home," said the barber. "As soon as it is dark I will drive you out to the old stone quarry. That's the place, but we must wait until dark."

They left the wagon and its driver on the road and climbed up to the quarry. All about them the rocks loomed like great stone faces in the moonlight. And when John Brown stepped out of the shadows, it was as if a rock had moved toward them. His old clothes, covered with dust; his white hair and hard-cut face, like granite in the moonlight; his strained, worn face with the two burning coals that were his eyes. Douglass' heart missed a beat. Something was very wrong.

"What is it, John Brown? What has happened?"

The old man looked at him without speaking. He studied the brown face almost as if he had not seen it before. Then he spoke briefly.

"Come!"

He led them between the rocks and stooped to enter a cave. Inside was Kagi and in a niche in the wall was a lighted torch. There were boulders about, and at a sign from the old man they sat down— John Brown, Kagi, Shields Green and Frederick Douglass. They waited for Brown to speak. He did so, leaning forward and putting a thin, gnarled hand on Douglass' knee.

"Dougless, we can wait no longer. Our move now must be a decisive one."

Douglass was bitterly chiding himself. He should have come

sooner. These last months had drained the old man's strength. He needed help here. The dark man spoke gently.

"But you said the time to begin calling in the slaves would come after the crops are gathered, as the Christmas approaches. Then many can get away without being missed right away. Is your ammunition distributed? Are your stations ready to receive and defend the fugitives?"

John Brown shook his head.

"No. We are not ready with all that." He drew a long breath, and it was obvious it caused him pain. "You were right about Hugh Forbes," he said then. "He has deserted us and," Brown hesitated, hating to say it, "I fear he has talked."

Douglass' face expressed his shock. Why had he not strangled the tinseled fool with his own hands?

"We are being watched: my men are certain of it. At any moment we may be arrested. Don't forget, I'm still an outlaw in Kansas." He added the last dryly, almost indifferently. Then suddenly the flame flared. John Brown was on his feet, his head lifted. He shook back his white hair.

"But God is with us! He has delivered the gates into our hands! We hold the key to the Allegheny Mountains. They stand here, our sure and safe defense!"

Douglass stared at him. Was it the torchlight that so transfigured his old friend? He stood like an avenging angel, illumined by the force that rose up in him. It charged his whole being with power—his eyes, his frame, the leashed, metallic voice.

"I am ready!"

Douglass looked at Kagi. Kagi's eyes fixed on the lifted face. He turned and looked at Green, and on that black giant's countenance he saw the same imprint. He wet his trembling lips. An icy hand had closed about his heart. He was afraid.

"The map, Kagi!" John Brown spoke sharply.

Kagi was ready. Brown knelt on the ground, and Kagi spread a wide sheet in front of him. He brought the torch near and knelt holding it, while Brown traced the lines with his finger.

"Here is the long line of our mountain fortress," he said tersely. "Right here east of the Shenandoah, the mountains rise to a height of two thousand feet or more. This natural defense is right at the entrance to the mountain passage. See! An hour's climb from this point and a hundred men could be inside an inaccessible fastness.

Here attacks could be repelled with little difficulty. Here are Loudon Heights—then beyond the passage plunges straight into the heart of the thickest slave districts. The slaves can get to us without difficulty, after we have made our way through here."

His finger had stopped. Douglass leaned forward. He was holding his breath. He could feel Brown's eyes upon him.

"But that—that is Harpers Ferry!" Douglass said, and his voice faltered.

He could feel the surge of strength in the other man.

"Yes," he said, "Harper's Ferry is the safest natural entrance to our mountain passage. We shall go through Harper's Ferry, and there we'll take whatever arms we need."

So little children speak, and fools, and gods!

For a moment there was silence in the cave. Then Douglass got up, striking his head against the low wall. He did not heed the blow, but took John Brown by the arm.

"Come outside, Captain Brown," he said. "Let's talk outside. I— I can't breathe in here!"

And so they faced each other in the open. Night in the mountains, stars over their heads, and stark, jagged rocks white in the shadows.

"You can't do it, John Brown!" Douglass' voice was strained. "You would be attacking an arsenal of the United States— This is war against the federal government. The whole country would be arrayed against us!"

"You do not understand, Douglass. We're not going to kill anybody. There are only a handful of soldiers guarding that ferry. We'll merely make them prisoners, hold them until we take the arms and get up into the mountains. Of course, there'll be a great outcry. But all the better. The slaves will hear of it. They'll know we're in the mountains, and they'll flock to us."

"Do you really believe this, John Brown? Do you really believe you can take a fort so easily?"

A hard note had come again into the old man's voice.

"Am I concerned with ease, Frederick Douglass? What is this you are saying? Our mission is to free the slaves! This is the plan!"

"There was no such plan," Douglass interposed hotly. "You said that fighting would only be in self-defense. This is an attack!"

John Brown's passion matched his.

"And when I rode down into the marshes of Kansas it was an

attack! You did not condemn then! Here we merely force our way through a passage!"

"This is treason! This is insurrection! This is war! I am not with you!"

The old man's voice cut like a whip.

"So! You have escaped so far from slavery that you do not care! You have carried the scars upon your back into high places, so you have forgotten. You prate of treason! You are afraid to face a gun!"

Douglass cried out in anguish. "John! John! For God's sake, stop!"

He stumbled away, sank down on a rock and buried his face in his hands. Some time later he felt a hand upon his shoulder, and Brown's voice, softened and subdued, came to him.

"Forgive an old man, son."

Douglass took the hand in his and pressed it against his face. The old man's hand was rough and knotty, but it was very firm.

"This is no time for soft words or for oratory," he said. "We have a job to do. Years ago I swore it—that I would do my part. God has called me to lift his crushed and suffering dark children. Twenty-five years have gone by making plans. Now unless I move quickly all of these years will have been spent in vain. I will take this fort. I will hold this pass. I will free the slaves!"

The stars faded and went out one by one, the gray sky blended through purple and rose to blue, and still they talked. Kagi brought them food.

At last Douglass lay down inside the cave. His eyes were closed, but his mind feverishly leaped from one possibility to another.

Then Brown was laying other maps before him. He had gone over it all so carefully. Now he showed each step of the way—where the men would stand, how they would hold the bridge, where they would cut the telegraph wires, how the engine-house in the arsenal would be occupied.

"Without a shot being fired, Douglass. I tell you we can take it without a shot!"

Douglass brought all the pressure of his persuasive power against him. He threw reason, logic, common sense at the old man.

"You'll destroy all we've done!"

John Brown looked at him and his voice and face were cold.

"*What* have you done?" The question bit like steel.

Another day passed. That night a storm came up. They sat huddled in the cave, while outside the rain beat down upon the rocks and tore up twisted roots. The mountains groaned and rumbled and the winds howled. During the storm the old man slept serenely.

When the rain stopped Douglass went out into the dripping morning. Puddles of water splashed beneath his feet, shreds of clouds lingered in the pine tops and broke against the side of the hills; the sky was clearing and soon the sun would come through. The fresh-washed earth gave off a clean, new smell. The morning mocked him with its promise of a bright, new day.

He heard John Brown behind him and stopped. He knew that strong, elastic step. He heard the voice—full, clear and renewed with rest.

"Douglass," Brown asked, "have you reached your decision?"

Without turning, Douglass answered. And his voice was weary and beaten.

"I am going back."

The old man made no sound. Douglass turned and saw him standing straight and slender in the morning light, a gentle breeze lifting his soft white hair, his wrinkled face carved against the sky. With a cry of utter woe Douglass threw himself upon the ground, encircling the slight frame in his arms.

"Oh, John—John Brown—don't go! You'll be killed! It's a trap! You'll never get out alive—I beg you, don't go! Don't go!"

Terrible sobs shook him; he could not stop.

"Douglass! Douglass!"

Brown took him by the shoulders, pressed his face against him, spoke as to a child.

"For shame, Douglass! Everything will be all right." Then, when he saw the big man was still, he added, "Come and go with me. You shall see that everything will be all right."

Douglass shook his head. He clung to the rough, gnarled hands.

"This is the hardest part of all. I cannot throw my life away with you! Years ago in Maryland I knew I had to live. That's *my* task, John—that I live."

"You shall have a trusted bodyguard!" The old man looked down at him with a twisted smile. Douglass made a gesture of resignation. He raised his eyes once more.

"Will nothing change you from this course?" he asked.

"Nothing," answered John Brown. He gently pulled himself away and walked to the edge of the cliff, looking out into the morning. Douglass sagged upon the ground.

"You may be right, Frederick Douglass." His words came slowly now. "Perhaps I'll not succeed at Harpers Ferry. Maybe—I'll never leave there alive. Yet I must go! Until this moment I had never faced that possibility, and I could not give you up. Now that I do, I see that only through your living can my dying be made clear. So, let us have an end of all this talk. Perhaps this is God's way."

Douglass pulled himself up. He was very tired.

"I must tell Green," he said.

John Brown turned. His face was untroubled, his voice alert.

"Yes. I had forgotten. Get him."

They came upon Shields Green and Kagi leaving the cave. Over their shoulders were fishing poles. Douglass spoke.

"Shields, I am leaving. Are you going back with me?"

John Brown spoke, the words coming easily, a simple explanation.

"Both of you know that Douglass disagrees with my plan. He says we'll fail at Harpers Ferry—that none of us will come out alive." He paused a moment and then said, "Maybe he is right."

Douglass waited, but still Shields Green only looked at him. At last he asked, "Well, Shields?"

"The Emperor" shifted the fishing rod in his hand. Then his eyes turned toward John Brown. Douglass knew even before he spoke. Shields looked him full in the face and said, "Ah t'ink Ah goes wid tha old man!"

And he and Kagi turned away and went off down to the stream.

Brown held his hand a moment before speaking.

"Go quickly now, and go without regrets. You have your job to do and I have mine."

Douglass did not look back as he stumbled over the wet, slippery rocks. Never in his life had he felt so desolate, never had a day seemed so bleak and empty, as alone he went down the mountain *to live* for freedom. He had left John Brown and Shields Green to die for freedom. Whose was the better part?

CHAPTER THIRTEEN

"Give them arms, Mr. Lincoln!"

THE NEWS of Harpers Ferry stunned Washington. *"A United States arsenal attacked—Slaves stampeding!"* *"The mad man from Kansas run amuck!"* *"The slaves are armed!"* Panic seized the South, and Capitol Hill rocked and reeled with the shock.

Jack brought home copies of the *New York Herald,* and Amelia read how the old man lay bleeding on a pallet with his two sons cold and still at his side. Governor Wise, leaning over to condemn, had drawn back before a courage, fortitude and simple faith which silenced him.

"There is an eternity behind and an eternity before," John Brown had said, and his voice did not falter. "This little speck in the center, however long, is comparatively but a minute. The difference between your tenure and mine is trifling, and I therefore tell you to be prepared. I am prepared. You have a heavy responsibility, and it behooves you to meet it. You may dispose of me easily, but this question is still to be settled . . . the end is not yet."

"Why did he let the train through?" people asked. *"Is* he crazy?"

"I came here to liberate slaves." All his explanations were so simple. "I have acted from a sense of duty, and am content to await my fate; but I think the crowd have treated me badly. . . . Yesterday I could have killed whom I chose; but I had no desire to kill any person, and would not have killed a man had they not tried to kill me and my men. I could have sacked and burned the town, but did not; I have treated the persons whom I took as hostages kindly. If I had succeeded in running off slaves this time, I could have raised twenty times as many men as I have now, for a similar expedition. But I have failed."

An old man had been stopped—a crazy old man, whose equally

crazy followers were killed or captured. It was over and very little harm done. An unpleasant incident to be soon forgotten.

But no one would have done with it. Papers throughout the country sowed John Brown's words into every town and hamlet; preachers repeated them in their pulpits; people gathered in small knots on the roadside and shouted them defiantly or whispered them cautiously; black men and women everywhere bowed their heads and wept hot, scalding tears. And William Lloyd Garrison, the man of peace, the "non-resister," said, "How marvelous has been the change in public opinion during thirty years of moral agitation. Ten years ago there were thousands who could not endure the slightest word of rebuke of the South; now they can swallow John Brown whole and his rifle in the bargain."

The old man never lost his calm. Frenzy shook every slave state in the Union. Rumors spread and multiplied. Black and white men were seized, beaten, and killed. Slaves disappeared. A hue and cry arose.

"The Abolitionists! Get the Abolitionists! They are behind John Brown!"

Amelia read of letters and papers found in the farmhouse near Harper's Ferry. *"Many people are implicated! Indictments being drawn up!"* She looked at Jack, her face white.

"Do you suppose—could it be—would *he* be among them?" She bit her trembling lips.

Jack Haley frowned. He had heard talk at the office. He knew they were looking for Frederick Douglass. He knew they would hang this Negro whom they hated and feared more than a dozen white men—*if* they got him. He patted Amelia on the shoulder.

"I wouldn't worry," he comforted her. "Your Frederick is a smart man."

"He might be needed to testify—he may have something to say." Amelia was certain Frederick Douglass would not turn aside from his duty.

"He is not a fool," Jack said, shaking his head. "The Dred Scott decision renders his word useless. No word of his can help John Brown."

Amelia heard the bitterness in Jack's voice and she sighed. Time had dealt kindly with Amelia. At sixty her step was more elastic, her skin smoother and her shoulders straighter than the day, fifteen years before, when she had walked away from Covey's place. Mrs.

Royall, intrepid journalist, was dead. Amelia had stayed on in the house, assumed the mortgage, and took in as roomers a score of clerks and secretaries who labored in the government buildings a few blocks away. "Miss Amelia's" house was popular, and her rooms were in demand.

Jack had married and talked of going away, of starting his own paper, of becoming a power in one of the new publishing houses—Then suddenly, during a sleeting winter, an epidemic had struck Washington. Afterward, there had been quite a stir about "cleaning up the city." Certain sections had got new sewers and rubbish was collected. But Jack's wife was dead. So a grim-faced, older Jack had moved in with Amelia. He had stayed on with the paper, contemptuous of much he saw and heard. For Jack Haley, as for many people in the United States the fall of 1859, John Brown cleared the air. *Somebody's doing something, thank God!*

Amelia continued to scan the papers, dreading to see Frederick Douglass' name. And one day she did, but as she read farther a smile lit up her face. The story was an angry denunciation of "this Frederick Douglass" by Governor Wise of Virginia. Douglass, he announced, had slipped through their fingers. He was known to have boarded a British steamer bound for England. "Could I overtake that vessel," the Governor was quoted as saying, "I would take him from her deck at any cost."

Off the coast of Labrador, in weather four degrees below zero, the *Scotia* strained and groaned. There was something fiercely satisfying to one passenger in the struggle with the elements. Frederick Douglass, pacing the icy deck or tossing in his cabin, felt that the sky *should* be black. The waters *should* foam and dash, the winds *should* howl; for John Brown lay in prison and his brave sons were dead!

Back in Concord, the gentle Thoreau was ringing the town bell and crying in the streets, "Old John Brown is dead—John Brown the immortal lives!"

By the time Douglass docked at Liverpool, England was as much alive to what had happened at Harper's Ferry as the United States. Once more Douglass was called to Scotland and Ireland—this time to give an account of the men who had thus flung away their lives in a desperate effort to free the slaves.

Having accepted an invitation to speak in Paris, he wrote for a passport. A suspicion current at the time, that a conspiracy against the life of Napoleon III was afoot in England, had stiffened the French passport system. Douglass, wishing to avoid any delay, wrote directly to the Honorable George Dallas, United States Minister in London. That gentleman refused to grant the passport at all on the ground that Frederick Douglass was not a citizen of the United States. Douglass' English friends gaped at the Ministry letter. The "man without a country," however, merely shrugged his shoulders.

"I forget too easily," he said. "Now I'll write to the French minister."

Within a few days he had his answer—a "special permit" for Frederick Douglass to visit "indefinitely" in any part of France. He was packed to go when a cable from home arrived.

Little Annie was dead. The sudden loss of his baby daughter seemed to climax all the pain and heartbreak of these months.

Heedless now of peril to himself, he took the first outgoing steamer for Portland, Maine.

During the seventeen dragging days of his voyage, Douglass resolved to make one stop even before going home. He had two graves now to visit—Annie's and John Brown's. Annie too had loved the old man. She would not mind if her father went directly to the house in the Adirondacks.

No one was expecting the haggard dark man who descended from the train at North Elba. He could not find a driver to take him up to John Brown's house. But from the livery stable he secured a horse. And so he rode up through the Indian Pass gorge, between two overhanging black walls, and came out under tall, white clouds above wine-colored mountains rising in a blue mist. And there beside a still, green pool, reflecting a white summit in its depths, he saw the house, with its abandoned sawmill.

Mrs. Brown exhibited no surprise when he stood before her. Her husband's strength sustained her now. John Brown and the sons that she had borne were no longer hers. They belonged to all the peoples of the world. She greeted Frederick Douglass with a smile.

"I've been expecting you. Come in, my friend." She talked quietly, transmitting to him John Brown's final words and admonitions. Then she rose. "He left something for you."

"Oh—John!" Until that moment he had listened without interrupting, his eyes on the woman's expressive face. The words broke from him unbidden.

At her gesture, he followed her up the bare stairs and into the bedroom that had been hers and John Brown's. The roof sloped down; he had to stoop a little, standing beside her before the faded, furled flag and rusty musket in the corner. She nodded her head, but could not speak.

"For me?" Douglass' words came in a whisper.

"He wanted you to have them." She had turned to the chest of drawers and handed him an envelope.

"He sent this in one of my letters. I was to give it to you when you came."

His hands were trembling as he drew forth the single white sheet on which were written two lines.

"I know I have not failed because you live. Go forward, and some day unfurl my flag in the land of the free. Farewell." And then was sprawled, "John Brown."

He left the farmhouse with the musket in his hands. They had wrapped the flag carefully, and he laid it across his shoulders. So many times she had stood in the narrow doorway and watched John Brown ride away. He had never looked back. But on this evening the rider paused when he came to the top of the hill. He paused and looked back down into the valley. His eyes found the spot where John Brown lay beside his sons. She could not see his lips move, nor could she hear his words—words the winds of the Adirondacks carried away:

"I promise you, John Brown. As I live, I promise you."

Then he waved his hand to John Brown's widow and was gone.

Douglass' homecoming was weighted with sorrow. But in the mountains of North Elba he had drawn strength. He was able to comfort the grieving mother and the older children. For the first time in years he sat quietly with his three fine sons. He told Rosetta how pretty she was—like her mother in the days of the plum-colored wedding dress. The family closed its ranks, coming very close together. Douglass managed to remain in his house nearly a months before knowledge got around that he was back in the country. Then a letter from William Lloyd Garrison summoned him:

> The investigating committee appointed by Congress is being called off. The net thrown out over the country yielded very little. As you know, Captain Brown implicated nobody. To the end he insisted that he and he alone was responsible for all that happened, that he had many friends, but no insti-

gators. In their efforts this committee has signally failed. Now
they have asked to be discharged. It is my opinion that the
men engaged in this investigation expect soon to be in rebellion themselves, and not a rebellion for liberty, like that of
John Brown, but a rebellion for slavery. It is possible that they
see that by using their Senatorial power in search of rebels
they may be whetting a knife for their own throats. At any
rate the country will soon be relieved of the Congressional
drag-net, so your liberty is no longer threatened. We are
planning a memorial to the grand old man here at Tremont
Temple and want you to speak. I know you'll come.

Douglass hastened to Boston. The great mass meeting was more
than a memorial. It was a political and social conclave. Arguments
and differences of opinions were laid aside. They had a line of action.
Douglass saw that he had returned to the United States in time for
vital service.

"It enabled me to participate in the most important and mem-
orable presidential canvass ever witnesses in the United States," he
wrote, looking back on it later, "and to labor for the election of a man
who in the order of events was destined to do a greater service to his
country and to mankind than any man who had gone before him in
the presidential office. It was a great thing to me to be permitted to
bear some humble part in this. It was a great thing to achieve American independence when we numbered three millions, but it was a
greater thing to save this country from dismemberment and ruin
when it numbered thirty millions. He alone of all our presidents was
to have the opportunity to destroy slavery, and to lift into manhood
millions of his countrymen hitherto held as chattels and numbered
with the beasts of the field." *

Not for nearly a hundred years was the country to see such a presidential campaign as the one waged in 1860.

Garrison was drawn into the fray early. He mocked the Democrats
when they tore themselves apart at their convention in Charleston and
cheered "an independent Southern republic." With the Democrats
divided, the Republicans would win; and into the Republican party
now came the Abolitionists—including William Lloyd Garrison.
Douglass was very happy.

A few weeks before the Republicans met in convention at Chicago,
Frederick Douglass at his home in Rochester had a caller. The man
identified himself as a tradesman from Springfield, Illinois.

* Douglass, *Life and Times of Frederick Douglass*, chap. ix, p. 397.

"I'm here, lookin' over the shippin' of some goods, and I took the liberty to come see you, Mr. Douglass," he said, resting his hands on his knotty knees.

"I'm very glad you did, sir." Douglass waited for the man to reveal his errand. He leaned forward.

"I ain't a talkin' man, Mr. Douglass. I'm much more for doin'." Douglass smiled his approval. The man lowered his tone. "More than once I took on goods for Reverend Rankin."

Douglass knew instantly what he meant. John Rankin was one of Ohio's most daring Underground Railroad agents. Douglass' face lit up, and for the second time he grasped his visitor's rough hand.

"Any Rankin man is a hundredfold welcome in my house! What can I do for you?"

"Jus' listen and think on what I'm sayin'. We got a man out our way we're namin' for president!"

The unexpected announcement caught Douglass up short.

"But I thought—" The man waved him to silence.

"Yep! I know. You Easterners got your man all picked out. I ain't sayin' nothin' 'bout Mr. Seward. I donno him. But the boys out West *do* know Abe Lincoln—and we're gonna back him!"

"Abe Lincoln?" Douglass was puzzled. "I never heard of him."

"Nope? Well, it don't matter. You will!"

He was gone then, leaving Frederick Douglass very thoughtful. The Westerner was right. Senator William Seward, a tried and true antislavery man, had been picked. The only question had been whether or not the entire party would accept such a known radical.

Douglass reached Chicago the evening before the nominations were taken up. He found the city decked out with fence rails which they said "Honest Abe" had split. Evidently the people in the streets knew him, the cab drivers and farmers in from the surrounding country. They stood on street corners, buttonholed workmen hurrying home from work, and they talked about "our man."

Something was in the air. The convention was a bedlam. Even while the thunder of applause that had greeted the nomination of William Seward still hung in the far corners of the hall, Norman B. Judd, standing on a high chair, nominated the man who habitually referred to himself as a "jackleg lawyer." The roar that greeted Lincoln's name spread to the packed street outside and kept up until the

Seward men were silenced. The cheering died away in the hall, as they began taking the third ballot; but the steady roar in the street found an echo in the chamber, when it was found that Lincoln had received two hundred thirty-one and a half votes, lacking just one and a half votes for nomination. Then Ohio gave its four votes to the "rail-splitter," and Abraham Lincoln became the Republican candidate for President of the United States.

Three candidates were in the field. Stephen A. Douglas, absolute leader of the Democratic party in the West, had been nominated at Baltimore after a bitter and barren fight at Charleston. The "seceding" Southern wing of the party had nominated John C. Breckinridge. Three candidates and one issue, *slavery*.

Stephen Douglas' position was: Slavery or no slavery in any territory is entirely the affair of the white inhabitants of such territory. If they choose to have it, it is their right; if they choose not to have it, they have a right to exclude or prohibit it. Neither Congress nor the people of the Union, outside of said territory, have any right to meddle with or trouble themselves about the matter.

The Democrats of Illinois laughed at the others for hailing forth the Kentuckian. But Breckinridge represented the powerful slavocracy which said: The citizen of any state has a right to migrate to any territory, taking with him anything which is property by the law of his own state, and hold, enjoy, and be protected in the use of, such property in said territory. And Congress is bound to furnish him protection wherever necessary, with or without the co-operation of the territorial legislature.

Abraham Lincoln's voice had never been heard by the nation. Easterners waited with misgivings to hear what the gangling backwoods lawyer would say. He did not mince words: Slavery can exist only by virtue of municipal law; and there is no law for it in the territories and no power to enact one. Congress can establish or legalize slavery nowhere but is bound to prohibit it in, or exclude it from, any and every Federal territory, whenever and wherever there shall be necessity for such exclusion or prohibition.

Frederick Douglass was convinced not only by his words but by the fact that Abraham Lincoln was so clearly the choice of the people who knew him. He threw his pen and voice into the contest. Many of the Abolitionists hung back; many an "old guard" politician sulked. Wendell Phillips dug up evidence that Lincoln had supported enforcement of the hated Fugitive Slave Law in Illinois.

But Douglass shook his leonine mane and campaigned throughout New York State and in Boston, Philadelphia, Cleveland, Chicago—wherever Negroes could vote.

"Here is a man who knows your weariness," he told them. "This is your opportunity to make your voice heard. Send Lincoln to the White House! Strengthen his hand that he may fight for you!"

Fear gripped the South. They called Lincoln the "Black Republican." No longer was the North divided. Young Republicans organized marching clubs and tramped through the city streets; torchlight processions turned night into day: *John Brown's body lies a-moldering in the grave.* . . . A new singing could be heard in the remotest pine woods of the South:

"Oh, freedom
Oh, freedom!

Oh, freedom ovah me—
An' befo' I'd be a slave
I'd be buried in mah grave
An' go home to my Lawd
An' be free."

On November 6, Wendell Phillips congratulated Frederick Douglass: "For the first time in our history, the slave has chosen a President of the United States."

Garrison and Douglass decided to attend the inauguration together.

"I want to show you the White House, Douglass. You must see the Capitol to which you have sent Lincoln."

Douglass smiled. He had never been in Washington, and he was glad they were together again.

Garrison was far from well. The winter months had tried his failing strength. After electing Lincoln, the North drew back, in large part disclaiming all participation in the "insult" to their "sister states" in the South. The press took on a conciliatory tone toward slavery and a corresponding bitterness toward antislavery men and measures. From Massachusetts to Missouri, antislavery meetings were ruthlessly stoned. The second John Brown Memorial at Tremont Temple was broken up by a mob, some of the wealthiest citizens of Boston taking part in the assault on Douglass and the other speakers. Howling gangs followed Wendell Phillips for three days wherever he appeared on the pavements of his native city, and hoodlums broke the windowpanes in Douglass' Rochester printing shop.

These things weighed heavily on Garrison's spirits. For a while he had been uplifted by the belief that moral persuasion was winning over large sections of the country. Now he saw them fearfully grasping their possessions—repudiating everything except their "God-given" right to pile up dollars.

But across the country stalked one more grim man. His face was turned to the east—to the rising sun; his lanky, bony body rose endless on a prop of worn, out-size shoes.

And deep in the hollows of the South, behind the lonesome pine trees draped with moss, down in the corners of the cotton fields, in the middle of the night—the slaves were whispering. And their words rumbled like drums along the ground: *"Mistah Linkum is a-comin'! Praise da Lawd!"*

Washington was an armed city. "The new President of the United States will be inaugurated—" General Scott was as good as his word. But the crowds did not cheer when Abraham Lincoln appeared. There was a hush, as if all the world knew it was a solemn moment.

Douglass looked on the gaunt, strange beauty of that thin face—the resemblance to John Brown was startling—and as he bared his head, Douglass whispered, "He's our man, John Brown. He's our man!"

Amelia saw Frederick Douglass in the crowd. She tugged frantically at Jack Haley's arm.

"Look! Look!" she said. "It's him!"

Jack, turning his head, recognized the man he had heard speak years ago in Providence, Rhode Island. Older, yes, broader and grown in stature, but undoubtedly it was the same head, the same wild, sweeping mane.

As the crowd began to disperse and Douglass turned, he felt a light pull on his sleeve and looked down on a slight, white-haired woman whose piquant upturned face and bright blue eyes were vaguely familiar.

"Mr. Douglass?" Her voice fluttered in her throat.

"At your service, ma'am." Douglass managed to make a little bow, though the crowd pressed upon them. Her eyes widened.

"Still the same lovely manners!" she said. At this the tall man at her elbow spoke.

"Mr. Douglass, you will pardon us. I am Jack Haley, and this is Mrs. Amelia Kemp."

"Don't you remember me—Frederick?" She smiled wistfully as she said his name, and the years dissolved. He remembered the dahlias.

"Miss Amelia!" He took her hand, and his somber face lit up with delight.

"Could you come with us? Have you a little time?" Her words were bubbling over.

Douglass turned to Garrison, who was regarding the scene with some misgiving. They two were far from safe in Washington.

"I think we'd better leave at once," he said with a frown.

Douglass' face showed his disappointment. He said, and it was clear he meant it, "I'm terribly sorry, Miss Amelia."

Jack Haley turned to Garrison. His voice was low.

"I understand the situation, sir. But if I drove you directly to our house, I assure you we shall encounter no difficulties. We would be honored."

Once more Douglass looked hopefully at Garrison. The older man shrugged his shoulders.

The fringed-top carryall stood at the curb. Garrison helped Amelia into the back seat and sat down beside her. Douglass climbed into the front seat with Jack. As Jack picked up the reins, Douglass grinned and said, "I could drive, you know."

Jack gave a short laugh. "I realize, Mr. Douglass, that we're uncivilized down here. But stranger things than this are seen on Pennsylvania Avenue. Relax, we'll get home all right."

So they drove down the avenue past soldiers and visitors and legislators, all intent upon their own affairs. Louisiana Avenue with its wide greensward and early violets was loveliest of all.

For two days in the short period before the guns opened fire at Fort Sumter, Frederick Douglass and William Lloyd Garrison rested from their labors on a shaded side-street off Louisiana Avenue.

Up North the countryside was still locked in the hard rigors of winter, but here spring was in the air. He walked out in the yard, and told Miss Amelia about his big sons who kept the paper going during his many absences.

Succulent odors rose like incense from Amelia's kitchen—Maryland fried chicken, served with snowy mounds of rice, popovers and cherry pie—their fragrance hung in the air and brought her lodgers tumbling down from their rooms to inquire, "What's going on here?"

Amelia told them about her guests, swearing them to secrecy. They tiptoed out into the hall and peeped into the living room. On the second evening Miss Amelia gave in to their urgent requests.

"A few of my young friends to meet you, Frederick. You won't mind?" After supper they gathered round. Far into the night they asked questions and talked together, the ex-slave and young Americans who sorted mail, ran errands and wrote the letters of the legislators on Capitol Hill.

They were the boys who would have to drag their broken bodies across stubble fields, who would lie like filthy, grotesque rag dolls in the mud. They were the girls who would be childless or widowed or old before their lives had bloomed.

"It's been wonderful here, Miss Amelia." Douglas held her hand in parting.

"I've been proud to have you, Frederick." Her blue eyes looked up into his, and Douglass saw her tears.

He stooped and kissed her on the soft, withered cheek.

They said the war was inevitable. Madmen cannot hear words of reason. On only one thing was Lincoln unswerving—to preserve the Union. As concession after concession was made, it became more and more evident that this was what the slaveholders did not want. They were sick to death of the Union! In Georgia, Tennessee, North Carolina and Virginia white men struggled against the octopus of slavery. They did all they could to prevent the break. But the slavers had control—they had the power, they had the money, and they had the slaves.

So there was war, and slaves were set to digging ditches and building barricades.

From the beginning Frederick Douglass saw in the war the end of slavery. Much happened the first two years to shake his faith. Secretary of State William Seward instructed United States ministers to say to the governments where they were stationed that "terminate however it might, the status of no class of the people of the United States would be changed by the rebellion; slaves will be slaves still, and masters will be masters still." General McClellan and General Butler warned the slaves in advance that "if any attempt was made by them to gain their freedom it would be suppressed with an iron hand." Douglass grew sick with despair when President Lincoln quickly withdrew the emancipation proclamation made by General John C. Frémont in Missouri. Union soldiers were even stationed about the farmhouses of Virginia to guard the masters and help them hold their slaves.

The war was not going well. In the *North Star* and from the platform, Douglass reminded the North that it was fighting with one hand only, when it might strike effectually with two. The Northern states fought with their soft white hand, while they kept their black iron hand chained and helpless behind them. They fought the effect while they protected the cause. The Union would never prosper in the war until the Negro was enlisted, Douglass said.

On every side they howled him down.

"Give the blacks arms, and loyal men of the North will throw down their guns and go home!"

"This is the white man's country and the white man's war!"

"It would inflict an intolerable wound upon the pride and spirit of white soldiers to see niggers in the United States uniform."

"Anyhow, niggers won't fight—the crack of his old master's whip will send him scampering in terror from the field."

They made jokes about it.

White men died at Bull Run, Ball's Bluff, Big Bethel, and Fredericksburg. The Union Army needed more soldiers. They began drafting men—white men. In blind rage the whites turned on the helpless blacks.

"Why should we fight for you?" they screamed. On the streets of New York, black men and women were beaten, their workshops and stores destroyed, their homes burned. They burned the Colored Orphan Asylum in New York. Not all the children could be dragged from the blazing building.

Dougless wrote letters to Congress and got up petitions. "Let us fight!" he pleaded. "Give us arms!"

He pointed out that the South was sustaining itself and its army with Negro labor. At last General Butler at Fort Monroe announced the policy of treating the slaves as "contrabands" to be made useful to the Union cause. General Phelps, in command at Carrollton, Louisiana, advocated the same plan. The story of how the slaves flocked into these camps, how they worked, how they were glad to sustain their half-starved bodies on scraps left over by the soldiers, how they endured any and all hardships for this opportunity to do something to "hep Massa Linkum win da war" cannot be told here. But it convinced the administration that the Negro could be useful.

The second step was to give Negroes a peculiar costume which should distinguish them from soldiers and yet mark them as part of the loyal force. Finally so many Negroes presented themselves that it was proposed to give the laborers something better than spades and shovels with which to defend themselves in case of emergency.

"Still later it was proposed to make them soldiers," Douglass wrote, "but soldiers without blue uniform, soldiers with a mark upon them to show that they were inferior to other soldiers; soldiers with a badge of degradation upon them. However, once in the army as a laborer, once there with a red shirt on his back and a pistol in his belt, the Negro was not long in appearing on the field as a soldier. But still, he was not to be a soldier in the sense, and on an equal footing, with white soldiers. It was given out that he was not to be employed in the open field with white troops . . . doing battle and winning victories for the Union cause . . . in the teeth of his old masters; but that he should be made to garrison forts in yellow-fever and otherwise unhealthy localities of the South, to save the health of the white soldiers; and, in order to keep up the distinction further, the black soldiers were to have only half the wages of the white soldiers, and were to be commanded entirely by white commissioned officers."

Negroes all over the North looked at each other with drawn faces.

Almost the cup was too bitter. But up from the South came stories of how black fugitives were offering themselves as slaves to the Union armies—of the terrible retaliation meted out to them if caught—of how the Northern armies were falling back.

Then President Lincoln gave Governor Andrew of Massachusetts permission to raise two colored regiments. The day the news broke, Douglass came home waving his paper in the air. Anna's face blanched. Up from the table rose her two sons, Lewis and Charles.

"We'll be the first!" They dashed off to sign up. Young Frederic was in Buffalo that morning. When he got back, he heard where they had gone, and turned to follow them.

"Wait! Wait!" The mother's cry was heartbroken.

His father too said, "Wait." Then Douglass explained.

"This is only the first, my son. We'll have other regiments. There will be many regiments before the war is won. We must recruit black men from every state in our country—South as well as North." He looked at his tall son and sighed. "Unfortunately, I am known. I would be stopped before I could reach them in the South. Here is a job for some brave man."

They faced each other calmly, father and son, and neither was afraid.

"I understand, sir. I will go!"

A few evenings later, before an overflow audience at Corinthian Hall in Rochester, Frederick Douglass delivered an address which may be placed beside Patrick Henry's in Virginia. It appeared later in leading journals throughout the North and West under the caption "Men of Color, to Arms!"

"Action! Action, not criticism, is the plain duty of this hour. Words are now useful only as they stimulate to blows. The office of speech now is only to point out when, where, and how to strike to the best advantage." This was Douglass the spellbinder, Douglass, who had lifted thousands cheering to their feet in England, Ireland, and Scotland. "From East to West, from North to South, the sky is written all over 'Now or Never.' Liberty won by white men alone would lose half its luster. . . . Who would be free themselves must strike the blow."

The applause swept across the country. White men read these words and were shamed in their prejudices; poor men read them and thanked God for Frederick Douglass; black men read them and hurried to recruiting offices.

They were in the crowd on Boston Common the morning the Fifty-fourth Massachusetts marched away—a father and a mother come to see their two sons off to war. Douglass was not thinking of the credit due him for the formation of the first Negro regiment. He was remembering how Lewis had always wanted a pony and the way Charlie always left his shoes in the middle of the floor, to be stumbled over. He tried to stay the trembling in Anna's arm by pressing it close to his side. He wished he had somehow managed to get that pony.

The soldiers were standing at ease in the street when Charlie saw her. He waved his hand, and though he did not yell, she saw his lips form the words, "Hi, Mom!" She saw him nudge his brother and then—

They were marching, holding their colors high, the sun glinting on polished bayonets and reflected in their eyes. They marched away behind their gallant Captain Shaw, and as they went they sang a song:

"John Brown's body lies a-moldering in the grave
But his soul goes marching on."

CHAPTER FOURTEEN

Came January 1, 1863

THE TALL MAN'S footsteps made no sound upon the thick rug. Muffled and hushed, his weary pacing left no mark upon the warp and woof underneath his feet. No sign at all of all the hours he had been walking back and forth, no sound.

To save the Union—this was the aim and purpose of everything he did. He had offered concession after concession—he had sent men out to die to hold the Union together and he had seen the horror of their dying. And yet no end in sight. Could it be that God had turned his face away? Was He revolted by the stench of slavery? Was this the measure He required?

The President had sought to reason with them. In his last annual message to Congress he had proposed a constitutional amendment by which any state abolishing slavery by or before the year 1900 should be entitled to full compensation from the Federal government. So far he had postponed the day when a slave owner must take a loss. Nothing had come of the proposal—nothing.

To save the Union! Would emancipation drive the border states into revolt? Would it let loose a terror in the night that would destroy and rape and pillage all the land? He had been amply warned. Or were the Abolitionists right? George Thompson, the Englishman, had been very convincing; the President had talked with William Lloyd Garrison, who all these years had never wavered from his stand; and in this very room he had received the Negro, Frederick Douglass.

Douglass had stated his case so well, so completely, so wrapped in logic that the President had found himself defending his position to the ex-slave. He had sat quietly, listened patiently, and then spoken.

"It is the only way, Mr. Lincoln, the only way to save the Union," Douglass said.

Outside, the day was dark and lowering. The sun hid behind banks of muddy clouds; dirty snow lay heaped against the Capitol. The tall man dropped to his knees and buried his haggard face in his hands. "Thy will be done, oh God, Thy will!" He, Abraham Lincoln, fourteenth president of the United States, would stake his honor, his good name, all that he had to give, to preserve the Union. And down through the ages men would judge him by one day's deed. He rose from his knees, turned and pulled the cord that summoned his secretary.

In Boston they were waiting. This was the day when the government was to set its face against slavery. Though the conditions on which the President had promised to withhold the proclamation had not been complied with, there was room for doubt and fear. Mr. Lincoln was a man of tender heart and boundless patience; no man could tell to what lengths he might go for peace and reconciliation. An emancipation proclamation would end all compromises with slavery, change the entire conduct of the war, give it a new aim.

They held watch-meetings in all the colored churches on New Year's Eve and went on to a great mass meeting in Tremont Temple, which extended through the day and evening. A grand jubilee concert in Music Hall was scheduled for the afternoon. They expected the President's proclamation to reach the city by noon. But the day wore on, and fears arose that it might not, after all, be forthcoming.

The orchestra played Beethoven's *Fifth Symphony*, the chorus sang Handel's *Hallelujah Chorus*, Ralph Waldo Emerson read his "Boston Hymn," written for the occasion—but still no word. A line of messengers was set up between the telegraph office and the platform of Tremont Temple. William Wells Brown, the Reverend Mr. Grimes, Miss Anna Dickinson, Frederick Douglass—all had said their lines. But speaking or listening to speeches was not the thing for which people had come together today. They were waiting.

Eight, nine, ten o'clock came and went, and still no word. Frederick Douglass walked to the edge of the platform. He stood there without saying a word, and before the awful stillness of his helplessness the stirrings of the crowd quieted. His voice was hoarse.

"Ladies and gentlemen—I know the time for argument has passed. Our ears are not attuned to logic or the sound of many words. It is the trumpet of jubilee which we await."

"Amen, God of our fathers, hear!" The fervent prayer had come from a black man who had dropped to his knees on the platform behind Douglass. There was a responding murmur from the crowd. Douglass stood a moment with his head bowed. Then he continued:

"We are watching for the dawn of a new day. We are waiting for the answer to the agonizing prayers of centuries. We—" His eyes were caught by a movement in the crowd packed around the doors. He held his breath. A man ran down the aisle.

"It's coming— It's coming over the wires! Now!" he shouted.

The shout that went up from the crowd carried the glad tidings to the streets. Men and women screamed—they tossed their hats into the air—strangers embraced one another, weeping. Garrison, standing in the gallery, was cheered madly; Harriet Beecher Stowe, her bonnet awry, tears streaming down her cheeks, was lifted to a bench. After a while they quieted down to hear the reading of the text . . . "are, and henceforward shall be, free." Then the Reverend Charles Rue, the black man behind Douglass, lifted his magnificent voice and led them as they sang,

> "Sound the loud timbrel o'er Egypt's dark sea,
> Jehovah hath triumphed, his people are free."

Cables carried the news across the Atlantic. Crowds thronged the streets of London and Liverpool. Three thousand workmen of Manchester, many of them present sufferers from the cotton famine, adopted by acclamation an address to President Lincoln congratulating him on the Proclamation. George Thompson led a similar meeting in Lancashire, and in Exeter Hall a great demonstration meeting was addressed by John Stuart Mill.

But it was from the deep, deep South that the sweetest music came. It was an old song—old as the first man, lifting himself from the mire and slime of some dark river bed and feeling the warm sun upon his face, old as the song they sang crossing the Red Sea, old as the throbbing of drums deep in the jungles, old as the song of all men everywhere who would be free. It was a new song, the loveliest thing born this side of the seas, fresh and verdant and young, full as the promise of this new America—the Delta's rich, black earth; the tall, thick trees upon a thousand hills; the fairy, jeweled beauty of the bayous; the rolling plains of the Mississippi. Black folks made a song that day.

They crouched in their cabins, hushed and still. Old men and women who had prayed so long—broken, close to the end, they waited for this glorious thing. Young men and women, leashed in their strength, twisted in bondage—they waited. Mothers grasped their babies in their arms—waiting.

Some of them listened for a clap of thunder that would rend the world apart. Some strained their eyes toward the sky, waiting for God upon a cloud to bring them freedom. Anything was possible, they whispered, waiting.

They recognized His shining angels when they came: a tired and dirty soldier, in a torn and tattered uniform; a grizzled old man hobbling out from town; a breathless woman, finding her way through the swamp to tell them; a gaunt, white "cracker" risking his life to let them know; a fleet-footed black boy, running, running down the road. These were the messengers who brought them word.

And the song of joy went up. Free! Free! Free! Black men and women lifted their quivering hands and shouted across the fields. The rocks and trees, the rivers and the mountains echoed their voices—the universe was glad the morning freedom's song rang in the South.

Part IV

TOWARD MORNING

The seeds of the Declaration of Independence are slowly ripening.

—JOHN QUINCY ADAMS

CHAPTER FIFTEEN

When lilacs last in the dooryard bloomed

"WHEN THE HEBREWS were emancipated they were told to take spoil from the Egyptians. When the serfs of Russia were emancipated, they were given three acres of ground upon which they could live and make a living. But not so when our slaves were emancipated. They were sent away empty-handed, without money, without friends, and without a foot of land to stand upon. Old and young, sick and well were turned loose to the open sky, naked to their enemies."

Fifteen years later Douglass was to say this to a tense audience, their large eyes, so bright that "freedom morning," veiled again with pain. If only Lincoln had been spared! How many times in the months and years had they harked back to that towering figure and asked, *"Why?"*

It is true that Lincoln's freeing of the slaves was a war measure, but with the enactment of that measure the President steered the Ship of State into uncharted waters. To whom could he turn for counsel? Not to a Cabinet dolefully prophesying disaster; not to a Secretary of War who had considered the occupation of Sumter by United States soldiers a deadly insult to the Southern states; not to a General who vacillated, delayed, quarreled and called his own men "a confused mob, entirely demoralized."

Lincoln sent for Frederick Douglass. It was proof of how far and how fast he was traveling. He had no precedent. Everything the President read or heard in his day treated all colored peoples as less than human. He was born and nurtured in the church which said fervent prayers of thanks that slavers "tore the savage from the wilds of Africa and brought him to Christianity." The unquestioned inferiority of a black man was in the very air that Lincoln breathed. And yet he turned to Douglass.

He did not receive the dark man in the office of the Executive Mansion, but out on the back porch. There were times when the tinted walls, drapes and heavy rugs of the imposing house stifled this "common man" from the West. At such times he chose the porch, with its vista of green.

"Sit down, Mr. Douglass," he said, motioning to a wide, easy chair. "I want to talk to you."

Mainly he wished to confer that afternoon about the best means, outside the Army, to induce slaves in the rebel states to come within Federal lines.

"I fear that a peace might be forced upon me which would leave the former slaves in a kind of bondage worse even than that they have known." Then he added, his voice heavy with disappointment, "They are not coming to us as rapidly and in as large numbers as I had hoped."

Douglass replied that probably many obstacles were being placed in their path.

The President nodded his head. He was troubled in heart and mind. He said he was being accused of protracting the war beyond its legitimate object and of failing to make peace when he might have done so to advantage. He saw the dangers of premature peace, but mainly he wanted to prepare for what lay ahead when peace did come, early or late.

"Four millions suddenly added to the country's population!" Lincoln said earnestly. "What can we do, Douglas?" Before Douglass could reply, the President leaned forward, his eyes intent. "I understand you oppose every suggestion for colonization."

"That is true, Mr. Lincoln. Colonization is not the answer."

"Why?"

"These people are not Africans. They know nothing about Africa —whatever roots they had have been destroyed. We were born here, in America."

The President sighed.

"I realize our responsibility, Douglass. We cannot set back the clock. We brought your people here, we made them work for us. We owe them for all these years of labor. But the fact remains that they are alien and apart. Can they ever fit into the life of this country?"

Douglass spoke very gently.

"This is the only land we know, Mr. Lincoln. We have tilled its fields, we have cleared its forests, we have built roads and bridges. This is our home. We are alien and apart only because we have been forced apart." Then he began to tell the President of Negroes who had been living and working in free states. He told of artisans and skilled craftsmen, of bakers, shoemakers and clockmakers; he told about schoolteachers, doctors, Negroes who, after being educated in Europe, had chosen to return.

Mr. Lincoln listened with growing amazement. Perhaps he thought to himself, *If only all of them were like this man Douglass!* But being the simple, honest soul he was, it is certain another thought came after, *Few men are like this Douglass!*

They sat together through the long summer afternoon, and worked out a plan. Other callers were turned away. "The President can see no one," they were told.

They decided that Douglass would organize a band of colored scouts who would go into the South, beyond the Union Army lines, and bring the slaves together as free workers.

"They will be paid something. I can't say what."

"They will come, sir!"

From time to time Douglass scribbled a note of instruction for the President's aides. Neither noticed the time. They were only concerned in mapping out a clear course of action. At last the President leaned back and the visitor gathered up his papers.

"From here," Lincoln said, "we'll move as we must. You will have to—"

His secretary came out on the porch. "Sir!" Lincoln nodded his head. "A courier has just arrived. He brings a communication from General Stephenson."

Lincoln jerked himself erect.

"Show him out here!"

There was despair in the way the President pressed his hand against his forehead.

"It is bad news," he explained. "Otherwise they would have wired."

"I'll go, sir!" Douglass rose to his feet. Lincoln's tall form lifted itself. He looked out across the lawn without seeing it.

"Navy guns have been bombarding Fort Wagner for several days. We were planning an attack. Surely—" He stopped as the two men came out on the porch.

The courier was only a boy. His eyes were bloodshot, and his uniform was streaked and spattered. He swayed a little as he bowed and extended a letter.

"General Stephenson sends his greetings, sir."

Lincoln's eyes were on the boy as his shaking fingers tore at the envelope.

"Why do you not come from General Strong?"

"General Stephenson is now in command of the two brigades." He stopped, but the President's eyes still questioned him and he added, "General Strong and Colonel Putnam have been killed."

Then Lincoln looked down at the single sprawled sheet. His lips began to move, and some of his words were distinct enough for Douglass to hear.

"On the night of July 18 we moved on Fort Wagner . . . the Sixth Connecticut, Forty-eighth Infantry New York, Third New Hampshire, Seventy-sixth Pennsylvania, Ninth Maine. . . ." He read on, then cried out, "Douglass! Listen to this!"

"The honor of leading the charge was given to the Fifty-fourth Massachusetts. I must report, sir, that these black soldiers advanced without flinching and held their ground in the face of blasting fire which mowed them down cruelly. Only a remnant of the thousand men can be accounted for. Their commander, Colonel Robert Shaw, is missing. We had counted on aid from the guns of the fleet—troops in the rear could not—" The President stopped.

Douglass' breath had escaped from his tense body in a groan. Now he gasped.

"I must go— Forgive me. I must go to my wife!"

The President took a step toward him, understanding and concern in his face. "You mean—?"

"Our sons—Lewis and Charles—in the Fifty-fourth."

Lincoln laid his hand on Douglass' arm, then spoke quickly to his secretary.

"See that the courier has food and rest. Wire General Stephenson for the list."

Then he was walking to the door with Douglass, his arm through his.

"Extend to your wife my deepest sympathy. I commend you both to God, who alone can give you strength. Keep me informed. You will hear from me."

The news of the defeat ran on ahead of him. Anna was standing in the hall, waiting. He took her in his arms, and for a few moments neither spoke. Then she said, "There is no word—yet."

Days passed, and they told themselves that no news was good news. Gradually names were made public. Horace Greeley hailed the Fifty-fourth Massachusetts as the "black phalanx." Newspapers throughout the North said that the Negro soldier had "proven himself." Southern papers used different words to tell the story, but they verified the fact that it was black bodies which filled the hastily dug trenches all around Fort Wagner. They had come upon a white body which was identified as the commander. It was said the order had been given to "dump him among his niggers!"

Anna Douglass wrote a letter to Robert Shaw's mother, who lived in Boston.

"The struggle is now over for your brave son. Take comfort in the thought that he died as he lived, that he lies with those who loved him so devotedly."

And still no word of Charles and Lewis.

Douglass did not tell Anna about a letter he had written to Abraham Lincoln. But when the reply came, he showed her the enclosed note, which read:

To whom it may concern:

The bearer of this, Frederick Douglass, is known to us as a loyal, free man, and is hence entitled to travel unmolested.

We trust he will be recognized everywhere as a free man and a gentleman.

Respectfuly,
A. Lincoln, President
I. K. Usha, Secretary

August 10, 1863

Anna lifted her eyes in a question.

"I'm going to South Carolina."

She pressed her hand against her shaking lips.

"They'll kill you—too!" she said. He shook his head.

"Our troops are encamped on the islands in and about Charleston harbor. The regiments are mixed up. There are so many wounded that I can be a real help by straightening out the record. Many homes do not know." And he kissed her.

She watched him shave off his beard. She gave him a large box of food.

"I'll find the boys!" His assurance cheered her.

He did find them—each on a different island—among the wounded. Charles thought him simply another figment of his feverish dreams. Lewis had been trying to get word out.

The news ran along the cots and out into the swamps:

"Frederick Douglass is here!"

Their cause was not lost.

There were times that fall when strong hearts quailed. Criticism against Abraham Lincoln mounted. Finally it became clear that Lincoln would not be re-elected by the politicians, the bankers, big business, or the press. The campaign of 1864 was, therefore, waged in country stores, at crossroads, from the backs of carts driving along city streets, in public squares and on church steps.

The young Republican party now had to face a completely united Democratic party which came forward with the story that the war was a failure. They chose the dismissed General George B. McClellan as their candidate and wrapped him in the ambiguous mist of an abused hero. But they reckoned without the inspired tactics of his successor, Ulysses S. Grant. The tide turned. "Lincoln's man" was doing the job. Now Sherman was "marching to the sea," and the backbone of the Confederacy was broken.

The people returned Abraham Lincoln to the White House.

With Lincoln safe, Douglass took the stump for the strengthening of the Emancipation Proclamation. The next step was to pass the Thirteenth Amendment, abolishing slavery by law.

In October, Douglass and John Langston called a National Convention of Colored Men for a four-day session in Syracuse. People still could not believe that the war would end in complete emancipation of all slaves. Douglass called upon this convention of free artisans, craftsmen and laborers in the free Northern states to take their place inside the governmental framework.

"Events more mighty than men—eternal Providence, all-wide and all-controlling," he told them, "have placed us in new relations to the government and the government to us. What that government is to us today, and what it will be tomorrow, is made evident by a very few facts. Look at them, colored men. Slavery in the District of Columbia is abolished forever; slavery in all the territories of the United States is abolished forever; the foreign slave trade, with its ten thousand revolting abominations, is rendered impossible; slavery in ten states of the Union is abolished forever; slavery in the five remaining states is as certain to follow the same fate as the night is to follow the day. The independence of Haiti is recognized; her minister sits beside our "Prime Minister," Mr. Seward, and dines at his table in Washington, while colored men are excluded from the cars in Philadelphia . . . a black man's complexion in Washington, in the presence of the Federal government, is less offensive than in the City of Brotherly Love. Citizenship is no longer denied us under this government."

The minutes of the convention were sent to President Lincoln. In December Lincoln laid the Thirteenth Amendment before Congress, and in January, 1865, slavery was forever abolished from any part of the United States "or any place subject to their jurisdiction."

Tirelessly, ceaselessly, Lincoln weighed every move he made. No harsh words, no condemnation—he recognized human weakness. "*Our* responsibility," he said. Not the South's alone, not merely the slaveholder's. He did not cant of "sins" and "virtues."

He read the appeal addressed to Governor Shepley by the "free men of color" in New Orleans, asking to be allowed to "register and vote." They reminded him of their defense of New Orleans against the British under General Jackson, and declared their present loyalty to the Union. In March he wrote the following letter to the newly elected Governor Hahn:

EXECUTIVE MANSION, WASHINGTON
March 13, 1864

Honorable Michael Hahn

MY DEAR SIR: In congratulating you on having fixed your name in history as the first Free State Governor of Louisiana, now you are about to have a convention which, among other things, will probably define the elective franchise, I barely suggest, for your private consideration, whether some of the colored people may not be let on, as for instance, the very intelligent, and especially those who have fought gallantly in our ranks. They would probably help in some trying time in the future to keep the jewel of Liberty in the family of freedom. But this is only suggestion, not to the public, but to you alone.

Truly yours,

A. LINCOLN *

* Du Bois, *Black Reconstruction*, chap. vi, p. 157.

Long afterward Douglass wondered if it was some awful presentiment that made his heart so heavy on the second Inauguration Day. Abraham Lincoln's voice lacked the resonance and liquid sweetness with which men stirred vast audiences. He spoke slowly, carefully, as if each word were a gift of himself to them—his last words to his people.

"With malice toward none, with charity for all, with firmness in the right as God gives us to see the right, let us strive to finish the work we are in, to bind up the nation's wounds, to care for him who shall have borne the battle, and for his widow and his orphans, to do all which may achieve and cherish a just and lasting peace among ourselves and with all nations."

A blackness engulfed Douglass for a time. He was unconscious of having pushed forward. The ceremonies over, there was jostling and movement all around him. Then over the heads of all the crowd, he saw President Lincoln looking at him—he saw his face light up with a smile of welcome. Douglass started toward him when he was stopped by something else. Andrew Johnson, the Vice-President, stood beside Lincoln.

"Mr. Lincoln touched Mr. Johnson and pointed me out to him," Douglass wrote, describing the incident. "The first expression which came to his face, and which I think was the true index of his heart, was one of bitter contempt and aversion. Seeing that I observed him, he tried to assume a more friendly appearance, but it was too late; it is useless to close the door when all within has been seen. His first glance was the frown of the man; the second was the bland and sickly smile of the demagogue." *

He turned aside, again engulfed in gloom. "Whatever Andrew Johnson may be," he thought, "he certainly is no friend of my race."

The same evening in the spacious East Room, at such an affair as he had never in his own country been privileged to attend before, he tried to put aside his misgivings. He simply ignored the startled glances turned in his direction. His card of admission was beyond question.

Even in this most brilliant of gatherings, Frederick Douglass was an impressive figure. He was faultlessly groomed. His magnificent head towered over any crowd, and he moved with poise and dignity. It is no wonder that the President saw him standing in line among the others.

* Douglass, *Life and Times of Frederick Douglass*, chap. xii, p. 442.

"Ah! Here comes my friend Douglass," Lincoln said playfully.

Taking Douglass by the hand he said, "I saw you in the crowd today, listening to my speech. Did you like it?"

Douglass smiled, a little embarrassed. He had no desire to hold up the line.

"Mr. Lincoln, I mustn't detain you with my opinions," he almost whispered. "There are a thousand people waiting to shake hands with you."

Lincoln was in an almost jovial mood that evening. He laughed softly.

"Nonsense," he said, "stop a little, Douglass. There's no man in the country whose opinion I value more than yours. I really want to know what you thought of it."

Douglass tried to tell him. In the years to come he wished he had found better words.

"Mr. Lincoln, your words today were sacred," he said. "They will never die."

Lincoln seemed satisfied. His face lit up.

"I'm glad you liked it."

Douglass rejoiced that Lincoln had his hour—an hour when he was bathed in joyful tears of gratitude. It happened on a soft, spring day in Richmond. General Weitzel had taken the city a few days before, with the Twenty-ninth Connecticut Colored Regiment at his back. Now on this April morning, the battered city was very still. White people who could leave had fled. The others shut themselves inside, behind closed doors and drawn shades. But lilacs were blooming in their yards.

It was a Negro soldier who saw the little rowboat pull up at the dock and a tall gaunt man, leading a little boy, step out. He waved back the sailors, who moved to follow him.

"We'll go alone," he said. Taking the little boy by the hand, he started up the embankment to the street.

"Which way to our headquarters?" he asked the soldier. The soldier had never seen Abraham Lincoln, but he recognized him. He saluted smartly.

"I'll direct you, sir," he offered. He was trembling. The President smiled and shook his head.

"Just tell me."

It was straight ahead up the street—Jefferson Davis' mansion. He couldn't miss it. The soldier watched him go. He wanted to shout.

He wanted to run—to spread the news—but he could not leave his post.

No conquering hero he—just a tired man, walking down the street, his deeply lined, sad face lifted to the few trees showing their spring leaves. All around him lay the ravages of war. Suddenly a black boy turned into the way and stared.

"Glory! Hit's Mistah Lincoln!" he yelled.

And then they came from all the by-streets and the lanes. They came shouting his name, flinging their hats into the air, waving their hands. The empty streets thronged with black folks. They stretched their hands and called out:

"Gawd bless yo', Mistah Lincolm!"

"T'ank yo' kin'ly, Mistah Lincolm!"

"T'ank yo'! Praise de Lawd!"

An old man dropped upon his knees and kissed his hand.

They saw the tears streaming down Lincoln's face, and a hush fell over those nearest him as he laid his hand upon the bowed white head, then stooped and helped the old man to his feet.

"God bless you—God keep you all!" Lincoln could say no more at the moment. They allowed him to move along his way, but by the time he had reached his destination as far as he could see the streets were black.

They waited while he went inside—waiting, cheering, and singing at intervals. When he came out he stood on the high steps and lifted his hands for silence. Many of them dropped on their knees and all listened, their faces turned to him as to the sun. He spoke simply, sharing their joy. He accepted their devotion, but he said, "God has made you free." They knew he had come from God.

"Although you have been deprived of your God-given rights by your so-called masters, you are now as free as I am; and if those that claim to be your superiors do not know that you are free, take the sword and bayonet and teach them that you are—for God created all men free, giving to each the same rights of life, liberty and the pursuit of happiness."

He went away with their voices in his ears. A few days later came Appomattox; and Lincoln, his face flushed, his eyes bright, his strength renewed by secret wells of energy, covered his desk with plans for reconstruction. Not a day to lose, not a moment. The wounds must be healed, a better, stronger nation rise.

The President called his Cabinet together for April 14, then sent a wire off to William Lloyd Garrison asking him to go to Fort Sumter for the raising of the Stars and Stripes there. Garrison joyfully obeyed. With him were Henry Ward Beecher and George Thompson, antislavery men who could now rejoice.

The flag was raised, and singing filled the air; the waters were covered with flowers, and the guns fired their triumphant salute. They were on the steamer headed farther south when, at Beaufort, they were handed a telegram.

Abraham Lincoln was dead!

"I mourn'd, and yet shall mourn with ever-returning spring."

CHAPTER SIXTEEN

Moving forward

THE AMERICAN ANTI-SLAVERY SOCIETY disbanded and its agents were withdrawn from the fields. The last number of the *Liberator* came out.

"The object for which the *Liberator* was commenced thirty-five years ago having been gloriously consummated—" wrote the white-haired editor. He could now close his office. The slaves were free—his job was finished. Garrison sailed for England and the Continent.

Frederick Douglass, dragging himself through the weeks, hardly heeded what was being done. He caught some words of Wendell Phillips' passionate plea: the Thirteenth Amendment had not yet become law; even after ratification it had to be carried out. But he had taken no part in the discussions. His occupation was gone and his salary—the Anti-Slavery Society had paid him about five hundred dollars a year—cut off. Lewis came home. Frederic was working with the Freedman's Bureau in Mississippi. Douglass made sporadic attempts to think of how he would earn a living. The newspaper hung heavy on his hands. An idea occurred to him. With the few thousand dollars Anna had saved from the sales of his book, *My Bondage and My Freedom*, he had best buy a farm, settle down and earn an honest living by tilling the soil.

But nothing seemed of any real importance.

"John Brown and Abraham Lincoln!" He lay awake at night linking the two names. Time seemed endless.

Yet it was only the latter part of June when President Johnson made Benjamin F. Perry, former member of the Confederate legislature, the Provisional Governor of South Carolina. Perry promptly put things back the way they had been "before Lincoln." He conferred

240

suffrage upon all citizens who had been legal voters prior to Secession.
He called for an election by these people of delegates to a Constitutional Convention to be held in September. In his opening address as
Provisional Governor, the Honorable Mr. Perry stated his platform
very clearly. "This is a white man's government, and intended for
white men only."

Horace Greeley reported the facts in the *Tribune* together with
a grim editorial.

Douglass shook with rage. His anger was directed not at the
Southern Provisional Governor but at the man who now sat in Abraham Lincoln's place. For a moment his hate for Andrew Johnson
consumed every rational thought. Then his mind began to clear—to
race, to leap forward. The moment broke his lethargy.

"John Brown and Lincoln—yes!" He spoke aloud. "But I'm
living. *I* am still here!" He struck the desk with his fist. "And by
God we'll fight!"

Then, seizing his pen, he swept aside the papers that had been
gathering dust, and on a clean white page he began to write.

"The liberties of the American people are dependent upon the
ballot-box, the jury box and the cartridge box. . . . Freedmen must
have the ballot if they would retain their freedom!"

His words sounded across the country. In many instances they
filled people, already worn out and war-weary, with dismay. The
ballot was such a vast advance beyond the former objects proclaimed
by the friends of the colored race that it struck men as preposterous
and wholly inadmissible. Antislavery men were far from united as to
the wisdom of Douglass' stand. At first William Lloyd Garrison was
not ready to join in the idea, but he was soon found on the right side.
As Douglass said of him, "A man's head will not long remain wrong,
when his heart is right."

But if at first Garrison thought it was too much to ask, Wendell
Phillips saw not only the justice, but the wisdom and necessity, of the
measure.

"I shall never leave the Negro until, so far as God gives me the
power, I achieve [absolute equality before the law—absolute civil
equality]," he thundered from his pulpit.

Enfranchisement of the freedmen was resisted on two main
grounds: first, the tendency of the measure to bring the freedmen into
conflict with the old master-class and the white people of the South
generally; second, their unfitness, by reason of their ignorance, ser-

vility and degradation, to exercise over the destinies of the nation so great a power as the ballot.

"We've set them free! By Heaven, that's enough! Let them go tc work and prove themselves!" So spake the North, anxious to get back to "business as usual."

But deep down in the land there was a mighty stirring. Words had been said that could not be recalled—*henceforth, and forever free.*

There were no stories of killings, massacre or rape by the freed blacks. Whitelaw Reid, touring the South, reported: "The Negroes everywhere are quiet, respectful and peaceful; they are the only group at work." And the Alexandria *Gazette* said "the Negroes generally behave themselves respectfully toward the whites."

At first there was much roaming about. Husbands set out to find wives; and wives, idle, sat on the flat ground, believing they would come. Mothers who had never set foot off the plantation, struck out across the country to find their children; and children—like dirty, scared, brown animals—swarmed aimlessly. There was sickness and death. Freedman's Aid Societies floundered around in a vacuum, well-intentioned, doling out relief here and there; but what the black man needed was a place where he could stand—a tiny, little part of the great earth and a tool in his right hand.

William Freeland, master of Freelands, sat on his high-pillared porch staring at the unkempt, tangled yard. Weeds and briers choking everything—shrubbery, close-fisted, intricately branched, suffocating the rambler. In the fields beyond, nothing was growing save long grass, thistles and fierce suckers; and over the pond a scum had gathered, frothing and buoyed with its own gases.

Though past sixty when the war began, William Freeland, ashamed that Maryland was undecided, had gone to Richmond and volunteered. He had cut a fine figure riding away on his horse—his well-tailored gray uniform setting off the iron gray of his hair. The ladies of Richmond had leaned from their windows, fluttering lace handkerchiefs. They would not have recognized him when he came back to Freelands. His hair was thinned and white, his uniform a tattered, filthy rag; the bony nag he rode could scarcely make it to the old sycamore.

But the house still stood. It had not been pillaged or burned. His land had not been plowed with cannon; it was not soaked with blood. Suddenly the spring evening was cold, and he shuddered. Involuntarily his hand reached toward the bell. Then it fell back. No one would answer. Old Sue was in the kitchen, but she was too deaf to hear.

He would have to get some help on the place. The thought of paying wages to the ungrateful blacks filled him with rage. The cause of all the suffering and woe, they had turned on their masters, running after Yankees. Some of them had even shot white men! Gall bit into his soul as he remembered the strutting colored soldiers in Richmond.

The sound of a cart coming up the drive broke into his gloomy meditation. The master frowned. A side road led around to the back. Peddlers' carts had no place on the drive. Then he remembered. This was probably the man he was expecting—impudent upstart! His hand shook, but he braced himself. He had promised to listen to him.

"He's likely a damn Yankee, though he claims he's from Georgia," Freeland's friend, the Colonel, had said. "But he's got a scheme for getting the niggers back in their place. He says they're dying like flies on the roads, they'll be glad to get back to work. Just bide your time, old man, we'll have all our niggers back. Where can they go?"

The master did not rise to greet his guest. He hated the sniveling oaf. But before the cart went rumbling back along the drive the owner of Freelands had parted with precious dollars.

Similar transactions were being carried on all over the South that spring.

"Were the planters willing to bestow the same amount of money upon the laborers as additional wages, as they pay to runners and waste in dishonest means of compulsion, they would have drawn as many voluntary and faithful laborers as they now obtain reluctant ones. But there are harpies, who, most of them, were in the slave trade, and who persuade planters to use them as brokers to supply the plantations with hands, at the same time using all means to deceive the simple and unsophisticated laborer." *

But things were stirring in the land. Frederick Douglass in Rochester sending out his paper—sending it South! The handsome, popular Francis L. Cardoza, charming young Negro Presbyterian minister in New Haven, Connecticut, resigning his Church and saying, "I'm going South!"

"What!" his parishioners exclaimed.

* Du Bois, *Black Reconstruction*, chap. xi, p. 464.

"Going to Charleston, *South* Carolina." And he grinned almost impishly while they stared at him, wondering if they had heard right. Francis Cardoza had been in school in Europe while the Anti-Slavery Societies were lighting their fires. Having finished his work at the University of Glasgow, he had accepted a call from New Haven. But now he heard another call—more urgent. He packed up his books. He would need them in South Carolina—land of his fathers.

Three colored refugees from Santo Domingo pooled their assets and started a paper in New Orleans. They called it the *New Orleans Tribune*, and published it as a daily during 1865. After that year it continued as a weekly until sometime in 1869. It was published in French and English, and copies were sent to members of Congress. Its editor, Paul Trevigne, whose father had fought in the War of 1812, wanted to bring Louisiana "under a truly democratic system of labor." He cited a new plan of credit for the people being tried in Europe. "We, too, need credit for the laborers," he wrote. "We cannot expect complete and perfect freedom for the workingmen, as long as they remain the tools of capital and are deprived of the legitimate product of the sweat of their brow." *

It was in September that a friend in South Carolina sent Douglass a clipping from the *Columbia Daily Phoenix*, certainly *not* an Abolitionist sheet. It was dated September 23, 1865, and as Douglass read his face lighted up with joy. Here was the right and proper challenge to Provisional Governor Perry—a challenge from within his own state! "A large meeting of freedmen, held on St. Helena Island on the 4th instant" had adopted a set of resolutions—five clearly stated, well-written paragraphs. Douglass reprinted the entire account in his own paper, crediting its source. People read and could scarcely believe what they read—coming as it did from the "ignorant, servile blacks" in the lowlands.

1. *Resolved,* That we, the colored residents of St. Helena Island, do most respectfully petition the Convention about to be assembled at Columbia, on the 13th instant, to so alter and amend the present Constitution of this state as to give the right of suffrage to every man of twenty-one years, without other qualifications than that required for the white citizens of the states.
2. *Resolved,* That, by the Declaration of Independence, we believe these are rights which cannot justly be denied us, and

* *New Orleans Tribune,* Jan. 17, 1865.

we hope the Convention will do us full justice by recognizing them.

3. *Resolved*, That we will never cease our efforts to obtain, by all just and legal means, a full recognition of our rights as citizens of the United States and this Commonwealth.

4. *Resolved*, That, having heretofore shown our devotion to the Government, as well as our willingness to defend its Constitution and laws, therefore we trust that the members of the Convention will see the justice of allowing us a voice in the election of our rulers.

5. *Resolved*, That we believe the future peace and welfare of this state depends very materially upon the protection of the interests of the colored men and can only be secured by the adoption of the sentiments embodied in the foregoing resolutions.

The week of the thirteenth came and went. Douglass scanned the papers in vain for any mention of the petition or of anything concerning the "new citizens" of South Carolina. In October came a letter from Francis Cardoza, whom Douglass had met but did not know very well. He said, "I wish to thank you for giving publicity to the petition sent in by our people on St. Helena. Your cooperation strengthened their hearts. As you know, as yet nothing has come of it, nor of the longer document drawn up and presented by 103 Negroes assembled in Charleston. I have a copy of the Charleston petition. Should you be in Washington any time soon I'll gladly meet you there with it. These men are neither to be pitied nor scorned. They know that they are only at the beginning. With the ballot they will become useful, responsible, functioning citizens of the state. Without the ballot—sooner or later, there will be war."

Douglass immediately got in touch with certain influential men. "I propose," he said, "that a committee go to Washington and lay the matter of the freedmen's enfranchisement squarely before President Johnson." His face darkened for a moment. "Perhaps I misjudge the man," he added. "He is faced with a gigantic task. It is our duty to give him every assistance."

They rallied round, and a delegation of colored people from Illinois, Wisconsin, Alabama, Mississippi, Florida, South Carolina, North Carolina, Virginia, Maryland, Pennsylvania, New York, the New England states and the District of Columbia was called together. George Downing, of Rhode Island, and Frederick Douglass were named spokesmen. A letter was dispatched to the White House requesting an interview with the President.

After several weeks, the answer came. The President would receive the delegation February 7. Douglass sent off a note to Cardoza saying when he would be in Washington and suggesting the home of "my dear friend, Mrs. Amelia Kemp" as the place of meeting.

An account of Johnson's interview with the "Negro delegation" has gone into the historical archives of Washington. It received nationwide publicity both because of what was said and because of Frederick Douglass' gift for rebuttal.

"Until that interview," Douglass wrote in his *Life and Times*, "the country was not fully aware of the intentions and policy of President Johnson on the subject of reconstruction, especially in respect of the newly emancipated class of the South. After having heard the brief addresses made to him by Mr. Downing and myself, he occupied at least three-quarters of an hour in what seemed a set speech, and refused to listen to any reply on our part, although solicited to grant a few moments for that purpose. Seeing the advantage that Mr. Johnson would have over us in getting his speech paraded before the country in the morning papers, the members of the delegation met on the evening of that day, and instructed me to prepare a brief reply, which should go out to the country simultaneously with the President's speech to us. Since this reply indicates the points of difference between the President and ourselves, I produce it here as a part of the history of the times, it being concurred in by all the members of the delegation."

1. The first point to which we feel especially bound to take exception, is your attempt to found a policy opposed to our enfranchisement, upon the alleged ground of an existing hostility on the part of the former slaves toward the poor white people of the South. We admit the existence of this hostility, and hold that it is entirely reciprocal. But you obviously commit an error by drawing an argument from an incident of slavery, and making it a basis for a policy adapted to a state of freedom. The hostility between the whites and blacks of the South is easily explained. It has its root and sap in the relation of slavery, and was incited on both sides by the cunning of the slave masters. Those masters secured their ascendancy over both the poor whites and blacks by putting enmity between them.

They divided both to conquer each. There was no earthly reason why the blacks should not hate and dread the poor whites when in a state of slavery, for it was from this class that their masters received their slave-catchers, slave-drivers, and overseers. They were the men called in upon all occasions by the masters whenever any fiendish outrage was to be committed upon the slave. Now, sir, you cannot but perceive that, the cause of this hatred removed, the effect must be removed also. Slavery is abolished. . . . You must see that it is altogether illogical to legislate from slaveholding premises for a people whom you have repeatedly declared it your purpose to maintain in freedom.

2. Besides, even if it were true, as you allege, that the hostility of the blacks toward the poor whites must necessarily project itself into a state of freedom, and that this enmity between the two races is even more intense in a state of freedom than in a state of slavery, in the name of heaven, we ask how can you, in view of your professed desire to promote the welfare of the black man, deprive him of all means of defense, and clothe him whom you regard as his enemy in the panoply of political power? Can it be that you recommend a policy which would arm the strong and cast down the defenseless? . . . Peace between races is not to be secured by degrading one race and exalting another; by giving power to one race and withholding it from another; but by maintaining a state of equal justice between all classes.

3. On the colonization theory you were pleased to broach, very much could be said. It is impossible to suppose, in view of the usefulness of the black man in time of peace as a laborer in the South, and in time of war as a soldier in the North . . . that there can ever come a time when he can be removed from this country without a terrible shock to its prosperity and peace. Besides, the worst enemy of the nation could not cast upon its fair name a greater infamy than to admit that Negroes could be tolerated among them in a state of the most degrading slavery and oppression, and must be cast away, driven into exile, for no other cause than having been freed from their chains.*

The open letter written, one of the delegation hurried away with it to the press. They had repaired to the home of John F. Cook, Washington member of the delegation. He invited Douglass to re-

* Douglass, *Life and Times of Frederick Douglass*, chap. viii, pp. 467–68.

main for the night, but Douglass explained that he had yet another
appointment and that he was expected at the home of an old friend.
Douglass now stood up and, shaking his shoulders, made ready to
leave.

The weather outside was nasty. A wet, driving snow had turned
the streets into muddy slush; the wooden sidewalks were slippery
and the crossings were ditches of black water. Douglass fastened his
boots securely and turned up the collar of his coat.

"Can you find your way, Douglass?" asked Dr. Cook. "The streets
are so poorly lighted, and on a night like this a stranger could easily
get lost. If you'll wait a little I'll be glad to—"

Douglass interrupted. "No, indeed, Doctor. I know the way very
well. It's not far."

Meanwhile, "Miss Amelia" was finding Francis Cardoza good
company. He was one of the handsomest men she had ever seen.
The little lady's eyes twinkled, and her cheeks were flushed.

Tom's widow was not as spry as she once was. Days and nights
of nursing in the Soldiers' Home had brought weights heavier than
years upon her valiant frame. Now she was old. But she could take
things easy. Jack Haley was head of the house. The boarders could
not be prevailed upon to move, and the dark woman in the kitchen
would have served just as faithfully without wages. Frederick's supper
was being kept warm on the back of the stove and his room was ready.
She lifted the shade and peered anxiously out into the dark night.

"I do hope he gets a cab. This is a bad night for him to be out on
these streets alone." Her guest smiled.

"Frederick Douglass can take care of himself, madam," he said.
"You should not worry about him."

"Oh, but I *do*!" And Amelia's blue eyes opened wide. Francis
Cardoza, his eyes on the white hands and pulsing, crinkled throat,
marveled anew at the children of God.

When Douglass came he was deeply apologetic, but they waved
aside his concern.

"It is nothing," they said. "We knew you were busy."

Amelia would not let them talk until he had eaten, and when he
shook his head, saying he could not keep Mr. Cardoza waiting any
longer, Cardoza laughed.

"Might as well give in, Mr. Douglass."

So they all went to the dining room, and Amelia insisted that the
young man join her Frederick in his late supper.

Here in the friendly room, beside the roaring fire, the happenings of the day no longer seemed so crushing. He told them everything, and they listened, feeling his disappointment. Then Amelia spoke their thought aloud.

"If only Mr. Lincoln had lived!"

She left them then after explaining to Douglass, "I invited Mr. Cardoza to spend the night, but he has relatives here in Washington."

They were both on their feet, bowing as she left. Amelia smiled and thought, "Always such lovely manners."

The two men settled down before the fire for serious talk. Francis Cardoza was well informed. He might easily be taken for a white man, and so had heard much not intended for his ears.

"I talked today with Thaddeus Stevens," he told Douglass. "I told him what I had seen of the black codes, and he told me of Senator Sumner's magnificent speech in the Senate two days ago. He swears they'll get the Civil Rights Bill through in spite of Johnson."

"And I believe they will!" Douglass agreed. He leaned forward eagerly. "You have brought the petition?"

"Yes, sir." Cardoza was unfolding a manuscript. "Here is an exact copy of the document presented by us to the Convention assembled at Columbia. These words of the freedmen of South Carolina are our best argument. Read!" He handed the sheets to Douglass.

It was a long document and Douglass read slowly. This then came from "those savage blacks"!

. . . Our interests and affections are inseparably interwoven with the welfare and prosperity of the state. . . . We assure your honorable body that such recognition of our manhood as this petition asks for, is all that is needed to convince the colored people of this state that the white men of the state are prepared to do them justice.

Let us also assure your honorable body that nothing short of this, our respectful demand, will satisfy our people. If our prayer is not granted, there will doubtless be the same quiet and seemingly patient submission to wrong that there has been in the past. The day for which we watched and prayed came as we expected it; the day of our complete enfranchisement will also come; and in that faith we will work and wait.*

* The original of this petition was recently unearthed in the Historical Archives of South Carolina. On the back of the document was a notation: "This petition was not read in the Convention." *Signed*; John T. Sloa, Clerk of Convention. Printed in article by Herbert Aptaker, *Journal of Negro History*, January, 1946.

Douglass sat staring at the last sheet a long time. The simple majesty of the words rendered him speechless. His voice was husky.

"I wish I could have read this to President Johnson today. No words of mine can equal it."

"President Johnson was already incensed by Senator Sumner's words," Cardoza reminded him.

Douglass was silent for a moment. Then he spoke slowly.

"I want to be fair to President Johnson. In criticizing our friend Charles Sumner he said, 'I do not like to be arraigned by someone who can get up handsomely-rounded periods and deal in rhetoric and talk about abstract ideas of liberty, who never periled life, liberty, or property.'" Douglass tapped the closely written sheets. "Well, here are men who even now are imperiling life, liberty and property. Perhaps he would have listened."

"When he spoke to the Negroes of Nashville before his election, Johnson expressed his eagerness to be another Moses who would lead the black peoples from bondage to freedom." Cardoza had been in Nashville a short time before.

"Notice that even then he said he would do the leading." There was bitterness in Douglass' voice. "Apparently he's not willing for the black man to stand up and walk to freedom on his two feet."

Washington was emerging from the enveloping darkness when Francis Cardoza took his leave.

As he walked through the silent, gray street past the Representatives Office Building he saw a light faintly showing through one of the windows. He murmured his thought aloud.

"We're beating a nation out upon the anvil of time. The fires must be kept hot!"

Inside the building a tired, thin man with deeply furrowed face pushed back his chair and for a moment covered his eyes with his hand. Then he glanced toward the window, and his mouth crooked into a smile. He'd have to explain at home. Again he had stayed out all night. His desk was covered with papers. He would go home now, drink some coffee. That morning he proposed to demand the floor. He had something to say. He paused a moment and re-read one scribbled paragraph:

"This is not a white man's Government, in the exclusive sense in which it is said. To say so is political blasphemy, for it violates the fundamental principles of our gospel of liberty. This is Man's Government, the Government of all men alike; not that all men will have equal power and sway within it. Accidental circumstances, natural and acquired endowment and ability, will vary their fortunes. But equal rights to all the privileges of the Government is innate in every immortal being, no matter what the shape or color of the tabernacle which it inhabits. Our fathers repudiated the whole doctrine of the legal superiority of families or races, and proclaimed the equality of men before the law. Upon that they created a revolution and built the Republic." *

Thaddeus Stevens arranged the papers in a neat pile, straightened his wig and stood up. Then he took down his overcoat from the rack and put it on. His feet echoed in the dim, empty corridor. A Negro attendant in the lobby saw him coming. The dark face lit up with a smile and his greeting sang like a tiny hymn.

"Good mawnin', Mistah Stevens—*Good* mawnin' to you, sah!"

And Thaddeus Stevens did not feel the chill in the air as he walked down the steps and out into the wet, gray dawn.

"The war is not over!" Douglass said grimly to his son Lewis. "The battle is far from won. Not yet can I unfurl John Brown's flag in a land of the free!"

On the other hand, he knew the battle was not lost. But the Abolitionists' fundamental tenet of "moral persuasion" would have to have a firm structure of legislation—or the house would come tumbling down.

Stout girders for this structure were being lifted all over the land, in the least expected places.

On January 1, 1867, the African Baptist Church of Richmond, Virginia, was packed for an Emancipation Celebration. In the midst of the singing and praying and shouting a young white man rose in the audience and, going forward, asked if he might say a word.

"My name's James Hunnicut and I'm from South Carolina," he said. A mother hushed her child with a sharp hiss. The dark faces were suddenly cautious. The young man went on.

"This is a happy birthday for you—a day to be remembered with great joy." He waited until the fervent "Amens" and "Hallelujahs" had died away. He took a step forward and his voice grew taut.

"But now each time you come together I urge you to look into the future."

* Congressional Globe, "39th Congress," I, p. 74.

Then in simple words that all could understand he talked to them of what it meant to be a citizen. He explained the machinery of government. He told them they must register and vote in the fall elections. Some of the men grew tense. They had discussed plans. To others it was new, and all leaned forward eagerly.

"When you are organized," he said, "help to elect a loyal governor and loyal congressmen. Do not vote for men who opposed your liberty—no matter what they say now. Keep your eyes and ears open and your mouths shut. Educate yourselves—and go to the ballot boxes with your votes tight in your hands!"

The young folks cheered him with a kind of madness. But some of the older ones shook their heads.

A week after this happened, Frederick Douglass, on his way to Chicago, found that he could stop off at Galesburg, Illinois, in time for a local emancipation mass meeting. Galesburg was known as an Abolitionists' town. In the town's old Dunn Hall they had hauled up the biggest guns of the 1860 campaign. The county had gone almost solid for Abraham Lincoln, though the Hall had given its greatest ovation to one of the stoutest advocates of Stephen A. Douglas. The speaker had been Robert Ingersoll, a young man from Peoria. Now seven years later, when they planned to celebrate emancipation, the Negroes asked Robert Ingersoll to deliver the main address. Douglass had been wanting to hear Ingersoll for a year.

"On one of the frostiest and coldest nights I ever experienced," Douglass wrote, "I delivered a lecture in the town of Elmwood, Illinois, twenty miles from Peoria. It was one of those bleak and flinty nights, when prairie winds pierce like needles, and a step on the snow sounds like a file on the steel teeth of a saw. My next appointment after Elmwood was on Monday night, and in order to reach it in time, it was necessary to go to Peoria the night previous, so as to take an early morning train. I could only accomplish this by leaving Elmwood after my lecture at midnight, for there was no Sunday train. So a little before the hour at which my train was expected at Elmwood, I started for the station with my friend Mr. Brown. On the way I said to him, 'I'm going to Peoria with something like a real dread of the place. I expect to be compelled to walk the streets of that city all night to keep from freezing.' I told him that the last time I was there I could obtain no shelter at any hotel and I knew no one in the city. Mr. Brown was visibly affected by the statement and for some time was silent. At last, as if suddenly discovering a way out of a painful situation, he said, 'I know a man in Peoria, should the hotels be closed against you there, who would gladly open his doors to you—a man who will receive you at any hour of the night, and in any weather, and that man is Robert G. Ingersoll.' 'Why,' said I, 'it would not do to disturb a family at such a time as I shall arrive there, on a night so cold as this.' 'No matter about the hour,' he said; 'neither he nor his family would be happy if they thought you were shelterless on such a night. I know Mr. Ingersoll, and that he will be glad to welcome you at midnight or at cockcrow.' I became much interested by this description of Mr. Ingersoll. Fortunately I had no occasion for disturbing him or his family that night. I did find quarters for the night at the best hotel in the city." *

He had left Peoria the next morning. But his desire to meet the Peoria lawyer had increased with the passing months—not the least because he usually heard him referred to as "the infidel."

The train was late pulling into Galesburg. Douglass took a cab at the station and was driven directly to Dunn's Hall. The place was jammed with people, and the meeting well under way. Douglass saw that the crowd was largely colored. That meant a lot of them had come a long distance. Among so many strangers he hoped to get in without attracting attention.

He succeeeded, but it was because the attention of the throng was riveted on the speaker who faced them on the platform far up front. Only those persons whom he pushed against even saw the big man with the upturned coat collar.

Douglass later described Robert G. Ingersoll as a man "with real living human sunshine in his face." It was this quality of dynamic light about the man up front which made him stare on that January night. He had come prepared to be impressed, but he was amazed at the almost childlike freshness of the fair, smooth face with its wide-set eyes. Ingersoll was of fine height and breadth, his mouth as gentle as a woman's, but, as Douglass began taking in what the man was saying, his wonder grew.

"Slavery has destroyed every nation that has gone down to death. It caused the last vestige of Grecian civilization to disappear forever, and it caused Rome to fall with a crash that shook the world. After the disappearance of slavery in its grossest forms in Europe, Gonzales pointed out to his countrymen, the Portuguese, the immense profits that they could make by stealing Africans, and thus commenced the

* Douglass, *Life and Times of Frederick Douglass*, chap. xvii, p. 561.

modern slave trade—that aggregation of all horror—infinite of all cruelty, prosecuted only by demons, and defended only by fiends.

"And yet the slave trade has been defended and sustained by every civilized nation, and by each and all has been baptized 'legitimate commerce' in the name of the Father, the Son and the Holy Ghost."

Douglass felt a chill descend his spine.

He told them that every great movement must be led by heroic, self-sacrificing pioneers. Then his voice took on another quality.

"In Santo Domingo the pioneers were Oge and Chevannes; they headed a revolt, they were unsuccessful, but they roused the slaves to resistance. They were captured, tried, condemned and executed. They were made to ask forgiveness of God and of the King, for having attempted to give freedom to their own flesh and blood. They were broken alive on the wheel and left to die of hunger and pain. The blood of those martyrs became the seed of liberty; and afterward in the midnight assault, in the massacre and pillage, the infuriated slaves shouted their names as their battle cry, until Toussaint, the greatest of the blacks, gave freedom to them all."

He quoted Thomas Paine: *No man can be happy surrounded by those whose happiness he has destroyed.* And Thomas Jefferson: *When the measure of their tears shall be full—when their groans shall have involved heaven itself in darkness—doubtless a God of justice will awaken to their distress and, by diffusing light and liberality among the oppressors or at length by his exterminating thunder, manifest his attention to the things of this world and that they are not left to the guidance of a blind fatality.*

He named Garrison, who was "for liberty as a principle and not from mere necessity."

A cheer went up from the crowd. Douglass' heart was glad as he heard it. Ingersoll then talked of Wendell Phillips, and of Charles Sumner, who at that moment was battling for the freedmen in Congress. His voice deepened, his great eyes became soft pools of light.

"But the real pioneer in America was old John Brown," he said. There was no cheer this time. They bowed their head and the golden voice was like a prayer.

"He struck the sublimest blow of the age for freedom. It was said of him that he stepped from the gallows to the throne of God. It was said that he had made the scaffold to Liberty what Christ had made the cross to Christianity."

They wept softly. Douglass, his hands clenched, lost himself in memories. When he heard the voice again it was ringing.

"In reconstructing the Southern states . . . we prefer loyal blacks to disloyal whites. . . . Today I am in favor of giving the Negro every right that I claim for myself.

"We must be for freedom everywhere. Freedom is progress— slavery is desolation and want; freedom invents, slavery forgets. Freedom believes in education; the salvation of slavery is ignorance.

"The South has always dreaded the alphabet. They looked upon each letter as an Abolitionist, and well they might." There was laughter.

"If, in the future, the wheel of fortune should take a turn, and you should in any country have white men in your power, I pray you not to execute the villainy we have taught you." The old Hall was still. Ingersoll was drawing to a close. ". . . Stand for each other and above all stand for liberty the world over—for all men." *

Douglass slipped out. He heard the thunder of applause. It filled the winter night as he hurried away. He walked for a long time down the unfamiliar streets, the snow crunching under his feet, but he did not feel the cold. His blood raced through his veins, his brain was on fire, his heart sang.

He had seen a shining angel brandishing his sword.

He had also found a friend. He would clasp Ingersoll's hand in his maturity, as the young Douglass had clasped the hands of William Lloyd Garrison and John Brown.

* C. P. Farrell (Editor), *The Political Speeches of Robert Ingersoll*, Dresden edition.

CHAPTER SEVENTEEN

Fourscore years ago in Washington

"THE FUTURE of the freedmen is linked with the destiny of Labor in America. Negroes, thank God, are workers."

New words being added to the song of freedom. In 1867, in the District of Columbia, colored workers came together in a mass meeting. They asked Congress to secure equal apportionment of employment to white and colored labor. Their petition was printed, and a committee of fifteen was appointed to circulate it. Similar meetings were held in Kentucky, Indiana and in Pennsylvania.

A year and a half later, in January, 1869, they called a national convention in Washington. Among the one hundred and thirty delegates from all parts of the country came Henry M. Turner, black political leader of Georgia. Resolutions were passed in favor of universal suffrage, the opening of public lands in the South for Negroes, the Freedman's Bureau, a national tax for Negro schools, and the reconstruction policy of Congress. They opposed any plan for colonization.

Frederick Douglass was elected permanent president. Resolutions were passed advocating industrious habits, the learning of trades and professions, distribution of government lands, suffrage for all—including women—and "free school systems, with no distinction on account of race, color, sex or creed."

The January convention, though not primarily a labor group, backed industrial emancipation. Eleven months later a distinctly labor convention met and stayed in session a full week at Union League Hall in Washington.

In February, 1870, the Bureau of Labor ran an article on the need of organized Negro labor. Shortly afterward, the Colored National

Labor Union came into being, with the *New Era*, a weekly paper, its national organ. Frederick Douglass was asked to become editor-in-chief.

People wanted Douglass to go into politics. Rochester, with a population of over sixty thousand white citizens and only about two hundred colored, had sent him as delegate to a national political convention in the fall of 1866. The National Loyalists' Convention held in Philadelphia was composed of delegates from the South, North and West. Its object was to lay down the principles to be observed in the reconstruction of society in the Southern states.

Though he had been sent by a "white vote," all was not clear sailing for Douglass. His troubles started on the delegates' special train headed for Philadelphia. At Harrisburg it was coupled to another special from the southwest—and the train began to rock! After a hurried consultation it was decided that the "Jonah" in their midst had better be tossed overboard. The spokesman chosen to convey this decision to the victim was a gentleman from New Orleans, of low voice and charming manners. "I credit him with a high degree of politeness and the gift of eloquence," said Douglass.

He began by exhibiting his knowledge of Douglass' history and of his works, and said that he entertained toward him a very high respect. He assured the delegate from Rochester that the gentlemen who sent him, as well as those who accompanied him, regarded the Honorable Mr. Douglass with admiration and that there was not among them the remotest objection to sitting in convention with so distinguished a gentleman. Then he paused, daintily wiping his hands on a spotless handkerchief. Having tucked the linen back into his pocket, he spread his hands expressively and leaned forward. Was it, he asked, not necessary to set aside personal wishes for the common cause? Before Douglass could answer, he shrugged his shoulders and went on. After all, it was purely a question of party expediency. He must know that there was strong and bitter prejudice against his race in the North as well as in the South. They would raise the cry of social as well as political equality against the Republicans, if the famous Douglass attended this loyal national convention.

There were tears in the gentleman's voice as he deplored the sacrifices which one must make for the good of the Republican cause. But, he pointed out, there were a couple of districts in the state of Indiana so evenly balanced that a little thing was likely to turn the scale against them, defeat their candidates, and thus leave Congress without the necessary two-thirds vote for carrying through the so-badly needed legislation.

"It is," he ended, lifting his eyes piously, "only the good God who gives us strength for such sacrifice."

Douglass had listened attentively to this address, uttering no word during its delivery. The spokesman leaned back in his seat. The three delegates who had accompanied him and who had remained standing in the aisle, turned to leave. They stopped in their tracks, however, at the sound of Douglass' voice. It was a resonant voice, with rich overtones, and his words were heard distinctly by everyone in the car.

"Gentlemen," he said, "with all due respect, you might as well ask me to put a loaded pistol to my head and blow my brains out as to ask me to keep out of this convention, to which I have been duly elected!"

The Louisianian's face froze. One of the men in the aisle swore— none too swiftly. Douglass reasoned with them.

"What, gentlemen, would you gain by this exclusion? Would not the charge of cowardice, certain to be brought against you, prove more damaging than that of amalgamation? Would you not be branded all over the land as dastardly hypocrites, professing principles which you have no wish or intention of carrying out? As a matter of policy or expediency, you will be wise to let me in. Everybody knows that I have been fairly elected by the city of Rochester as a delegate. The fact has been broadly announced and commented upon all over the country. If I am not admitted, the public will ask, 'Where is Douglass? Why is he not seen in the convention?' And you would find that enquiry more difficult to answer than any charge brought against you for favoring political or social equality." He paused. No one moved. Their faces remained hard and unconvinced. Douglass sighed. Then his face also hardened. He stood up.

"Well, ignoring the question of policy altogether, I am bound to go into that convention. Not to do so would contradict the principle and practice of my life."

They left then. The charming gentleman from New Orleans did not bother to bow.

No more was said about the matter. Frederick Douglass was not excluded, but throughout the first morning session it was evident that he was to be ignored.

That afternoon a procession had been planned to start from Independence Hall. Flags and banners lined the way and crowds filled the streets. Douglass reached the starting point in good time. "Almost everybody on the ground whom I met seemed to be ashamed or afraid of me. I had been warned that I should not be allowed to walk through the city in the procession; fears had been expressed that my presence in it would so shock the prejudices of the people of Philadelphia as to cause the procession to be mobbed."

The delegates were to walk two abreast. Douglass stood waiting, grimly determined to march alone. But shortly before the signal to start Theodore Tilton, young poet-editor of the *New York Independent* and the *Brooklyn Worker*, came hurrying in his direction. His straw-colored hair was rumpled and his face flushed.

"This way, Mr. Douglass! I've been looking for you."

He grinned as he seized Douglass' arm and with him pushed well up toward the head of the procession. There they took a place in the line. Tilton gayly ignored the sour faces around them.

"All set, captain, we're ready to march!" he called.

Douglass tried to murmur something to express his appreciation, but the writer winked at him.

"Watch and see what happens!" he chuckled.

The band struck up and the line began to move. Someone on the sidewalk pointed to the sweeping mane of Douglass' head and shouted, "Douglass! There's Frederick Douglass!"

They began to cheer. The cheering was heard by those farther down the street, and heads craned forward. People leaned out of windows overhead to see. They waved their flags and shouted, hailing the delegates of the convention.

And Douglass was the most conspicuous figure in the line. The shout most often heard all along the way was:

"Douglass! Douglass! There is Frederick Douglass!"

After that there was no further question of ignoring Douglass at the convention. But any ambitions which he might have had for a political career cooled. He realized that a thorough-going "politician" might well have acceded to the delegates' politely expressed wish "for the good of the party," but he knew that he would never place the good of the party above the good of the people as a whole. After the adoption of the Fourteenth and Fifteen Amendments, both white and colored people urged him to move to one of the many districts of the South where there was a large colored vote and get himself a seat in Congress. No man in the country had a larger following. But the thought of going to live among people simply to gain their votes was repugnant to his self-respect. The idea did not square with his better judgment or sense of propriety.

When he was called to Washington to edit the *New Era* he began to turn the thought over in his mind. The problem of what to do with himself after the Anti-Slavery Society disbanded had been taken care of. He was in demand as a lecturer in colleges, on lyceum circuits and before literary societies. Where before he had considered himself well-off with his four-hundred-fifty- to five-hundred-dollar-a-year salary, he now received one hundred, one hundred fifty, or two hundred dollars for a single lecture. His children were grown. Lewis was a successful printer, Rosetta was married, and the youngest son was teaching school on the Eastern Shore of Maryland not far from St. Michaels.

Douglass had campaigned for Ulysses S. Grant because he was fond of, and believed in, Grant. There had been scarcely any contest. The people were sick to death of the constant wrangling which had been going on in Congress. President Johnson's impeachment had fizzled like a bad firecracker. The kindest thing they said about Johnson was that he was weak. Everybody agreed that what was needed now was a strong hand. So by an overwhelming majority they chose a war hero.

Undoubtedly, Washington would be interesting, reasoned Douglass. It was the center of the hub, the Capital of all the States. He would also be nearer the great masses of his own people. But Anna Douglass—for the first time in thirty years neither overworked nor burdened with cares—was reluctant to leave Rochester.

Douglass provided for his family, but making money had never been his chief concern. Anna had always stretched dollars. The babies were all little together, so Anna could not go out and work. But while they were little, she often brought work home, sometimes without her husband's knowledge. During the years when runaway slaves hid in their attic, Anna was always there at any hour of the day or night with food, clean clothing, warm blankets; and it was Anna who kept her husband's shirts carefully laundered, his bag neatly packed. No one knew better than Douglass how Anna carried the countless, minute burdens of the days and nights. He loved her and depended upon her. But, like Anna Brown, she was the wife of a man who belonged to history. So now, though she would have preferred to relax under the big shade tree he had planted years before, enjoy the cool spaciousness of the home which they had made very comfortable, gossip a bit with her neighbors and relish the many friendly contacts she had made in Rochester, she nodded her head.

"If Washington is the place for you, of course we'll go." And she smiled at her husband, who was growing more handsome and more famous every day.

Douglass was in his prime. He cut an imposing figure. He knew it and was glad. For he regarded himself as ambassador of all the freedmen in America. He was always on guard—his speech, his manners, his appearance. Now that he could, he dressed meticulously, stopped off at New York on his way to Washington and ordered several suits, saw to it that he was well supplied with stiff white shirts. He intended that when he walked down Pennsylvania Avenue, across Lafayette Square, or through the Capital grounds, men would ask, "Who is he? What embassy is he from?" Sooner or later they would learn that he was "Frederick Douglass, ex-slave!"

Yes, he was proud. And this same naïve pride almost tripped him.

Since the paper needed him at once, it was decided Douglass would go on ahead, find a house, and later they would move their things and Anna would follow him.

He plunged into his work and almost immediately into difficulties. The *New Era* was not his own paper. It was the national organ of the Colored National Labor Union, and Douglass soon found he was not in step with the union leaders. The only one he knew personally was George Downing of Rhode Island. Even Downing seemed to have developed strange, new ideas.

James H. Morris was an astute and courageous reconstruction leader of North Carolina who saw politics and labor in clear alliance.

"What the South needs is a thorough reconstruction of its classes," he argued, "and that's a long ways from being a sharp division of white and black."

"With the ballot the Negro has full citizenship. He can make his way." Douglass did not grasp the significance of organized labor.

"The unions have been shutting out the black man's labor all these years."

"White workers had to learn."

It must be remembered that by adoption Douglass was New England and Upper New York. Puritan individualism with all its good and bad qualities had sunk deep. He had himself fought for Irish cottiers and British labor, but could not at this time envision black and white workers uniting against a common enemy in the United States.

After a series of what he called "bewildering circumstances," he purchased the paper and turned it over to Lewis and Frederic, his two printer sons. After a few years they discontinued its publication. The "misadventure" cost him from nine to ten thousand dollars.

Meanwhile, in another world—a world of international intrigue and power politics that took little account of Frederick Douglass— events were shaping themselves "according to plan." United States expansionists waited until President Grant took office and renewed their efforts to strengthen our hand in the Caribbeans.

The islands of the Caribbean Sea were heavy with potential wealth. Fortunes lay in the rich, black soil; cheap labor was there in the poor, black peoples who had been brought from Africa to work the islands. The key was Santo Domingo—the old Saint Domingue at which Spain, France and Great Britain had clutched desperately.

Since Columbus first landed there December 6, 1492, the history of the island had been written in blood. On one side had been born the second republic in the Western Hemisphere, called Haiti. When U. S. Grant became President of the United States, Haiti had stood for sixty-six years—in spite of the fact that it was looked upon as an anomaly among nations. On the other side of the island was the weaker Santo Domingo. After declaring its independence in 1845, it had been annexed by Spain while the Civil War was keeping the United States busy. When this happened, the "Black Republic" of Hait sought with more zeal than power to take the place of the United States as defender against aggression by a European power. Santo Domingo did manage to wrench herself from Spain in 1865, but she was far from secure. The need for military bases and coaling stations in the Caribbean was obvious to a President skilled in military tactics. Admirals and generals of many nations had looked with longing eyes on Haiti's Môle St. Nicolas, finest harbor in the Western world. But the Haitians were in a position to hold their harbor, and meanwhile Santo Domingo's Samoná Bay was not bad. So President Grant offered the "protection" of the powerful United States to a "weak and defenseless people, torn and rent by internal feuds and unable to maintain order at home or command respect abroad."

But the ever-watchful Charles Sumner rose in the Senate, and for six hours his voice resounded through the chamber like the wrath of

God. He set off a series of repercussions against this annexation which reverberated across the country.

Douglass, in the midst of his own perplexities, heard the echoes and defended President Grant. Men working with him, particularly labor men, stared at him in amazement.

"How can you, Douglass!" they exclaimed. "Don't you see what this means? And how can you side against Sumner? He's the most courageous friend the black man has in Congress!"

"I'm not against Charles Sumner. Our Senator sees this proposed annexation as a measure to extinguish a colored nation and therefore bitterly opposes it. But even a great and good man can be wrong."

George Downing, his eyes on Douglass' earnest, troubled face, thought to himself, *How right you are!*

Charles Sumner, lying on a couch in the library of his big house facing Lafayette Square, listened with closed eyes while Douglass gently remonstrated. His strength was ebbing. Every one of these supreme efforts drained him of life. Sumner was one of the few men of his day who saw that the Union could yet lose the war. He had been very close to Lincoln in the last days. He was trying to carry out the wishes of his beloved Commander in Chief. He listened to Douglass, who he knew also loved Lincoln, with a frown. He sat up impatiently, tossing aside the light shawl with a snort.

"You're caught up in a rosy cloud, Douglass. The lovely song of emancipation still rings in your ears drowning all other sounds. You're due for a rude awakening." His large eyes darkened. "And I'm afraid it won't be long in coming!"

It was several days later when Douglass, responding to an invitation from the White House, felt a chill of apprehension. The President greeted him with a blunt question.

"Now, what do you think of your friend, Sumner?" he asked bitterly.

"I think, Mr. President," said Douglass, choosing his words carefully, "that Senator Sumner is an honest and a valiant statesman. In opposing the annexation of Santo Domingo he believes he is defending the cause of the colored race as he has always done." Douglass saw the slow flush creeping above the President's beard. He continued evenly. "But I also think that in this he is mistaken."

"You do?" There was surprise in the voice.

"Yes, sir, I do. I see no more dishonor to Santo Domingo in making her a state of the American Union than in making Kansas,

Nebraska, or any other territory such a state. It is giving to a part the strength of the whole."

The President relaxed in his chair, a slight smile on his lips. Douglass leaned forward.

"What do you, Mr. President, think of Senator Sumner?"

President Grant's answer was concise.

"I think he's mad!"

The Commission which President Grant sent to the Caribbean was one of many. Secretary Seward himself had gone to Haiti in the winter of 1865. And in 1867 Seward had sent his son, then Assistant Secretary of State. But the appointment of Frederick Douglass on Grant's Commission was a pretty gesture. A naval vessel manned by one hundred marines and five hundred sailors, with the Stars and Stripes floating in the breeze, steaming into Samoná Bay bringing Frederick Douglass and a "confidential reconnaissance commission" of investigation! A reporter from the *New York World* went along, and much was made of Douglass' "cordial relations" with the other members and of the fact that he was given the seat of honor at the captain's table. It was a delightful cruise.

After thirty-six hours in port, they were ready to leave with the report that the people were "unanimously" in favor of annexation by the United States. Douglass heard nothing of the insurrection going on in the hills, nor of the rival factions bidding for American support, nor of the dollars from New York.

In spite of the commission, however, Horace Greeley and Charles Sumner defeated the bill—a bitter disappointment to certain interests, but far from a knockout blow.

The "old settlers" of Rochester tendered a farewell reception to Frederick Douglass and his family when he took formal leave of the city which had been his home for thirty years. All the old-time Abolitionists who had weathered the long and bitter storm were invited. Gerrit Smith, shrunken and feeble, was there. Joy and sadness sat down together at that board. But everyone was proud of the dark man whom Rochester now acclaimed as her "most distinguished son."

Gideon Pitts's father, old Captain Peter Pitts, had been the first settler in the township of Richmond, so Gideon Pitts and his wife were among the sponsors of the affair.

"Those were trying days even in our quiet valley," Pitts's eyes twinkled. Douglass was trying to recall the grizzled face. "But we licked 'em!"

It was the chuckle that brought it all back—the house offering shelter from pursuers, his pounding on the door and the old man in his nightshirt and bare feet!

"Mr. Pitts!" He seized his hand. "Of course, it's Mr. Pitts!" He turned to his wife, "My dear, these are the folks who took me in that night on Ridge Road. You remember?"

"Of course, I remember." Anna smiled. "I've always intended to ride out some afternoon and thank you, but—" She made a little rueful gesture, and she and Mrs. Pitts began to chat. They spoke of their children, and Douglass remembered something else.

"You had a little girl— How is she?"

The father laughed proudly. "My little girl's quite a young lady now. She's one that knows her own mind, too—belongs to Miss Anthony's voting society. She says that's the next thing—votes for women!"

Douglass nodded his head. "She's right. We're hoping the *next* amendment will make women citizens. Remember me to her, won't you?"

"We sure will, Mr. Douglass!"

Then they were gone and Douglass said, "Good sound Americans, Anna—people of the land."

And Anna said a little wistfully, "We'll miss them." Deep in her heart, Anna was afraid of Washington.

The house Douglass had taken at 316 A Street, N.E., was not ready, but he wanted Anna close by to supervise repairs and redecorations. They took Lewis with them, leaving Rosetta and her husband in the Rochester home until everything was moved.

Douglass planned to send his twelve bound volumes of the *North Star* and *Frederick Douglass' Paper*, covering the period from 1848 to 1860, to Harvard University Library. The curator had requested them for Harvard's historical files. But first he had to dash off to New Orleans to preside over the Southern States Convention.

P. B. S. Pinchback, Lieutenant-Governor of Louisiana, had invited Douglass to be his guest at the Governor's Mansion. Indistinguishable from a white man, Pinchback had been educated in the North and had served as a captain in the Union Army. In appearance and actions he was an educated, well-to-do, genial Louisianian—intelligent and capable, but he was a practical politician and he played the politician's game. He might have left New Orleans, gone to France as so many of them did, or even to some other section of the country. He might easily have shrugged off the harness of the *cordon bleu*, but New Orleans was in his blood. He lived always on the sharp edge, dangerously, while around him swirled a colorful and kaleidoscopic drama. He was by no means a charlatan.

It was April when Douglass came to New Orleans. He was greeted most cordially. "I shall show you my New Orleans and you will not want to leave," Pinchback promised.

And Douglass was captivated by New Orleans—captivated and blinded. Camellias were in bloom, their loveliness reflected in stagnant waters. Soft, trailing beauty of mosses on damp walls in which stood high, heavy gates. The streets were filled with multicolored throngs—whites and blacks and all the colors in between, old women with piercing bright eyes under flaming *tignons*, hawkers crying out their wares, extending great trays piled high with figs, brown cakes and steaming jars—the liquid French accents—the smells!

They stepped over the carcass of a dog, which had evidently been floating in the street gutter for some time. "This is the old section," Pinchback explained. "When we cross Canal Street, you'll think you're in New York."

But there was nothing in New York like any part of New Orleans. The celebrated visitor found himself in gardens where fountains played and tiny, golden birds sipped honeysuckle, where flowering oleanders grew in huge jars and lovely ladies with sparkling eyes trailed black lace.

Into the Governor's courtyard, with its glistening flagstones, came men for a talk with the great Douglass: Antoine Dubuclet, State Treasurer, a quiet, dark man, who had lived many years in Paris; tall and cultured P. G. Deslone, Secretary of State; Paul Trevigne, who published the *New Orleans Tribune*.

Trevigne was not on the best of terms with the Lieutenant-Governor. He bowed stiffly from the waist and hoped that the host would leave him and Douglass alone together. But Pinchback ordered coffee served beside the fountain, and over the thin, painted cup his eyes laughed.

"M. Trevigne does not approve of me," he explained, turning to Douglass. "He thinks I should take life more vigorously—by the throat. I use other methods."

Douglass, observing them, realized that here were two men of very different caliber. He marveled anew that Pinchback had been able to gain the confidence of the black people of New Orleans.

"Undoubtedly, sir," Trevigne was saying frankly, "I understand better the more direct methods of our first Lieutenant-Governor." He turned to Douglass. "His name was Oscar Dunn, and he was the only one of the seven colored men in the Senate two years ago who had been a slave. He was by far the most able."

Pinchback had been in the Senate then. He studied the tray beside him and finally chose a heart-shaped pastry. He did not look up, but he said, "Oscar J. Dunn died—*very suddenly.*" His smile flashed. "I prefer to live."

Trevigne frowned. He continued almost as if the Governor had not spoken.

"Oscar Dunn was responsible for opening public schools to blacks and poor whites alike."

Douglass roused himself with a start. He looked at his watch.

"I'm sorry—but I'm going to be late. We must go. Let's continue our visit on the way." Trevigne welcomed the interruption.

"I'll send you over in the carriage. And do not worry," Pinchback lifted himself from the easy chair with languid grace. "The session will not begin on time."

But the session of the convention had begun when Douglass reached the hall. The efficient secretary was calling the roll.

The convention was not going very well. Division in the Republican ranks grew deeper and broader every day. Douglass blamed Charles Sumner and Horace Greeley who "on account of their long and earnest advocacy of justice and liberty to the blacks, had powerful attractions for the newly-enfranchised class." He ignored the persistent influence of the National Labor Union and its economic struggle. Douglass pointed to what the Republican party had done in Louisiana—to the legislators he had met. Six years later he was to hear all of them labeled "apes," "buffoons," and "clowns." He was to see the schools Dunn had labored so hard to erect burned to the ground; the painstaking, neat accounts of Dubuclet blotted and falsified; the studied, skilful tacts of Pinchback labeled "mongrel trickery."

There were those in New Orleans who saw it coming.

"Warmoth," they warned him, "is the real master of Louisiana. And he represents capital, whose business it is to manipulate the labor vote—white and black."

"The Republican party is the true workingmen's party of the country!" thundered Douglass. And what he did was to steer the convention away from unionism to politics—not seeing their interrelation.

And so, as white labor in the North moved toward stronger and stronger union organization, it lost interest in, and vital touch with, the millions of laborers in the South. When the black night came, there was no help.

But all this was later. Douglass returned to Washington singing the praises of Louisiana—its rich beauties and the amazing progress the people were making. He congratulated himself that he had succeeded "in holding back the convention from a fatal political blunder." His story was carried by the *New York Herald*—and pointedly omitted from the columns of the *Tribune*.

He found a letter awaiting him from Harvard: when was he sending on his newspaper files? There was some question of getting them catalogued before summer. Yes, he must attend to that—soon. And he laid the letter to one side.

On June 2, 1872, his house in Rochester burned to the ground. His papers were gone, and Douglass cursed the folly of his procrastination. Rosetta and her husband had managed to get out with a few personal possessions. Household furniture could be replaced, but Anna wept for a hundred precious mementos of the days gone by— little Annie's cape, the children's school books, the plum-colored wedding dress and Frederick's first silk hat.

But Douglass thought only of his newspaper files and how he ought to have sent them to Harvard.

The gods were not yet finished with Frederick Douglass. It was as if they conspired to strip him of the last small vestige of his pride, as if to make sure that henceforth and forevermore he should "walk humble."

"It is not without a feeling of humiliation that I must narrate my connection with the Freedmen's Saving and Trust Company," he wrote, when, later on, he felt he had to put down the whole unfortunate story.

The pathetically naïve account which follows is amazing on many counts. How could this little group of "church members" have expected to find their way within the intricate maze of national banking in the United States? From the start they were doomed to failure. Yet here stands an eternal monument to the fact that the newly emancipated men and women "put their money in banks," were thrifty and frugal beyond our most rigid demands. For these banks were in the

South among the masses of people who had just come out of slavery. The one Northern branch was in Philadelphia. Frederick Douglass did not see the reasons for the bank's failure. He blamed himself and the handful of black men who tried to scale the barricades of big business, only to have themselves broken and left with a corpse on their hands.

This was an institution designed to furnish a place of security and profit for the hard earnings of the colored people, especially in the South. There was something missionary in its composition, and it dealt largely in exhortations as well as promises. The men connected with its management were generally church members, and reputed eminent for their piety. Their aim was to instil into the minds of the untutored Africans lessons of sobriety, wisdom, and economy, and to show them how to rise in the world. Like snowflakes in winter, circulars, tracts and other papers were, by this benevolent institution, scattered among the millions, and they were told to "look" to the Freedmen's Bank and "live." Branches were established in all the Southern States, and as a result, money to the amount of millions flowed into its vaults.

With the usual effect of sudden wealth, the managers felt like making a little display of their prosperity. They accordingly erected, on one of the most desirable and expensive sites in the national capital, one of the most costly and splendid buildings of the time, finished on the inside with black walnut and furnished with marble counters and all the modern improvements. . . . In passing it on the street I often peeped into its spacious windows, and looked down the row of its gentlemanly colored clerks, with their pens behind their ears, and felt my very eyes enriched. It was a sight I had never expected to see. . . .

After settling myself down in Washington, I could and did occasionally attend the meetings of the Board of Trustees, and had the pleasure of listening to the rapid reports of the condition of the institution, which were generally of a most encouraging character. . . . At one time I had entrusted to its vaults about twelve thousand dollars. It seemed fitting to me to cast in my lot with my brother freedmen and to help build up an institution which represented their thrift and economy to so striking advantage; for the more millions accumulated there, I thought, the more consideration and respect would be shown to the colored people of the whole country.

About four months before this splendid institution was

compelled to close its doors in the starved and deluded faces of its depositors, and while I was assured by its President and its actuary of its sound condition, I was solicited by some of the trustees to allow them to use my name in the board as a candidate for its presidency.

So I waked up one morning to find myself seated in a comfortable armchair, with gold spectacles on my nose, and to hear myself addressed as president of the Freedmen's Bank. I could not help reflecting on the contrast between Frederick the slave boy, running about with only a tow linen shirt to cover him, and Frederick—President of a bank counting its assets by millions. I had heard of golden dreams, but such dreams had no comparison with this reality.

My term of service on this golden height covered only the brief space of three months, and was divided into two parts. At first I was quietly employed in an effort to find out the real condition of the bank and its numerous branches. This was no easy task. On paper, and from the representations of its management, its assets amounted to three millions of dollars, and its liabilities were about equal to its assets. With such a showing I was encouraged in the belief that by curtailing the expenses, and doing away with non-paying branches, we could be carried safely through the financial distress then upon the country. So confident was I of this, that, in order to meet what was said to be a temporary emergency, I loaned the bank ten thousand dollars of my own money, to be held by it until it could realize on a part of its abundant securities. *

One wonders how the trustees ever managed to pay back that loan before the final crash. But they did pay it.

Gradually I discovered that the bank had, through dishonest agents, sustained heavy losses in the South. . . . I was, six weeks after my election as president, convinced that the bank was no longer a safe custodian of the hard earnings of my confiding people.

Douglass' next move probably made bad matters worse. He reported to the Chairman of the Senate Committee on Finance that the federal assets of the bank were gone. A commission was appointed to take over the bank, and its doors were closed. Not wishing to take any

* Douglass, *Life and Times of Frederick Douglass*, chap. xiv, pp. 486–88.

advantage of the other depositors, Douglass left his money to be divided with the assets among the creditors of the bank.

In time—a long time—the larger part of the depositors received most of their money. But it was upon the head of the great Frederick Douglass that the wrath and the condemnation descended.

CHAPTER EIGHTEEN

"If slavery could not kill us, liberty won't"

SENECA FALLS' Union Woman's Suffrage Society hated to lose one of its most faithful and ardent members, but the manner of her leaving was cause for much rejoicing. *A Civil Service position in Washington! My goodness, what a break!*

"It's not a break." Miss Dean, secretary of the society, spoke indignantly. "Helen Pitts has passed the examination, and she is taking her well-earned place in the ranks of government workers."

"Sure," Matilda Hooker teased, "but isn't Susan B. Anthony wearing herself out all over the place just so women can have such rights? This is a significant step, and I say we women in Seneca can be proud of Helen Pitts."

"Hear! Hear!" they said. Then Helen Pitts came in, her face flushed, and after a little excited chatter the meeting was called to order.

It was true that Helen had taken the fall Civil Service examination by way of a "declaration of independence." When she presented herself at the post-office they had eyed her with disapproval.

"What's the schoolmarm here for?" they asked. And Sid Green remarked sourly that he'd heard tell she was one of those "advanced women." His wife rebuked him sharply.

"Miss Pitts is one of the nicest and most ladylike teachers we've ever had. You ought to be ashamed of yourself, Sid Green!"

But Sid hadn't taken it back. The School Board hadn't liked their teacher's marching in the suffrage parade last fall—and Sid knew it, no matter what his wife said. Anyhow, *he* wore the pants in *his* house. He hitched them up now with a jerk and went outside.

There was no question about the teacher's popularity with her pupils. The morning she mailed her resignation (to take effect at the end of the month) she decided not to tell the children until after the Christmas party. That wasn't going to be easy.

The teacher's mind was jerked back to the present by hearing her name.

"I move that Helen Pitts be our delegate," Lucy Payne said.

Helen blinked her eyes.

"I second the motion." Mrs. Huggins was nodding her head emphatically.

Helen nudged the girl next to her and whispered, "I didn't hear— What's going on?"

"Delegates to the National Convention," came the low answer.

"But—"

"Sh-sh! You're on your way to fame and fortune." The girl grinned as the chairman rapped for order. She was ready to put the motion.

"It has been moved and seconded that Miss Helen Pitts be our delegate in Washington next month. All those in favor say 'Aye'."

The "Ayes" had it, and everybody beamed at Helen.

"Get up! You're supposed to thank them!" Her friend nudged her.

It was silly to be nervous—they were all her friends. But the hazel eyes were dangerously bright and the neat, folded kerchief at her throat fluttered.

"Ladies, you do me great honor," she said. "I— I'll try to be a good representative." She swallowed and then spoke resolutely. "We know why we want votes for women—not for any of the silly reasons some men say. We must be very sure and as courageous as our leaders. They are taking the fight right to the Capital, and I promise you we'll fling it into the very teeth of Congress, disturbing their peaceful complacency until they will be forced to action."

They did not have enough funds in the treasury to send a delegate from Seneca Falls. Helen would go down to Washington a week before her job started.

Helen Pitts spent most of her Christmas holiday at home packing and harking to parental admonitions. Gideon Pitts regarded his daughter both with pride and apprehension. Schoolteaching had been a nice, quiet occupation, but he knew something about the "wiles" and "pitfalls" of big cities. He thought he ought to go down with her and see that she found a respectable place to live in. His wife held him back.

"That's silly, Pa. Helen's got plenty mother wit, for all she's so small and frail-looking." Her mother sighed. "I was hoping she'd be settling near home—that she might accept Brad."

Aunt Julia was a little more direct.

"I'd get this nonsense out of Helen's head if I was her mother." She spoke firmly. "Old maids soon fade, and all these new-fangled ideas ain't a-gonna keep her warm winter nights."

"Helen's no old maid yet," defended her mother.

" 'Pears like to me she'll be thirty come this spring. And if that ain't an old maid my mind's failing me," was the acid comment.

In due time Helen Pitts took her seat in the Fourth National Suffrage Convention, meeting in Washington the first week in January, 1874.

The air crackled with excitement. Now that the Fourteenth Amendment had gone to some length to define "citizenship" within the United States, "manhood suffrage" was being substituted by the politicians for the recent vanguard cry "universal suffrage." Susan B. Anthony was calling upon the women of America to have their say. The leaders of the movement were ridiculed, mocked and libeled, but they had come to Washington in full armor.

Her face aglow, eyes sparkling with indignation, Miss Anthony told the opening session that a petition against woman's suffrage had been presented in the Senate by a Mr. Edmunds. Mrs. General Sherman, Mrs. Admiral Dahlgren and other Washington wives had signed it.

"These are the women," she said, "who never knew a want, whose children are well fed and warmly clad. Yet they would deny these same comforts to other women even though they are earned by the toil of their hands. Such women are traitors not only to their best instincts, but to all mothers of men!"

Helen tried to applaud louder than anybody else. She would have liked to stand and tell them that her home was in Rochester, that she had been one of the youngest members of Susan B. Anthony's own club. But the women did not spend their time exchanging compliments. Helen voted for or against resolution after resolution; she was placed on one committee.

Lincoln Hall was packed for the big open session on Saturday afternoon. Many came just to hear the big speakers, but the women were happy because they were creating a real stir in Washington. They devoutly hoped it would be felt throughout the country.

A shiver of anticipation went through the crowd at the appearance of Robert Ingersoll.

"He's like a Greek god," a woman seated beside Helen moaned. "Any man as handsome as that is bound to be wicked!"

An outstanding editor had written at great length on how laws in the United States favored women. Word by word and line by line Ingersoll, the lawyer, cut the ground from underneath the editor's feet. Skilfully he analyzed the many laws upon the statute books which bound women and their children to the petty whims and humors of men.

"But these laws will not change until *you* change them," he told them. "Justice and freedom do not rain like manna from heaven upon outstretched hands. We men will not *give* you the ballot. You must *take* it!"

The secretaries rustled papers nervously. The chairman glanced at her watch. There was a hitch in the program, but the audience did not mind a little breathing spell. The side door up front opened, and Frederick Douglass entered as quietly as possible. He looked like a huge bear. He was covered with snow which clung even to his beard and hair. With some assistance he hurriedly removed this overcoat and rubbers. After wiping his face and hair with his big handkerchief, he mounted the steps to the platform.

Instantly the crowd burst into applause which continued while Susan B. Anthony took his hand and Mr. Ingersoll, leaning forward in his seat, greeted him warmly. When Douglass sat down facing the audience his broad shoulders sagged a little, and Helen fancied he closed his eyes for a moment as he rested his hands on his knees. She had not heard him since the close of the war. The touch of gray in his hair heightened his air of distinction, but she had not before noticed how his cheekbones showed above the beard. Perhaps his face was thinner.

To this convention Douglass was the very symbol of their strivings. He was one of the first to see that woman's suffrage and Negro citizenship were the same fight. He had appeared with Susan B. Anthony in her early meetings at Syracuse and Rochester. Now slavery was abolished and here he was still standing at her side.

Few in the big hall heard the effort in Frederick Douglass' voice that afternoon. They heard his words. But behind him Robert Ingersoll's mouth tightened and a little frown came on his face. *What can I do to help?* he wondered.

Afterward, Helen Pitts tried to speak to Mr. Douglass. He would not remember her, but it would be something to write to the folks at home. But the press of the crowd was too great, and her committee was called for a short caucus.

In front of the hall some time later she was surprised to see him just leaving the building. With him was Mr. Ingersoll. Helen was struck again by the somber shadows in Douglass' face, but Ingersoll was smiling, his face animated.

"Nonsense, Douglass!" she heard Ingersoll say. "What you've needed for a long time is a good lawyer." He laughed buoyantly. "Well, here he is!"

Douglass' voice was heavy.

"But, Mr. Ingersoll, I can't—"

Ingersoll had stepped to the curb and, lifting his cane, was hailing a passing cab.

"But you can. Come along, Douglass! First, we eat. Then I shall tell you something about banking. What a spot for *you* to be in!"

They climbed into the cab, and it rolled away through the gathering dusk. Helen walked to her room, wondering what on earth they had been talking about.

The next time Helen Pitts heard Douglass speak was on the occasion of the unveiling of the Freedmen's Monument in Lincoln Park. Negroes throughout the United States had raised the money for this monument to Lincoln; and on a spring day, when once more the lilacs were in bloom, they called together the great ones of the country to pause and think. Helen had never before witnessed such an array of dignitaries—the President of the United States, his Cabinet, judges of the Supreme Court, members of the Senate and House of Representatives.

"Few facts could better illustrate the vast and wonderful change which has taken place in our condition as a people," Douglass, the ex-slave, told the hushed crowd, "than our assembling here today. . . . It is the first time that, in this form and manner, we have sought to do honor to an American great man, however deserving and illustrious. I commend the fact to notice. Let it be told in every part of the Republic. Let men of all parties and opinions hear it. Let those who despise us, not less than those who respect us, know it and that now and here, in the spirit of liberty, loyalty and gratitude, we unite in this act of reverent homage. Let it be known everywhere, and by everybody who takes an interest in human progress and in the amelioration of the condition of mankind, that . . . we, the colored people, newly emancipated and rejoicing in our blood-bought freedom, near the close of the first century in the life of this Republic, have now and here unveiled, set apart, and dedicated a monument of enduring granite and bronze, in every line, feature, and figure of which men may read . . . something of the exalted character and great works of Abraham Lincoln, the first martyr-President of the United States."

Douglass spoke as one who loved and mourned a friend. And when the last word was said, men turned and walked away in silence.

"He is the noblest of them all!" Helen Pitts said to herself.

Douglass sat that night at home in his study, his head bowed in his hands. Lincoln had been struck down, his face turned toward the future; he had been struck down as he walked in the road. And they had not carried on. The nation had failed Lincoln and new chaos was upon them. *"You are caught up in a rosy cloud, Douglass."*

He had been with the Senator from Massachusetts when he died. With his last breath Charles Sumner had pleaded for the Civil Rights Bill—his bill. He had died fighting for it.

Douglass had pinned his faith on the ballot. He shuddered. Armed men were now riding through the night, marking their course by whipping, shooting, maiming and mutilating men, women and children. They were entering houses by force, shooting the inmates as they fled, destroying lives and property. All because the blacks were trying to use their ballot.

The summer saw a hesitating, weak old man pleading with Congress for assistance. Congress refused, and so the soldier had no other recourse but to call out troops to enforce the Reconstruction laws. Three times the soldiers restored to power candidates who had been ousted from office by force and fraudulent elections. In retaliation, the planters in Louisiana killed Negroes and whites in cold blood. Pitched battles raged in the streets of New Orleans.

The lowest ebb of degradation was reached with the election of 1876. School histories touch that month lightly and move quickly on. The deal was made, and Rutherford B. Hayes became President of the United States.

The calm was ominous. From several sections of the dead-still South groups of grim-faced men journeyed to Washington and gathered at Frederick Douglass' house.

"They say he will remove the soldiers. That means the end of everything for us. Only the Federal troops have held them back!"

"Is there nothing? Nothing you can cling to?" Douglass sought for one hope.

"There might have been had we cemented ties with Northern labor. They are just as intent on crushing the white worker." The black man's eyes on Douglass' face accused him. He had been a delegate to the Louisiana convention. And that was where the Negro labor union died!

"How bitter knowledge is that comes too late!" Douglass acknowledged his mistake with these words. The man from South Carolina spoke.

"They'll say we lost the ballot because we did not know how to use it."

"It is a lie—we could not do the things we knew to do!"

"The measures you have passed? Reforms?" Douglass searched the drawn faces.

"They'll all be swept away—"

"Like so much trash!"

"Go to the new President," they urged. "You cannot be accused of seeking favors. Go and tell him the truth. Plead with him to leave us this protection a little longer."

"A little longer, they ask a little more time, Mr. Hayes." Douglass was in the White House, begging understanding for his people's need. He leaned forward, trying to read the face of the man who held so much of their destiny in his hands.

President Hayes spoke calmly.

"You are excited, Douglass. You have fought a good fight—and your case is won. There is no cause for further alarm. Your people are free. Now we must work for the prosperity of all the South. How can the Negro be deprived of his political or civil rights? The Fourteenth and Fifteenth Amendments are part of the Constitution. Douglass, do you lose faith in your government?"

Douglass rose slowly to his feet. There was logic and reason in the President's words.

"I covet the best for my country—the true grandeur of justice for all," he said. "Humbly I do pray that this United States will not lose so great a prize."

He bowed and took his leave.

All restrictions were lifted from the South. Little by little, on one pretext or another, blacks and poor whites were disfranchised; and the North covered the ugliness with gossamer robes of nostalgic romance. The Black Codes were invoked; homeless men and women were picked up for vagrancy, chain gangs formed, and the long, long night set in.

Not all at once, of course. And that afternoon as Douglass walked away through the White House grounds, he could not be sure. The air was clean and sweet after a cleansing shower, and he decided to walk.

He swung along, hardly heeding his direction. Then he saw that he was on I Street, N.W., and, as he approached a certain building, his steps slowed. The Haitians had opened their Legation with such pomp and pride! At last the valiant little Republic had been recognized, and President Lincoln had invited them to send their ambassador. He had come, a quiet, cultured gentleman who spoke English and French with equal charm and grace. But almost immediately the Haitian Legation on I Street had closed, and Ernest Roumain moved to New York City. He had said very little, but everybody knew that Washington would not tolerate the Legation of Haiti.

Douglass sighed. He hesitated a moment. Then his face brightened. He would go and see Miss Amelia. Yes, it would do him good to talk to Miss Amelia a little while.

Over on Pennsylvania Avenue at Fifteenth Street government clerks and secretaries were leaving the Treasury Building. They glanced up at the clearing skies and set off in their several directions. Helen Pitts paused a moment at the top of the steps. She and Elsie Baker usually walked home together; but Elsie did not come, so Helen started walking rather slowly down the street.

It was nice to stroll along like this after the busy day. Her work had settled into a regular routine. Life in the civil service was by no means dull. There was always the possibility of being let in on some "important secret." Anything could and often did happen in Washington.

And now there was not even the slightest chance of her getting homesick. Her first lodging place had been respectable enough, but she used to look forward to times when she could go home. Now she was thinking about having her mother come down and spend a week with her. She'd love it.

Her good luck had come on a particularly cold night when

Elsie, whom she knew then only as the Senior Clerk, had spoken to her.

"You have an awfully long ways to go, don't you, Miss Pitts?"

"Yes, it is far. But it's only in weather like this that I really mind it."

Mrs. Baker—she was a war widow—regarded her for a few minutes and then murmured, "I wonder!"

"You wonder what?" asked Helen pleasantly.

"I was just wondering if *maybe* Miss Amelia wouldn't let you have Jessie Payne's room."

"And why should I have Jessie Payne's room? I don't know the lady."

The Senior Clerk laughed.

"You probably won't because she went home Christmas to be married. And her room *is* empty."

"Is it a nice room?"

"Miss Amelia's house is special." Elsie smiled. "All of us have been there for ages. John and I both lived there when we— Naturally, afterward, when I came back I went straight to Miss Amelia. But she doesn't take new people. She isn't able to get about much any more. Mr. Haley's really the boss, and she doesn't have to do anything. So you see, it isn't a lodging house at all. You'd love it."

"It sounds wonderful!"

"Why not come home with me tonight for supper? We could sound Miss Amelia out."

They sat around the big table in the dining room—eight of them when a chair was placed for Helen—with the nicest little blue-eyed lady smiling at them from behind a tall teapot. Helen knew that the tall, stoop-shouldered Mr. Haley was city editor of one of the daily papers. He didn't talk much, but he was a pleasant host.

"Where are you from, Miss Pitts?"

Her reply brought Miss Amelia's full attention.

"Rochester!" Miss Amelia exclaimed. "We have a very distinguished friend who lives—or rather used to live—in Rochester. He's in Washington now. You've heard of Frederick Douglass?" She leaned forward, her eyes bright.

"Oh, yes, ma'am." Helen's enthusiasm was quite genuine. "Everybody in Rochester knows Frederick Douglass."

The little lady sat back, a smile on her face.

"I knew him when he was a boy."

Jack Haley chuckled. He turned to Helen, and his tired eyes smiled.

"Hold on to your hat, Miss Pitts. You're going to hear a story."

Everybody laughed. They all knew Miss Amelia's favorite story.

"You'll get the room!" whispered Elsie.

She was right, of course. The next day Helen Pitts moved into Jessie Payne's room.

They met just outside the gate. He saw that the lady was about to turn in and so, lifting his hat, he stepped back. She smiled and said, "How do you do, Mr. Douglass?"

"Good evening, ma'am." She walked up the path, and he cursed his inability to remember names. He was sure her face was familiar. It was dusk. When he saw her inside surely he would remember. At the door she turned.

"Stop cudgeling your brains," she said. "I've never been introduced to you."

"Then it's not really my fault if I don't know your name." He gave a sigh of relief.

They both laughed then, and Miss Amelia was calling, "Come in! Come in, both of you! Well, so at last you two have met again."

"Why no, Miss Amelia, the lady doesn't—"

"We haven't been introduced," Helen interrupted.

"Tck! Tck! You told me that—"

"But that was years ago, Miss Amelia."

Douglass was holding both Miss Amelia's hands in his.

"Please, ladies! This isn't fair. Now, please, won't you present me?"

Amelia was severe.

"After the length of time you've stayed away, Fred, I shouldn't."

Douglass bowed gravely when at last she complied with his request, his eyes still somewhat puzzled. Then Helen said, "I'm Gideon Pitts's daughter, from Rochester."

A few weeks later—to the horror of Washington—President Hayes appointed Frederick Douglass United States Marshal of the District of Columbia. It might almost seem that, having recalled the troops from the South, the President went out of his way to administer a rebuke where it would hurt most.

Fear was expressed that Douglass would pack the courts and jury-boxes with Negroes. Of even more concern was the time-honored custom that the Marshal presented all guests to the President at state functions! Immediately efforts were made by members of the bar to defeat Douglass' confirmation for office. But a one-time slaveholder, Columbus Alexander, of an old and wealthy Washington family, joined with George Hill, influential Republican, in presenting the necessary bond; and when the confirmation came up before the Senate the gentleman from New York, Senator Roscoe Conkling, won them over with a masterly and eloquent address on "Manhood."

So Frederick Douglass in "white kid gloves, sparrow-tailed coat, patent-leather boots and alabaster cravat" was at the President's side at the next White House reception. Nothing could be done now but wait for some overt act on his part to justify his removal. The opposition thought they had him a couple of months after he took office.

The Marshal had been invited to Baltimore to deliver a lecture in Douglass Hall—named in his honor and used for community educational purposes. He spoke on "Our National Capital." Everybody seemed to enjoy a pleasant evening. But the next morning Douglass awoke to find that he was being quoted and attacked by the press. Within a few days some of the newspapers had worked themselves into a frenzy, and committees were appointed to procure names to a petition demanding his removal from office.

It is said that the President laughed about the matter, and it is certain that after a statement made by Douglass was printed in the *Washington Evening Star* the hostility kindled against him vanished as quickly as it had come.

Douglass could be very witty, and he had made some humorous reflections on the great city. "But," he wrote the editor, "it is the easiest thing in the world, as you know, sir, to pervert the meaning and give a one-sided impression of a whole speech. . . . I am not such a fool as to decry a city in which I have invested my money and made my permanent residence."

As a matter of fact, Douglass had spoken in the most glowing terms of "our national center. . . . Elsewhere we may belong to individual States, but here we belong to the whole United States. . . ."

Douglass did love Washington. With his children and their families he occupied the double house at 316 and 318 A Street, N.E. But he wanted to buy some place on the outskirts of the city where Anna could have peace and rest. His house was only a few minutes' walk from the Capitol, and visitors were always knocking on their door. Besides, Anna missed her trees and flowers. She shrank from what she termed the "frivolities" of Washington and would seldom go anywhere with him. When he spoke of moving "out into the country" he saw her face brighten. He began looking for a place.

Marshal Douglass was on hand to welcome President James A. Garfield to the White House. According to long-established usage, the United States Marshal had the honor of escorting both the outgoing and the incoming presidents from the imposing ceremonies in the Senate Chamber to the east front of the Capitol where, on a platform erected for the purpose, the presidential oath was administered to the President-elect.

Hopes throughout the country ran high at the time of Garfield's inauguration. As Senator from Ohio, Garfield had been a reform advocate for several years.

There was no question about the serious state of affairs. "Under the guise of meekly accepting the results and decisions of war," Douglass noted, "Southern states were coming back to Congress with the pride of conquerors rather than with any trace of repentant humility. It was not the South, but loyal Union men, who had been at fault. . . . The object which through violence and bloodshed they had accomplished in the several states, they were already aiming to accomplish in the United States by address and political strategy."

In Douglass' mind was lodged a vivid and unpleasant memory which he thought of as "Senator Garfield's retreat."

In a speech on the floor the Ohio Senator had used the phrase "perjured traitors," describing men who had been trained by the government, were sworn to support and defend its Constitution, and then had taken to the battlefield and fought to destroy it. One Randolph Tucker rose to resent the phrase. "The only defense Mr. Garfield made to this brazen insolence," Douglass remembered, "was that he did not make the dictionary. This was perhaps the soft answer that turneth away wrath, but it is not the answer Charles Sumner, Benjamin Wade or Owen Lovejoy would have given. None of these men would have in such a case sheltered himself behind a dictionary."

Yet no one in the country felt the shock of President Garfield's assassination more deeply than Douglass. Not only had a good man been cruelly slain in the morning of his highest usefulness, but his sudden death came as a killing blow to Douglass' newly awakened hopes for further recognition of his people.

Only a few weeks before, Garfield had asked Douglass to the White House for a talk.* The President said he had wondered why his Republican predecessors had never sent a colored man as minister or ambassador to a white nation. He planned to depart from this usage. Did Douglass think one of his race would be acceptable in the capitals of Europe?

Douglass told President Garfield to take the step. Other nations did not share the American prejudice. Best of all, it would give the colored citizen new spirit. It would be a sign that the government was in earnest when it clothed him with American citizenship.

Again the country was in gloom. People in their sorrow came together; legislators and earnest men and women shook their heads and marveled at the struggles which seemed necessary for welding a nation of free men. The people as a whole were finding that freedom is a hard-bought thing.

Douglass rose before a huge audience in New York City. He was older. He had suffered because of failure to see, he had stumbled a little on the way—but he had never left the road. The lines in his face were lines of strength, the fire in his eyes was the light of knowledge, the sweet song of emancipation no longer filled his ears to the exclusion of everything else. He saw the scarred and blackened stumps that blocked his path, he saw the rocks and muddy pitfalls on the way, he knew that there were hidden snipers further up the road, but he went on—walking with dignity. The crowd listening to him was very still.

"How stands the case with the recently emancipated millions of colored people in our country?" he began. "By law, by the Constitution of the United States, slavery has no existence in our country. The legal form has been abolished. By law and the Constitution the Negro is a man and a citizen, and has all the rights and liberties guaranteed to any other variety of the human family residing in the United States."

Men who had recently come to these shores from other lands heard him. New York—melting pot of the world! They had come from Italy and Germany, from Poland and Ireland and Russia to the country of freedom.

"It is a great thing to have the supreme law of the land on the side of right and liberty," he said. "Only," he went on, "they gave the freedmen the machinery of liberty, but denied them the steam

* Douglass, *Life and Times of Frederick Douglass* (appendix), chap. ii, p. 631.

with which to put it in motion. They gave them the uniforms of
soldiers but no arms; they called them citizens and left them subjects;
they called them free and almost left them slaves. They did not
deprive the old master class of the power of life and death. Today
the masters cannot sell them, but they retain the power to starve them
to death!

"Greatness," the black orator reminded the citizens of New York,
"does not come to any people on flowery beds of ease. We must fight
to win the prize. No people to whom liberty is given can hold it as
firmly or wear it as grandly as those who wrench their liberty from
the iron hand of the tyrant."

He could take the cheers of the crowd with a quiet smile. He
knew that some of them would remember and in their own way
would act.

Anna joined her husband on the New York trip. And for a short
while they relived the time more than forty years before, when, after
the anxious days and nights, they were first free together. This trip,
their youngest son Charles was marrying Laura Haley, whose home
was in New York.

They had banks of flowers, organ music, smart ushers and lovely
bridesmaids. The marriage of Charles, son of Frederick Douglass,
was a very different affair from that wedding so long ago when Frederick, fugitive from slavery, took Anna Murray, freewoman, to be his
wife. As the bride all in white came floating down the aisle, Douglass
turned and smiled into Anna's clear, good eyes.

With his appointment as Recorder of Deeds for the District of
Columbia, Douglass knew that he could safely buy the house he
coveted. It was for sale, but until now he had only gazed with longing. It was on Anacostia Heights overlooking Washington across the
Potomac—a fine old house with spacious grounds, servants' quarters
and stables. As soon as he took office, and without saying anything to
Anna, he set about buying the property.

For many reasons Douglass' present appointment was far more
desirable than the post of Marshal. The Recorder's job was a local
office; though held at the pleasure of the President, it was in no sense
a federal or political post.

Douglass felt freer and more on his own. At that time the salary
was not fixed. The office was supported solely by fees paid for work
done by its employees. Since every transfer of property, every deed

of trust and every mortgage had to be recorded, the income was at times larger than that of any office of the national government except that of the President. Also, Douglass had that winter brought out the third of his autobiographies, *The Life and Times of Frederick Douglass.*

June promised to be a hot month, and everybody was talking about getting away from the city. Anna thought her husband seemed increasingly busy and preoccupied.

"Come along, dear," he said one Sunday. "We're going for a drive."

"Me too, Grandma!" Their grandchild, Rosetta's little girl, came running up.

"Not this time, honey," Douglass said. "Grandpa'll take you riding, but not right now." And he added for Anna's ears alone, "Today I only want your grandmother."

He was in a talkative mood that afternoon.

"Remember the morning the boat pulled into New Bedford?" he asked as they crossed the bridge over the Potomac River. "Remember the big house sitting up on the hill?"

He turned in the buggy seat and looked at her. And in that moment he was no longer the great Frederick Douglass—he was the slender, eager boy, just escaped from slavery, leaning on the rail of the boat, devouring with his young eyes every detail of their wonderful free home. The big white house far up on the hill had caught their eyes. *"Look! Some day we'll have a house like that! Look, Anna!"*

So now, when he asked, "Do you remember?" she only nodded her head. The smart little buggy was rolling along on land once more.

"Now we're in Anacostia," he said. "Close your eyes and keep them closed till I say!" She heard him chuckle like a boy, and then he said, "Now— Look!" He pointed with his whip.

It was the big white house high on a hill!

"There's our house, Anna, the house I promised you!"

She could only stare. Then the meaning of his words made her gasp.

"Frederick! You don't really mean— You haven't—?"

He laughed as she had not heard him laugh in a long time. They were winding up the hill now—toward the house.

That afternoon they planned and dreamed. The owners had let the house run down, but it would be perfect.

"We'll try to have it ready in time to escape the August heat. This is why I've been deaf to your talk about a vacation."

The afternoon almost exhausted Anna.

"Mamma's all fagged out," Rosetta told her father the next day. June was very hot, and Douglass began to worry about his wife.

"Perhaps you'd better go away for a few days." She shook her head.

"The house will be ready soon. When we get on our hill—" Her eyes were happy with anticipation.

When the doctor ordered her to bed, she was planning the moving.

"I'll just take it easy for a few days—then we'll start packing," she said.

Anna Murray Douglass died on August 4th, 1882.

CHAPTER NINETEEN

Indian summer and a fair harvest

THEY MOVED HIM out to the house in November.

"It must be settled before winter," Rosetta said, and his sons agreed.

"Pipes will freeze up unless someone is in the house."

So they packed the furniture—the piano—his books. It was a twelve-room house. They looked at each other in dismay. What were his plans? What to put in all those rooms?

"Buy what is needed." His voice was tired. He went into his room, closing the door softly behind him.

Meanwhile, Robert Ingersoll had moved to Washington. In spite of the many demands of his meteoric career he sought out Douglass, invited him to his home, sent him books.

"She was so happy, Douglass." Ingersoll laid his hand on the older man's arm. "Think of that. I wish—" He stopped and for a moment a shadow crossed his face. He was thinking of his brother. Then he said softly, "Blessed is the man who knows that through his own living he has brought some happiness into life."

Gradually Douglass' work reclaimed him. Nothing had been neglected at the office. Helen Pitts was now a Senior Clerk there. Everyone had cooperated in seeing that the work went on. His unfailing courtesy had endeared him to the whole staff.

He stopped in several times during winter for tea with Miss Amelia. The little old lady, grown very frail, kept a special biscuit "put by" for him. Jack Haley came in once and joined them. He kept Douglass talking quite late, for even after all these years Jack recalled the first long nights of his own loneliness.

Then the Supreme Court declared the Civil Rights Act of 1875 unconstitutional, and Frederick Douglass leaped into the fray.

He called a protest mass meeting at Lincoln Hall

"If it is a bill for social equality," Douglass said, opening the meeting, "so is the Declaration of Independence, which declares that all men have equal rights; so is the Sermon on the Mount; so is the golden rule that commands us to do to others as we would that others should do to us; so is the teaching of the Apostle that of one blood God has made all nations to dwell on the face of the earth; so is the Constitution of the United States, and so are the laws and the customs of every civilized country in the world; for nowhere, outside of the United States, is any man denied civil rights on account of his color."

He stood silent until the applause had died away, and introduced "the defender of the rights of men." The speech Robert Ingersoll made comes down to us as one of the great legal defenses of all time.

The voice was the voice of Robert Ingersoll, but as Douglass listened he heard the clear call of Daniel O'Connell, the fervent passion of Theodore Parker, the dauntless courage of William Lloyd Garrison. Sparks "flashing from each to each!"

So Frederick Douglass spoke the following winter when Wendell Phillips died. All Boston tried to crowd into Faneuil Hall for the memorial to this great "friend of man." Douglass was chosen to deliver the address.

"He is not dead as long as one man lives who loves his fellowmen, who strives for justice, and whose heart beats to the tread of marching feet."

In the spring the women, gathered in their Sixteenth National Suffrage Convention, paid tribute to Wendell Phillips, and Douglass heard Miss Helen Pitts speak briefly. When he rose he made his "coworker and former townswoman" a pretty compliment. The women on the platform smiled their approval at Helen.

In the summer Douglass went out on a speaking tour. The 1884 election was approaching, and throughout the country voices were questioning the party in power. Bloody crimes and outrages in the South, betrayal of all the principles and ideals of Abraham Lincoln, had not won over the Southern white vote. Negroes in the North—in some doubtful states their votes were important—began to leave "Lincoln's Party."

Douglass was steadfastly opposed to this trend. No possible good, he said, could come out of the Negro's lining up with the "Party of the South." It had been faithful to the slaveholding class during slavery, all through the war, and was today faithful to the same ideals.

"I hope and believe," he told friends, "that Abraham Lincoln's party will prove itself equally faithful to its friends . . . friends with black faces who during the war were eyes to your blind, shelter to your shelterless, when flying from the lines of the enemy. . . . Leave these men no longer compelled to wade to the ballot-box through blood. . . . A government that can give liberty in its constitution ought to have the power in its administration to protect and defend that liberty."

By midsummer it was clear that the campaign would be a hard one. James G. Blaine, the Republican candidate, was a popular figure. Grover Cleveland, Democratic candidate, was hardly known outside his own state. But the issues were not fought around two personalities.

When Douglass returned to Washington in August he heard about Miss Amelia.

"She wasn't sick at all," Helen told him.

"Why didn't you let me know? I would have come." Douglass was deeply distressed.

"There was no time. She wouldn't have wanted us to call you from your work when there was nothing you could do." She spoke gently as to an unhappy child, but her eyes were filled with tears.

And Douglass, beholding the understanding and compassion that lay in her blue eyes, could not look away. A minute or an hour—time did not matter, for the meaning of many years was compressed in that instant. No word was said, their hands did not touch, but in that moment the course of their lives changed.

Helen spoke first, a little breathlessly.

"Mr. Haley is breaking up the house. I'd— I'd like to take my vacation, now that you're back. I'll— I'll go home for a little while."

He had turned away, his hand shifting the papers on his desk. He did not look at her.

"Miss Pitts, may I— May I call to see you this evening?" he asked.

"Yes, Mr. Douglass," Helen Pitts answered simply. "I'll be at home."

The next morning Douglass called on a minister who was also his close friend. He told him that he was going to be married.

"I'd like for you to perform the ceremony."

The minister was all smiling congratulation. The announcement took him wholly by surprise. He had heard no whisper of romance involving the great Frederick Douglass who, for all his sixty-odd years, was a handsome figure of a man. The minister beamed.

"You're very wise. A man needs a good wife! And who is the fortunate lady?"

He repeated the name, trying to place it. Douglass' next words brought him to his feet.

"Douglass!" Real alarm sounded in his voice. "You can't! It's suicide!"

Douglass smiled quietly. A warm peace filled his heart. He knew that all the years of his living had not been barren. All the time he had been growing into understanding.

"I should be false to all the purposes and principles of my life," he said, "if I did not marry this noble lady who has done me the honor to consent to be my wife. I am a free man." He stood up, balancing his cane in his hands. He regarded his distraught friend with something like pity. "I am free even of making appearances just to impress. Would it not be ridiculous if, after having denounced from the housetops all those who discriminate because of the accident of skin color, I myself should practice the same folly?"

They said nothing about their plans to anyone, not even to Douglass' children, but were married three days later in the minister's home. Then Douglass drove his bride across the Potomac River and out to Anacostia. Within the next few days every paper in the country carried accounts of this marriage. Most of what they said was untrue. They were almost unanimous in condemnation.

When Grover Cleveland was elected President, white and black alike sat back complacently, jubilantly waiting for the Democratic President to "kick out" the Recorder of Deeds. Douglass himself did not expect anything else. His adherence to the Republican party was well known. He was a "staunch Republican" who had made no secret of his abhorrence of a Democratic administration. With his wife he paid his formal respects at the inauguration reception, but they did not linger in the parlors. He was surprised when, upon returning home a few evenings later, he was handed a large engraved card inviting Mr. and Mrs. Frederick Douglass to the Executive Mansion.

"He was a robust, manly man," Douglass said of Cleveland, "one who had the courage to act upon his convictions. . . . He never failed, while I held office under him, to invite myself and wife to his grand receptions, and we never failed to attend them. Surrounded by distinguished men and women from all parts of the country and by diplomatic representatives from all parts of the world, and under the gaze of late slaveholders, there was nothing in the bearing of Mr. and Mrs. Cleveland toward Mrs. Douglass and myself less cordial and courteous than that extended to the other ladies and gentlemen present." *

Within the course of the next two years Washington and the country recovered some equanimity so far as Douglass was concerned. But it is doubtful if anybody forgot.

Now Douglass decided on the fulfillment of a long-cherished desire. They sailed for Europe.

"Don't come back until you've really seen the world," Ingersoll urged them. "Take plenty of time. You'll be richly repaid."

They stayed away nearly two years. Douglass revisited England and Ireland and Scotland. He missed the people with whom he had worked in the old days, but their children received him royally. The two sisters, Anna and Ellen Richardson, who forty-five years before had written to Thomas Auld offering to buy his "runaway slave," were still living. Helen kissed their withered cheeks and breathed her thanks. They set up housekeeping in Paris, watched the ships sail from Marseilles, and climbed the old amphitheater in Arles. In Genoa Douglass was drawn, more than to anything else, to Paganini's violin exhibited in the museum. This was Douglass' favorite instrument. He had even learned to play it a little.

"We'll buy a violin while we're here," Helen promised. "It won't be Paganini's, but we'll get an instrument."

"Well, it won't sound like Paganini's, either!" Under the Italian sunshine that was enough to make them laugh. Pisa and then Rome, Naples and Pompeii, Sicily.

Then eagerly they turned toward the rising sun—Egypt, the Suez Canal, Libyan deserts, the Nile flowing through Africa.

Douglass' heart beat fast. Sandy's face came before him—Sandy and the bit of African dust he had held in his hand so long ago. Perhaps strength had flowed into him from that dust.

They made the voyage from Naples to Port Said in four days. The weather was perfect, and at dawn they found themselves face to face with old Stromboli, whose cone-shaped summit rises almost perpendicularly from the sea.

"Nothing in my American experience," Douglass claimed, "ever gave me such a deep sense of unearthly silence, such a sense of fast, profound, unbroken sameness and solitude, as did this passage through the Suez Canal, moving smoothly and noiselessly between two spade-

* Douglass, *Life and Times of Frederick Douglass*, III, chap. v, p. 647.

built banks of yellow sand, watched over by the jealous care of England and France. We find here, too, the motive and mainspring of English Egyptian occupation and of English policy. On either side stretches a sandy desert, to which the eye, even with the aid of the strongest field-glass, can find no limit but the horizon; land where neither tree, shrub nor vegetation of any kind, nor human habitation breaks the view. All is flat, broad, silent and unending solitude. There appears occasionally, away in the distance, a white line of life which only makes the silence and solitude more pronounced. It is a line of flamingoes, the only bird to be seen in the desert, making us wonder what they find upon which to subsist.

"But here, too, is another sign of life, wholly unlooked for, and for which it is hard to account. It is the half-naked, hungry form of a human being, a young Arab, who seems to have started up out of the yellow sand under his feet, for no town, village, house or shelter is seen from which he could have emerged. But here he is, running by the ship's side up and down the sandy banks for miles and for hours with the speed of a horse and the endurance of a hound, plaintively shouting as he runs: 'Backsheesh! Backsheesh! Backsheesh!' and only stopping in the race to pick up the pieces of bread and meat thrown to him from the ship. Far away in the distance, through the quivering air and sunlight, a mirage appears. Now it is a splendid forest and now a refreshing lake. The illusion is perfect." *

The memory of this half-naked, lean young Arab with the mirage behind him made an indelible impression.

After a week in Cairo, Douglass wrote, "Rome has its unwashed monks, Cairo its howling and dancing dervishes. Both seem equally deaf to the dictates of reason."

When they returned to Washington and to their home on Anacostia Heights they knew that they had savored the full meaning of abundant living. They had walked together in many lands and among many nationalities and races; they had been received together by peoples of all shades, who greeted them in many different languages; their hands had touched many hands. They had so much they could afford to be tolerant.

Arrows of ignorance, jealousy or petty prejudice could not reach them.

In June, 1889, Frederick Douglass was appointed Minister to Haiti.

* *Ibid.*, III, chap. ix, p. 707.

CHAPTER TWENTY

The Môle St. Nicolas

SECRETARY OF STATE BLAINE was disturbed. All morning bells had been ringing and secretaries scurrying around like mad. With the arrival of the New York shipowner, even the clerks in the outer offices knew that something was "in the wind."

The "problem of the West Indies" was perhaps the most important unfinished business left over from the former Secretary of State. Blaine had seen himself succeeding where William Seward had failed. Circumstances were propitious and favorably disposed; the Môle St. Nicolas, most coveted prize in the Caribbean, was practically within his grasp—or had been.

Haiti, after seventy-five years of maintaining itself as firm and invulnerable as its own Citadel, was now torn and weakened by civil war. Six years before, a provisional government had been set up under a General Légitime. Gradually Légitime assumed control, and two years later France recognized his government as official. But for reasons of their own, business interests in the United States preferred dealing with General Hyppolite's opposing forces, who termed the present régime that of "the usurpers of Port-au-Prince." President Cleveland had listened to their advice and not recognized any government in Haiti. That left everything wide open. The U. S.-West Indies Line and the Charleston & Florida Steamship Line tackled shutting out the rival British Atlas Steamship Company, and the dire need for coaling stations was stressed in certain circles. At long last the United States had high hopes of locking up the narrow Windward Passage, one of the strategic routes on the world's highway system of commerce.

Meanwhile Stephen Preston, Haitian Minister, was in the United States pleading for his country's recognition. Blaine played a cat-and-mouse game, putting the anxious Preston off from week to week, yet according him every ceremonial privilege as a minister and assuring him that the matter of official recognition only awaited its turn before the new President—Benjamin Harrison.

So matters stood in the latter part of May, 1889. Then Secretary Blaine made two moves. He told Preston his terms for recognition: a naval station in Haiti and representation of Haiti in European capitals by the American ambassador to those countries! The Haitian's olive face paled. He murmured a few words, bowed and departed. The Secretary then sent to President Harrison the names of an "investigating commission" to go to Haiti. It was to be headed by Colonel Beverley Tucker of Virginia.

Out of a clear sky, with no word of warning, Blaine's papers still lying unsigned on his desk, President Harrison recognized the Légitime government in Haiti. At the same time he appointed the most widely known Negro in America "Minister Resident and Consul-General to the Republic of Haiti and chargé d'affaires to Santo Domingo."

"A pretty kettle of fish!" stormed the shipowner.

Secretary Blaine struggled to maintain his dignity.

"A little premature, perhaps," he temporized. "But our President has gone on record as favoring the development of commerce with Latin America, and we have no reason to believe that Frederick Douglass will not co-operate in carrying forward the clearly expressed policies of his government."

"You are a fool!" snapped the shipowner.

The Secretary's face flushed, and a vein throbbed at his temple.

"You forget," he said evenly after a moment, "or perhaps you do not know, that Frederick Douglass was Secretary of President Grant's Santo Domingo Commission; and Douglass had no part in its failure."

"Whatever the reasons, what interests me is that the United States didn't get Samoná Bay." The shipowner's voice rasped. "I never trust those—those *people*. It's bad enough to have to do business with them in the islands. Well"—he made a gesture of resignation—"I didn't come here to quarrel. You'll simply have to handle this fellow."

The Secretary picked up a sheet of paper from his desk. He was wondering how well he or anybody else could "handle" Frederick Douglass.

"I've already dictated a letter to him in which I express the hope that he will accept President Harrison's appointment—"

The shipowner interrupted with something like a sneer.

"You're certainly going out of your way to be cordial."

"Ignorant calf!" was the Secretary's unspoken thought. Aloud he continued as if he had not heard. "—because his influence as minister," he said steadily, "is the most potent force we can send to the Caribbean for the peace, welfare and prosperity of those weary and unhappy people."

"Um—um." The idea was penetrating. "Not bad, not bad at all."

"It can be late fall before he arrives." They regarded each other across the flat-topped desk. "Meanwhile—"

"Meanwhile," the shipowner was getting to his feet, "much can happen."

"I was thinking that."

"Perhaps the usurper, Légitime, will not be on hand to greet our new Ambassador."

"Perhaps!"

The gentlemen bowed and separated.

That evening Stephen Preston sent a joyful letter home. "A miracle has taken place, truly a miracle!"

And on Cedar Hill the Douglasses sat on their porch and re-read the letter which a messenger had brought from Secretary of State Blaine.

"You deserve it, my dear. You deserve every bit of it!" She smiled at her husband, her eyes shining with happiness. Douglass' voice was a little husky. The letter trembled in his hand.

"Secretary Blaine is right. This is important to every freedman in the United States. It's important to that valiant small nation which owes its independence to a successful slave revolt. This recognition is important to dark peoples everywhere. I am so grateful that I'm here to do my part."

And Helen Douglass reached out and took his hand. She was proud, so very proud of him.

Telegrams and letters of congratulation came in, not only from all over the United States, but from Mexico, South America, Africa. A clockmaker in Zurich sent Douglass a great clock carved from a huge block of wood.

Newspapers in the United States only mentioned an unexpected "turn-over" in Haiti "because it might affect the recent appointment." But when on October 7, 1889, Légitime was thrown out of office and Hyppolite became president, the Administration declared it a purely

domestic matter, and the United States representative was instructed
to proceed to his post. Unexplained "troubles" had delayed Douglass'
departure, but now the reasons for keeping him in Washington
rapidly exhausted themselves. The first week in November, Douglass,
accompanied by his wife, sailed for Port-au-Prince.

Nature is lavish with her gifts in the Caribbean. They thought
they had seen her finest habiliments along the Riviera, but even
world travelers hold their breath or speak in awed whispers as out of
the violet distance emerges the loveliest jewel of the Antilles.

Across a bay of deepest blue, the purple of the mountains of La
Gonaïve loomed against the western sky as if tossed from the cerulean
depths of the gulf. Fanning up from the great bay rise the hills,
wrinkled masses of green and blue and gray and orange, their dim
wave of color relieved by crimson splotches of luxuriant gardens or
by the pointed spires of trees.

The city of Port-au-Prince spilled over into the water with its
crowded harbor, large and small boats and white sails skimming over
the surface. In the center of the city rose the great Gothic cathedral,
to one side the white palace occupied by Haiti's President.

Two smart, attentive officials were on the dock to meet Frederick
Douglass. Behind sleek, glistening horses they drove the new Minister
and his wife to the spacious villa which was to be their home. The
house was already staffed with servants, who gathered, European
fashion, to greet the new tenants. The maids smiled shyly at Mrs.
Douglass, then whisked her away to her rooms. The officials took their
leave, saying that the President would be happy to receive Mr.
Douglass at his pleasure.

That afternoon, accompanied by his secretary, who would also act
as interpreter, Douglass drove to the palace to present his creden-
tials. He was cordially received by a uniformed adjutant. In a short
while they were being ushered up a wide, sweeping staircase and into
a frescoed hall. They paused here.

"There is the anchor of the *Santa Maria*," the secretary whispered,
"the anchor Columbus lowered in the Môle St. Nicolas."

Douglass walked closer. He was so deeply absorbed that he did
not see the huge doors swing open. The secretary had to touch his
arm. The President of Haiti was coming to greet the representative
from the United States, his hand extended. They went in to his
study.

President Hyppolite was large and dark. He knew he was in a

dangerous game. He knew that he was only a pawn. Wary and watchful, he listened more than he talked. For underneath everything else—far deeper than personal ambitions—was his determination to keep Haiti out of the scheming hands that clutched at her so greedily.

He hated all Spaniards, Frenchmen, Englishmen and Americans with equal intensity. He studied this brown American, this ex-slave, who carried himself with such dignity and who spoke with such assurance. Hyppolite wondered how much the other man knew. He attended his visitor's words carefully, listening to catch any additional meanings in his voice. He understood English, but he remained silent, his large head slightly cocked to one side until the interpreter translated Douglass' words into French.

He answered in French. Choosing his words carefully, he expressed his approval of "growing commercial intercommunications," his hope for closer and "mutually helpful" relations with the United States. Then he touched upon Haiti's long and independent existence and said that each nation has the right to be proud of its autonomy.

"For a long time Haiti was an outcast among the nations of the world. But Haiti remembers that the victory of Toussaint L'Ouverture was as important to the United States as it was to Britain. By exterminating the armies of Leclerc, we at the same time destroyed Napoleon's dream of an empire in the Mississippi valley. He was glad to sell Louisiana at any price."

The President was satisfied with the expression which lighted Douglass' face when the interpreter had translated these words. His rather grim face broke into a smile.

"I speak a little English," he said in English.

Douglass grinned and returned with:

"J'ai étudié le francais—un—une peu—mais ma femme—" he stopped, spreading his hands hopelessly.

They laughed together then, and the rest of the visit Hyppolite spoke English.

"Here you will learn the French—but quick," he said. "Altogether we will help you."

Douglass expressed his own and his wife's appreciation of the preparations for their comfort, and President Hyppolite said that without doubt Mrs. Douglass would be very busy receiving the ladies of Port-au-Prince.

After Douglass had bowed out, the President stood for a few minutes drumming on his desk. Then he pulled a cord which summoned a certain gentleman of state.

"Your Excellency!" The man waited. President Hyppolite spoke rather slowly, in concise French.

"The Frederick Douglass is an honorable man. He intends to discharge his duties in a manner which will bring credit and distinction to his people and to his nation. It is to be remembered at all times that Mr. Douglass is, first of all, Ambassador of the United States."

"Yes, Your Excellency!"

The President dismissed him with a nod. Then he walked to the window and stood looking at the Square. From this window he could not see the middle of the Champs de Mars, but he was thinking of the statue there—the statue of a black soldier thrusting his sword toward the sky. This statue of Dessalines is Haiti's symbol of her struggle for freedom. Hyppolite sighed as he turned away from the window.

He wondered if there might be a better way.

Back in Washington activities had been bent upon getting John Durham sent as special consul to Port-au-Prince because of his "special fitness for the job." Once more President Harrison's action proved disappointing. He sent John Durham to Santo Domingo City. It began to be whispered about in Washington and New York that the Haitians had snubbed Frederick Douglass and his wife. Stephen Preston heard the rumors just before he sailed for home. He suspected their origin, but he decided to hold his peace until he reached Port-au-Prince.

"Frederick," Helen Douglass said, "this place will be my undoing! Such ease is positively shameful. My only exercise is changing clothes for another reception or dinner party. And the food!" Her voice became a wail of despair. "I'm getting fat!"

He laughed.

"Well, madam, I might suggest horseback riding. I'm feeling fine!"

She shook her head.

"You? I can't go galloping around these mountains the way you do."

It was true. Frederick Douglass estimated his age to be over seventy. Yet he was spending hours every day in the saddle.

"It's the only way one can see Haiti!"

They took the boat to Cap Haitien, and while Helen was entertained in one of the big white houses set on the slopes and surrounded by a tropical garden, Douglass, accompanied by other horsemen, rode up to the summit of Bonne-à-l'Evêque. Gradually the earth fell away until the rocky edges of the mountain showed like snarling teeth, and the foothills below seemed like jungle forest. An earthquake in 1842 was said to have shaken the Citadel to the danger point; but Douglass, viewing this mightiest fortress in the Western world, doubted whether any human army with all its modern equipment could take it. Christophe had built his Citadel at a height of twenty-six hundred feet—an amazing feat of engineering so harmoniously constructed through and through that, though thousands and thousands of natives must have died during the course of its construction, one could almost believe it the work of one man.

Douglass stood at the massive pile which is now the tomb of the most dominant black man in history.

"If a nation's greatness can at all be measured by its great soldiers," he thought, "then little Haiti, with its Toussaint L'Ouverture, Jean Jacques Dessalines and Henri Christophe, must surely be listed among the first!"

Another day they took him up a high cliff overlooking the Môle St. Nicolas.

"You have perhaps heard that Abbé Raynal called it the Gibraltar of the West Indies," the Haitian commented, watching Douglass' face.

"See," the second companion pointed with his riding crop, "the harbor is practically landlocked. The entrance is only four miles wide and deep enough on both sides to permit the largest vessels to pass close to shore. At two hundred yards from land bottom is not touched with an eighty-fathom line."

Douglass gazed in wonder. The waters of the bay spread out, smooth and unruffled as a great lake. The land on which they stood at the right of the entrance rose sharply. Opposite, a wooded plain extended. At the end of the bay clustered a group of buildings with the clear sheen of water right in the middle of them.

"Man could not have designed anything so perfect," Douglass murmured.

The first Haitian spoke again.

"They say all the fleets in Europe could lie here secure from every wind. And the largest vessels in fifty fathoms of water could have cables on land."

"It is incredible!"

The Haitian turned as if to mount his horse. He spoke carelessly.

"A powerful nation holding this harbor might easily control not only the Caribbeans but South America as well."

"But a friendly nation," Douglass reasoned with great sincerity, "with the means at hand might use this harbor to bring prosperity to all the Caribbean."

"*Ce soit possible!*"

Douglass did not know French well enough to catch the slight sarcasm in the Haitian's words.

As they rode down the trail they spoke only of the scenery.

In November the United States warship *Yantic* steamed into the Môle, and Douglass reported that frequent references in the American press to alleged desires on the part of his country to obtain bases there were arousing fears among the Haitian people. Strangely enough, Douglass now found himself the point of attack by the press. They said he was not the man for the post.

"The fault of my character," Douglass wrote later, "was that upon it there could be predicated no well-grounded hope that I would allow myself to be used, or allow my office to be used, to further selfish schemes of any sort for the benefit of individuals, either at the expense of Haiti or at the expense of the character of the United States." *

Events moved rapidly. Certain facts became apparent to Douglass, and in March, 1890, he wrote to Secretary Blaine that certain American business interests were bringing pressure upon Haiti. Douglass had not at this time seen a report recorded by the Bureau of Navigation, received January 22, 1890, which read:

> The strategical value of this Island from a naval point of view is invaluable, and this increases in direct proportion to the millions which American citizens are investing in the Nicaragua Canal. The United States cannot afford to allow any doubt to rest in the minds of any Haitian as to our fixed determination to allow no one to gain a foothold on, or establish a protectorate over this Island.

Home on leave for a few weeks in August, Douglass spoke on Haiti to a large audience in Baltimore. He noted he had recently been under attack by the press of the country.

"I believe the press has become reconciled to my presence in the

* Douglass, *Life and Times of Frederick Douglass*, III, chap. ix, p. 723.

office except those that have a candidate for it," he said, "and they give out that I am going to resign. At them I fling the old adage 'Few die, and none resign.' I am going back to Haiti."

Let us take Douglass' own account of what happened the following winter. It appeared in the *North American Review*, September, 1891.

On January 26, 1891, Rear Admiral Gherardi, having arrived at Port-au-Prince, sent one of his under-officers on shore to the United States Legation, to invite me on board his flagship, the *Philadelphia*. . . . I went on board as requested, and there for the first time I learned that I was to have some connection with negotiations for a United States coaling-station at the Môle St. Nicolas; and this information was imparted to me by Rear Admiral Gherardi. He told me in his peculiarly emphatic manner that he had been duly appointed a United States special commissioner; that his mission was to obtain a naval station at the Môle St. Nicolas; and that it was the wish of Mr. Blaine and Mr. Tracy, and also of the President of the United States, that I should earnestly co-operate with him in accomplishing this object. He further made me acquainted with the dignity of his position, and I was not slow in recognizing it.

In reality, some time before the arrival of Admiral Gherardi on this diplomatic scene, I was made acquainted with the fact of his appointment. There was at Port-au-Prince an individual, acting as agent of a distinguished firm in New York, who appeared to be more fully initiated into the secrets of the State Department at Washington than I was, and who knew, or said he knew, all about the appointment of Admiral Gherardi, whose arrival he diligently heralded in advance, and carefully made public in all the political and business circles to which he had access. He stated that I was discredited at Washington, had, in fact, been suspended and recalled, and that Admiral Gherardi had been duly commissioned to take my place. It is unnecessary to say that it placed me in an unenviable position, both before the community of Port-au-Prince and before the government of Haiti.

Anyone may read a carefully documented account of the negotiations which followed in Rayford Logan's *Diplomatic Relations of the United States with Haiti*. There can be no question that Douglass strove to carry out the wishes of his government while at the same time "maintaining the good character of the United States." He clearly regretted certain features of the negotiations.

Not the least, perhaps, among the collateral causes of our non-success was the minatory attitude assumed by us while conducting the negotiation. What wisdom was there in confronting Haiti at such a moment with a squadron of large ships of war with a hundred cannon and two thousand men? This was done, and it was naturally construed into a hint to Haiti that if we could not, by appeals to reason and friendly feeling, obtain what we wanted, we could obtain it by a show of force. We appeared before the Haitians, and before the world, with the pen in one hand and the sword in the other. This was not a friendly and considerate attitude for a great government like ours to assume when asking a concession from a small and weak nation like Haiti. It was ill-timed and out of all proportion to the demands of the occasion. It was also done under a total misapprehension of the character of the people with whom we had to deal. We should have known that, whatever else the Haitian people may be, they are not cowards, and hence are not easily scared.

Frederick Douglass was blamed for the failure of the negotiations. He did resign the summer of 1891.

Logan says, "My own belief is that Douglass was sincerely desirous of protecting the interests of a country of the same race as his, while at the same time carrying out the wishes of his government and upholding the integrity of that government. His failure was due rather to the fact that there was no real public demand for the Môle, that Harrison was not prepared to use force. . . . After all, the Panama Canal had not been built; the United States had not even obtained her release from the Clayton-Bulwer Treaty so that she could construct a canal under her own control. The use of force against Haiti had to wait until the canal had been constructed, until the United States had become a world power, until a new period of recurrent revolutions had increased the impatience in the State Department, and until the attention fixed upon the World War permitted the military occupation of Haiti without arousing too much protest in the United States." *

In 1893 the Haitian government appointed Douglass Haiti's Commissioner to the World Columbian Exposition at Chicago; and

---

* Logan, *Diplomatic Relations of United States with Haiti*, chap. xv, p. 457.

in 1899 Haiti contributed the first thousand dollars toward the bronze statue of Frederick Douglass now standing in one of the public parks of Rochester. Speaking in 1932, Dantes Bellegarde, Haitian Minister to the United States, expressed the belief that were Frederick Douglass still living he "would be among those who most ardently approved the doctrine of international morality. . . . A policy respectful of the rights of small nations such as had been exemplified in the activities of Douglass while United States Minister in Haiti, is the only policy capable of assuring to a powerful nation like the United States the real and profound sympathy of the states of Latin America."

Frederick Douglass was now nearly eighty years old. He had not retired from public life. His snow-white bushy hair, topping the straight, well-set figure was a familiar sight wherever people gathered to plan a stronger, nobler nation, to build a more understanding world. His faith in his country and in its ultimate destiny rendered him tolerant; his ready wit was gentle. Little knots of people gathered round him wherever he went and found themselves repeating his stories and remembering best of all his rare good humor. The villagers in Anacostia were proud of him. They told of the visitors who came from far and near seeking his home.

On the morning of February 15, 1895, Susan B. Anthony arrived in Washington to open the second triennial meeting of the National Woman's Council. This was her seventy-fifth birthday, and that afternoon Mr. and Mrs. Frederick Douglass called to express their good wishes and congratulations.

The big open meeting of the session was to be February 20. During the morning Frederick Douglass appeared and, amid resounding applause, was invited to the platform by the president, Mrs. Sewall. He accepted, but declined to speak, acknowledging the applause only by a bow.

It was one of those bitterly cold days, and Douglass reached home just in time for supper. He was in high good spirits. Even while he shook off the snow and removed his boots in the hall he was recounting the happenings of the day.

"Miss Anthony was at her best!" he said as he stood before the big open fire, warming his hands.

"I'm a little tired," he said after supper. He had started up the stairs and stopped, apparently to look at the picture of John Brown which hung there on the wall. His wife, in the living room, turned quickly. The phrase was unlike him.

And then he fell. He was dead before they could get him to his room.

All the great ones spoke at his funeral. Susan B. Anthony read Elizabeth Cady Stanton's memorial to the only man who had sustained her demand for the enfranchisement of women at the first convention back in 1848.

There have been many memorials to him—in marble and bronze, in song and poetry. But stone and wood are dead, and only we can make words come alive. Frederick Douglass' words reach us across the years:

> Though I am more closely connected and identified with one class of outraged, oppressed and enslaved people, I cannot allow myself to be insensible to the wrongs and suffering of any part of the great family of man. I am not only an American slave, but a man, and as such, am bound to use my powers for the welfare of the whole human brotherhood. . . . I believe that the sooner the wrongs of the whole human family are made known, the sooner those wrongs will be reached.*

* *The Liberator*, March 27, 1846.

Epilogue

ANY PORTION of the story of man's struggle for freedom is marvelously strange. This is a true story, and therefore some footnotes are necessary. In many instances I have quoted directly from Frederick Douglass' autobiographies. His own words, with their simple, forthright quality, form a clear picture of the man.

This book attempts to bring together many factors. I am therefore deeply indebted to all who have labored long and faithfully in compiling this story. Special mention must be made of W. E. B. Du Bois' *Black Reconstruction* and *John Brown*, W. P. and F. J. Garrison's *William Lloyd Garrison*, Ida Harper's *Susan B. Anthony*, Rayford Logan's *Diplomatic Relations of the United States with Haiti*, A. A. W. Ramsay's *Sir Robert Peel*, J. T. Wilson's *The Black Phalanx* and *The Journal of Negro History*, edited by Carter G. Woodson.

It was on a Sunday afternoon in April that I first climbed Anacostia Heights to Cedar Hill.

"Here are the terrace stairs," they told me.

But I knew of the winding path that he had used, and I chose that. It is tangled and overgrown in places now, but up I went until I reached the sloping gardens and yes, there it was, just as I had expected, a lilac bush blooming where the path met the graveled walk!

A typical Virginia homestead, with veranda, carriage house and servants' quarters, the house and grounds are preserved by the Douglass Memorial Association of Negro Women's Clubs. I stood beside the sundial and tried to read its shadow, looked down into the well, and sat for a while on a stone seat beneath a flowering trellis.

307

It was so easy to see them on the porch or in the sunny living rooms with wide window-seats and fireplaces. Pictures looked down at me from every side—Susan B. Anthony, William Lloyd Garrison, the young and handsome Charles Sumner, Wendell Phillips and Abraham Lincoln.

I sat dreaming at his desk a long time, fingering his notebooks and the yellowing accounting sheets upon which he had tried to balance that pitiful bank record. On three sides of the study books rose from floor to ceiling—worn and penciled books. Books about people were undoubtedly his favorites.

In the rooms upstairs were pictures and intimate small objects of family life, and in his room in a locked case I saw a rusty musket and a flag.

They opened the case for me, and I laid my face against the folds of John Brown's flag. There it was in this year of 1946, still furled and standing in the corner of Frederick Douglass' room.

I must have stayed in those rooms for some time, because suddenly I realized it was growing dark and that I was alone. A glass door stood ajar and I stepped through and out upon a little balcony, a tiny balcony where one could sit alone and think. Surely many times on just such spring evenings Douglass had stepped out on his balcony. Looking far over the group of houses clustered at the foot of the hill, he must have caught the gleam of the Potomac as I did, and beyond that all Washington spread out like a bit of magic. Washington Monument was not pointing to the sky in his day, but there was the beautiful rounded dome of the Capitol. He could see that Capitol of which he was so proud—he could contemplate all the intriguing pattern of the city which he loved so much, capital of the nation which he served so faithfully.

Then, all at once, as I stood there on the balcony, I knew why it was that in the evening of his life Frederick Douglass' eyes were so serene. Not because he was lost in illusions of grandeur, not because he thought the goal attained, not because he thought all the people were marching forward. But as he stood there on his little balcony he could lift his eyes and, looking straight ahead, could see over the dome of the Capitol, steadfastly shedding its rays of hope and guidance, the north star.

Bibliography

Austin, George Lowell, *The Life and Times of Wendell Phillips.* Boston. Lee & Shepard, 1888.

Buckmaster, Henrietta, *Let My People Go.* New York. Harper & Brothers, 1941.

Douglass, Frederick, *Narration of Frederick Douglass.* Boston. The American Anti-Slavery Society, 1845.

————, *My Bondage and My Freedom.* New York. Miller, Orton & Mulligan, 1855.

————, *Life and Times of Frederick Douglass.* Boston. De Wolfe, Fiske & Co., 1893.

Du Bois, W. E. Burghardt, *Black Reconstruction.* New York. Harcourt Brace & Co., 1935.

————, *John Brown.* Philadelphia. George W. Jacobs, 1909.

Garrison, W. P. and F. J., *William Lloyd Garrison.* Boston. Houghton, Mifflin & Co., 1894.

Greeley, Horace, *The American Conflict.* Hartford. A. D. Case & Co., 1864.

Harper, Ida, *Life and Work of Susan B. Anthony.* Indianapolis. The Bowen-Merrill Co., 1899.

Hart, Albert B., *Slavery and Abolition.* New York. Harper & Brothers, 1906.

Ingersoll, Robert, *Political Speeches.* New York. C. P. Farrell (editor), 1914.

Logan, Rayford W., *Diplomatic Relations of United States with Haiti.* University of North Carolina Press, 1941.

May, Samuel J., *Recollections of the Anti-Slavery Conflict.* Boston. Fields, Osgood & Co., 1869.

Mansergh, Nicholas, *Ireland in the Age of Reform and Revolution.* London. G. Allen & Unwin, Ltd., 1940.

Ramsey, A. A. W., *Sir Robert Peel.* London. Constable & Co., Ltd., 1928.

Wilson, Joseph Thomas, *The Black Phalanx: History of the Negro Soldiers of the United States*. Hartford. The American Publishing Co., 1897.

Woodson, Carter G. (editor), *Journal of Negro History*. Washington, 1935–46.